INTRODUCTION TO HISTORICAL GEOLOGY

Cretaceous chalk cliffs near Dover, England. Geological Survey of Great Britain.

Introduction to
HISTORICAL GEOLOGY

by Raymond Cecil Moore
UNIVERSITY OF KANSAS

McGraw-Hill Book Company Inc.   New York   Toronto   London   1949

INTRODUCTION TO HISTORICAL GEOLOGY

Preface

The aim of this book is to give an account of the salient features of earth history in a manner specially suited to needs of those who have no previous acquaintance with this subject. Here belong students enrolled in a beginning course in historical geology, which almost invariably comprises the second part of a first course in general geology, or is set up as a separate course immediately following elementary physical geology. Also, here belong a host of young and old who are not studying geology in school but who are curious about the world in which they live. This book is for them, although it is desirable that they should first read about the characters of minerals and rocks, the ways in which they are formed, and the geologic processes that operate to modify or destroy them and to reorganize them. These processes, which shape features of the earth surface by erosion and sedimentation, are the same as those which have been at work during many million years of past earth history.

Excepting introductory chapters, which deal with general principles and with origin of the earth, the book is directed primarily to the nature of changing physical conditions and the record of life during geologic history of the continent of North America. We must give some attention to areas in Europe, because most major divisions of the rock succession were recognized first and defined there. Naturally, however, the part of the world in which we live has greatest interest for us.

Many questions come to mind when we begin to think about the history of the land surface all around us. How old is the earth, and in what manner have its main surface features, the continents and ocean basins, come into being? Why are mountains such as the Appalachians and Rockies distributed as chains thousands of miles long in belts roughly parallel to the eastern and western borders of North America, whereas the continental interior is mostly a vast lowland plain? What is the explanation for occurrence of fossil marine shells in stratified rocks of far-inland localities, as in Kansas, and at elevations more than 10,000 feet above sea level, as in Colorado? Why are fossil remains of innumerable kinds of extinct animals and plants, both of sea and land, found to be arranged in an orderly sequence, the most primitive in lowermost rock layers, and near-modern types in uppermost strata? All these and many other questions pertaining to the geological history of our continent are answered with varying sureness on the basis of observations and deductions belonging in the province of this book. When we understand the evidence of past conditions and geological events, we can better comprehend our present surroundings, and we appreciate the immensity of the earth's geological history as compared with our small span of life. Historical geology brings us knowledge of great cultural value because it gives us comprehension and perspective. It also has much economic value, for when we know how rock formations, ores, fuel deposits, and other earth materials were made, we are guided in seeking and developing these things which are useful to man.

Features of "Introduction to Historical Geology" that call for special notice are (1) avoidance of including a mass of unfamiliar technical terminology in the text, (2) emphasis on clear explanation of principles, and (3) graphic presentation of most significant data with accompanying brief descriptions.

Many books on historical geology are burdened with a forbiddingly large vocabulary of technical words consisting largely of the scientific names of fossils and names of rock formations. The student is led to think, naturally enough, that acquisition of knowledge of historical geology consists mainly, if not essentially, of learning all these strange new terms. The task is to memorize, and some teachers do not help very much in developing a keen interest on the part of students in why's and wherefore's. If stress is put unduly on a catalogue of mere what's, the subject may seem dry and difficult indeed. It is dead, rather than alive with interest. Yet the names of fossils and of rock units are needed, especially by the student who goes on to more advanced work in geology. Accordingly, many such names are given in the illustrations used in this book, and without obtruding, they are available for such reference and attention as may be judged desirable by the student and teacher. They are not prerequisite to learning about geological history.

In preparing the text, effort has been made to write straightforwardly in plain English, with attention to stating as simply and clearly as possible each pertinent observation or conclusion. The discussion of historical meaning of these things is aimed at development of understanding by the reader of reasons for each deduction. To think accurately and to make sound analysis of any set of observations are abilities that a student needs much more than the ability to repeat something he has been told or to recite matter that he has memorized. The relation between cause and effect, therefore, is constantly held in view as data of the geological record are examined.

Most of the illustrations accompanying the several chapters are new. They consist of maps, sections, and block diagrams that are designed to express in graphic form subjects treated in the text, contributing to the ease and precision of full comprehension. They also include many photographs of typical rock exposures, topographic features, and characteristic fossils. Restorations of natural assemblages of ancient forms of life and of individual organisms aid in obtaining a vivid concept of the appearance of long-extinct plants and animals. They are species that once were actually living things. The brief descriptions that accompany the captions of most figures not only supplement discussion given in the text but independently serve to point out many important features belonging to study of earth history. One who closely examines these illustrations and their explanations cannot fail to acquire a good deal of understanding of historical geology, even without reading the text. It is my judgment that all beginning students will find the few lines of description or comment added to the titles of figures decidedly helpful, because they call attention to significant items otherwise readily overlooked. Teachers recognize the value of such assistance, just as they appreciate the advantage of all sorts of visual instruction.

I am indebted to friends whose authoritative knowledge of certain divisions of the geologic column in North America has been put generously at my disposal, especially in checking the charts of rock formations. Also, I have received valued aid in obtaining many geological and paleontological illustrations, for which acknowledgment is made mostly in notations accompanying the figures. I express appreciation here to C. Wythe Cooke, G. A. Cooper, R. W. Imlay, P. B. King, J. B. Knight, A. L. Loeblich, Jr., N. D. Newell, J. B. Reeside, Jr., L. W. Stephenson, and C. J. Stubblefield. I am grateful to Edith Lewis and Marjorie Bradley for secretarial assistance in preparing the manuscript, to Roy and Dorothy Jindra for work on illustrations of invertebrate fossils, and to Jack Koenig for drawing the outcrop maps representing the geologic systems. Most of the maps, sections, rock charts, and block diagrams have been drawn by me. The frontispiece photograph, obtained from the Director of the Geological Survey of Great Britain, is covered by copyright reserved for the British Crown and is published by permission of the Controller of H. M. Stationery Office.

RAYMOND CECIL MOORE

LAWRENCE, KAN.
January, 1949

Contents

1. Materials and Methods of Historical Geology

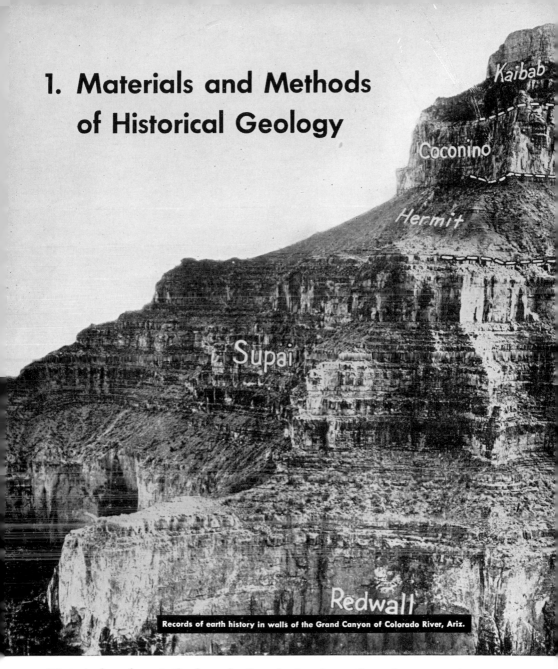

Kaibab

Coconino

Hermit

Supai

Redwall

Records of earth history in walls of the Grand Canyon of Colorado River, Ariz.

Historical geology is the branch of geologic science that relates to past history of the earth. It depends on virtually all knowledge in the field of physical geology gained in study of minerals, rocks, geologic processes and structures, and it utilizes this knowledge in deducing the

N. W. Carkhuff, U. S. Geological Survey

conditions and events of the earth's past. Among features belonging to study of earth history are the origin and development of the continents and oceans, the changing geography of seas and lands, the appearance and disappearance of great mountain systems, the occurrence of profound volcanic activity at different times and places, and great climatic changes. In addition, we find evidence of innumerable forms of prehistoric plants and animals, many of which represent types of life long vanished from the earth. The nature of this past life and its evolution during geologic time not only form an intrinsically interesting part of historical geology, but if these organic remains were not preserved in the rocks, many features of the earth record would not be decipherable. It is desirable to begin our study, then, by surveying the nature of historical geologic evidence and methods by which this is to be interpreted.

As foundation, we accept the conclusion that nature's laws are unchanging. This means that we have no reason to doubt that the principles of physics and chemistry, the operation of gravity, and the essential nature of geologic processes are independent of time. They are unchanging. During past earth history rocks must have been formed and some of them subsequently broken down physically or chemically in the same manner as now; we may be sure that rains fell, water flowed downhill, winds blew, and waves beat against shores, just as we can see on the earth at the present time. This concept, which has come to be known by the formidable term of "uniformitarianism," simply holds that the present is a key to the past. Our ability to analyze the rock record depends, first, on the completeness and accuracy of our understanding of these present-day laws and processes, and, second, on the extent to which the rock record is available for study.

Historical Meaning of Rock Characters

Rocks comprise igneous, sedimentary, and metamorphic types. We know that igneous rocks originate both as intrusions and extrusions, that sedimentary rocks are formed by the breaking down and deposition of preexisting rock material, and that metamorphic rocks are produced mainly by heat and pressure affecting other rocks. Inasmuch as the origin and history of all these differ, each must be considered separately from the standpoint of historical geology.

IGNEOUS ROCKS

Texture, form, and distribution. The occurrence of outcrops of igneous rocks anywhere obviously constitutes evidence of volcanism in the past history of the region. The nature, extent, and geologic date of the volcanism may be learned from study of the texture, form, and distribution of the igneous rocks, and especially from observation of their structural relations with associated rocks. Coarse, subequal-grained rocks, such as granite or diorite, represent deep-seated intrusions of batholithic type. Such intrusions seem to be associated characteristically with crustal deformations that produce mountain building. Dikes, sills, and other intrusive igneous bodies may be identified by their form and relations to associated rocks, and they are commonly distinguished also by texture.

The location and nature of extrusive volcanism may be read from observation of characteristic features corresponding to those of modern lava flows, ash falls, or pyroclastic materials mingled with sediment. Such igneous bodies commonly are layered, and some of them show columnar jointing; cindery or scoriaceous texture at the top of a basaltic layer may serve to distinguish it as an individual lava flow. Pumice, tuff, and agglomerate denote explosive volcanic activity, and layers of volcanic ash or dust (commonly altered chemically to the clayey material called "bentonite") denote wind action that served to transport the volcanic materials.

Structural relations. The geologic date of making igneous rocks can be determined with varying precision by observing structural relations with associated rocks. Intrusive igneous bodies are obviously younger than associated rocks that they intersect, but very often it is extremely difficult to tell how much younger. Extrusive igneous rocks are younger than the rocks that occur beneath them and older than the ones lying upon them. These age determinations are relative, and narrowness of geologic dating depends upon the accuracy with which the age of associated rocks is known.

SEDIMENTARY ROCKS

Composition, texture, and distribution. Most of historical geology has to do with sedimentary rocks and their contained organic remains. This is accounted for by the fact that events of earth history are

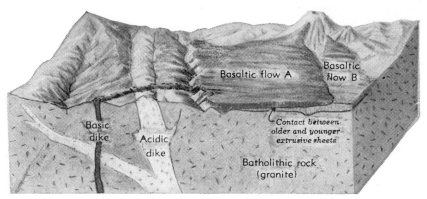

Basaltic flow A

Basaltic flow B

Basic dike

Acidic dike

Contact between older and younger extrusive sheets

Batholithic rock (granite)

1. Structural relations of igneous rock masses. The batholithic rock is deep-seated intrusive igneous rock that has become exposed by erosion of the original cover. It is older than the dikes that intersect it, and these, in turn, are older than the extrusive volcanics.

recorded mainly in terms of differing kinds of sedimentation, varying deformation of these sediments after they have been formed into rock layers, interruptions in rock building commonly accompanied by erosion, and evidence of evolution of life presented by fossils entombed in the sedimentary rocks.

Sedimentary rocks are divisible into clastic and nonclastic types. Clastic rocks, such as conglomerate, sandstone, arkose, and shale, are made up mainly of the broken fragments of preexisting rocks which denote mechanical disintegration of the source materials. The composition and degree of rounding of the clastic grains show the extent of sorting and reflect the effects of transportation. Applying knowledge of modern conditions of weathering, transportation, and sedimentation, study of the composition and texture of ancient sedimentary rocks permits deductions as to conditions under which they were formed. Thus, a very pure light-colored sandstone, 100 to 400 feet thick, that is widely distributed in the central and upper Mississippi Valley region, when examined with a lens or under the microscope, is seen to be composed of unusually well-sorted and rounded grains of quartz having frosted surfaces. This deposit, known as the St. Peter sandstone, evidently represents extensive sorting of the sedimentary materials in which all but the resistant quartz grains have been eliminated, and it shows prolonged transportation during which grains have been very well rounded and the surfaces frosted by impact of grain on grain. As shown by outcrops distributed through several states and by identifying the sandstone in innumerable well borings where younger strata overlie it, this deposit is known to be spread with essentially uniform characters over many ten-thousand square miles. What does this represent in terms of geologic history? What was the source of the sand and what were the agents of transportation and deposition? Conceivably, this sandstone indicates the former existence in the central United States of a Sahara-like desert where migrating sand dunes were spread by strong winds. On the other hand, perhaps the sand was laid down by water, being shifted by waves and currents of a shallow sea, or spread as beach deposits at the margin of such a sea. Possibly work by wind, streams, and a shallow sea may all have had part in making the St. Peter sandstone. Reliable conclusions must be based on a survey of all available evidence and proper interpretation of the meaning of each observation. Most of the bedding is parallel to the base and top of the deposit, which originally must have been nearly horizontal, and the evenness of the layers thus bespeaks

2. Grains of St. Peter sandstone. The rounded polished surfaces of quartz sand grains shown in this photomicrograph represent prolonged abrasion, probably by wind work mostly, but also including wear from other transporting agents. The purity and good sorting of the grains are effects of prolonged reworking.

other. Thus, parts of the western United States contain shale outcrops that represent offshore muds (Mancos shale) containing marine organisms; these muds were laid down contemporaneously with near-shore and onshore beds (Mesaverde sandstone) in which shallow water and beach deposits, coal-bearing marsh deposits, and stream-laid terrestrial deposits are respectively differentiated. Recognition of these sedimentary facies and their relations to one another aids importantly in understanding regional geography of the time and in interpreting geologic history.

The geologic date of sedimentary deposits is determined by study of their organic remains and by their relation to other deposits in vertical sequence, as discussed later in this chapter.

Stratification and features of bedding planes.   Historical interpretation of sedimentary strata calls for attention to features shown by bedding. The thickness of individual sedimentary rock layers ranges from a fraction of a millimeter to many feet. Very massive strata of uniform texture clearly mean relatively long persistence of uniform conditions of sedimentation. A bedding plane is introduced when these conditions are temporarily changed, as when a film of clay is spread over an area of accumulating sand or of pure calcium carbonate. These bedding planes, which may be very smooth or wavy, reflect the temporary configuration of the surface of sedimentation, generally a sea bottom.

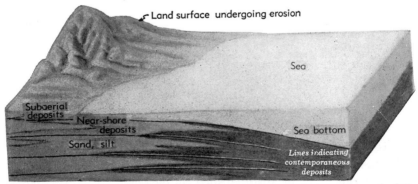

4. Variation in sedimentary facies. Types of sedimentary accumulations commonly differ according to the place and mode of their deposition. They may grade laterally one into another and interfinger as result of changing conditions. The deposits shaded most darkly represent off-shore sediments.

5. Evenly stratified, thin-bedded sandstone. These layers of sand and silt in the Allegheny River Valley near Oil City, Pa., indicate very regular alternation of conditions affecting deposition in shallow water. The strata belong to the great coal-bearing succession of deposits called the Pennsylvanian System. *(R. M. Leggette, U. S. Geol. Survey.)*

Ripple-marked bedding planes are of interest because they indicate agitation of the accumulating sediments by waves or currents; if the sediments are water-laid, this means that depth of water is sufficiently

6. Ripple-marked sandstone near Abingdon, Va. These markings plainly record wave movement in shallow water. They have been preserved by burial beneath layers of limestone, (Jonesboro formation, Upper Cambrian). *(Charles Butts, U. S. Geol. Survey.)*

7. Ancient rock surface showing mud cracks. The earthy limestone (Moccasin) of Middle Ordovician age in southwestern Virginia here shown reveals effects of exposure and drying that produced mud cracks, which subsequently were filled with sediment of slightly different nature.

small to permit agitation of the bottom. Study of the pattern and profile of ripples permits differentiation of various types, such as oscillation ripples made by waves, and current ripples produced by water currents or wind. This helps in interpreting conditions of ancient geography.

Some bedding planes show the characteristic polygonal pattern of mud cracks, which represent above-water desiccation of sediment, with subsequent filling of the cracks by other sediment.

Cross-bedding, formed by inclined deposition of granular sediments on the lee slopes of bars and dunes, denotes current action, and study of the pattern of cross-bedding may permit determination of whether this structure was produced by winds, by currents in streams, or in shallow water along a shore line.

Inasmuch as the original attitude of strata bearing mud cracks, ripple marks, and cross-bedding, as studied in physical geology, can be determined from study of these structures, they are useful in determining the top and bottom of a sequence of vertical or overturned beds, wherever found in such occurrence.

Organic remains. A characteristic feature of sedimentary rocks that is vitally important to historical geology is the common occurrence of fossilized remains of organisms. Fossils are the remains or traces of animals or plants preserved in rocks (Latin *fossilis,* meaning something dug out of the earth). Before the time of modern science, men

8. Irregularly cross-bedded sandstone. The weathered surfaces of this rock (Coconino sandstone of Permian age) in Walnut Canyon, Ariz., show the varying angle of inclined laminae of sand grains. This indicates shifting direction of sand transportation in the manner characteristic of wind deposits.

9. Evenly cross-bedded, coarse sandstone. Each main layer of this rock (Dakota sandstone of Cretaceous age) near Bennett, Neb., is composed of laminae that slope in the same direction. This feature of the cross-bedding, combined with coarse texture, indicates work of running water. *(N. H. Darton, U. S. Geol. Survey.)*

regarded shells, bones, or leaf imprints discovered in rocks as freaks of nature or the ineffective creative effort of some unknown plastic force within the earth. A few men interpreted them as actual remains of life that existed before the flood of Noah, death and burial in sediments having resulted from the great flood, but it is hard to explain why fishes and other aquatic creatures would have been drowned.

Shortly before 1800, the discovery was made that fossils of a given bed or group of beds are characteristic of it and serve to distinguish it from other fossil-bearing rock layers. Furthermore, the sequence of natural assemblages of animals (faunas) and assemblages of plants (floras), as represented by fossils in rocks, is constant. The geologic distribution of these fossil assemblages in one region corresponds to that oberved in others, and this provides the all-important foundation on which rock strata in different regions may be correlated and divisions that correspond in age may be recognized. If evidence derived from study of organic remains in the rocks were lacking, most of the record of earth history that is somewhat definitely and accurately known would be obscure or indecipherable, and we would have virtually no tangible evidence bearing on the history and evolution of life on the earth.

Preservation of organic remains as a fossil commonly depends on two chief requisites: (1) that the organism be buried quickly in some protecting medium and (2) that it possess some sort of hard parts, such as a skeleton or shell. The death of an animal or plant normally is followed quickly by decay that destroys tissues and eventually obliterates all traces of the organism. If such decay is inhibited or prevented, as in embalming bodies to make mummies or by sealing them in a protective medium, organic structures—especially resistant parts such as shells, teeth, and bones—may be preserved. Natural mummies may be made by the dry air of a desert or cave, and such remains later may be buried by sediment. Woolly mammoths and rhinoceroses of the Ice Age have been found solidly frozen in ice of northern

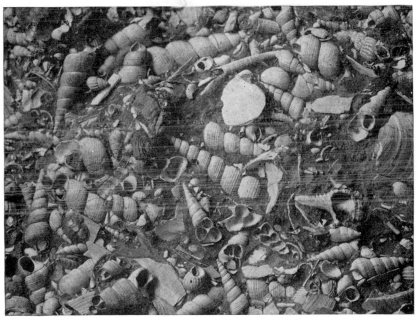

10. Highly fossiliferous marine sandstone. The abundant, well-preserved shells, mostly snails, shown on the weathered surface of this silty sandstone, indicate the abundance of life on a shallow sea bottom of mid-Tertiary (Miocene) time in the Chesapeake Bay region. The calcium carbonate shell substance has been preserved with virtually no change. The crowding and partial sorting of the shells suggest effects of current action. Natural size. (*U. S. Geol. Survey.*)

11. Quarrying out a dinosaur skeleton. The specimen here partly exposed is unusual in that the bones lie in undisturbed articulated position. The animal was lying on its side when buried in Cretaceous mud (Belly River beds, Alberta, Can.). (*American Museum of Natural History.*)

Siberia, so that even the flesh, internal organs, and undigested food in the stomach have been almost perfectly preserved. Insects showing every detail of structure and color have been found in amber, which is the fossilized resin of conifer trees.

The great majority of fossils have been made simply by covering by water in fine sediments. Although this does not ordinarily prevent bacterial decay of soft tissues, harder parts may be well preserved. Thus, chances of preservation of an organism as a fossil naturally are greatest in water bodies such as the sea where hard parts are buried in muds and sands of the sea bottom. On land, the best opportunity for fossilization is found in lakes and swamps. Fresh-water deposits, such as the Green River beds of Wyoming and the Florissant beds of Colorado, contain beautifully preserved fishes, insects, fresh-water shells, and the leaves and twigs of land plants that were blown by winds or carried by streams to the area in which they are preserved.

Eruptions of volcanic ash, such as descended on the Roman cities of Pompeii and Herculaneum, may smother and bury numerous animals and plants. In this way the forests of standing trunks in Yellowstone Park have been formed, and many fine fossil skeletons of mammals, as in the John Day Basin of Oregon, have been preserved.

The manner in which organic remains may be preserved in sediments varies widely. Some fossils consist of the hard parts of an animal or the woody tissues of a plant preserved unaltered in the sediment

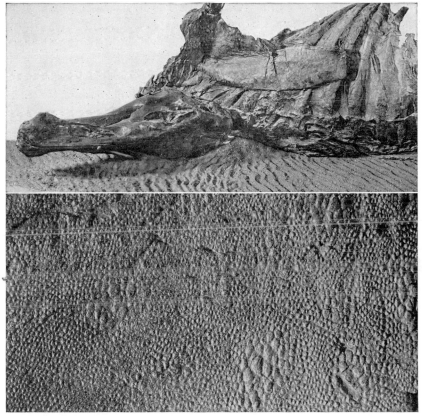

12. Mummified remains of a duck-billed dinosaur. The remarkable specimen here shown indicates desiccation of the remains after death of the animal, just as bones and skin may be preserved today in the dry desert air of parts of the southwestern United States. Eventually the bones of this dinosaur, with their covering of dried skin, were buried by drifting sand of Cretaceous age. The lower view shows the appearance of a part of the scaly skin. (*American Museum of Natural History.*)

that buried them. Most fossils, however, have undergone change. Shells composed of calcium carbonate may be made more dense by infiltration of calcite deposited by ground water. Commonly, also, there has been replacement of the original hard parts by some other mineral in submicroscopic particles; such replacement by calcium carbonate is termed *calcification;* by silica, *silicification;* and by iron pyrite, *pyritization.* This particle-by-particle replacement operates to preserve microscopic structures of the hard parts, even though chemical composition is changed. Slow decay under water of the tissue of plants (and less commonly of animals) may result in concentrations of carbon which shows the form of the original organism; this is termed *carbonization.*

13. Fossil brachiopods preserved by silicification. After burial in Permian limestone of western Texas, the substance of these marine shells, which originally was calcium carbonate, was replaced by silica carried by percolating ground water. The shells were removed from the rock matrix by dissolving the limestone in dilute hydrochloric acid. The spiny projections, which ordinarily break away in natural weathering, are here preserved intact. Natural size.

After burial in sediment, the hard parts of an organism may be removed by solution so as to leave merely the *mold* of its form in the surrounding rock. If the cavity is filled by some foreign mineral substance, just like metal poured into a foundry mold, the fossil is termed a *cast,* and such a cast retains no trace of original microscopic internal structure or shell substance.

Indirect evidence of the existence of organisms is found in the fossil tracks of land animals, the trails or borings of worms and other invertebrates, and coprolites (fossil excrement). Gizzard stones of some ancient reptiles may be identified by their form, surface polish, and manner of occurrence, associated perhaps with actual skeletal remains. The stone implements or weapons of prehistoric man also are indirect fossils.

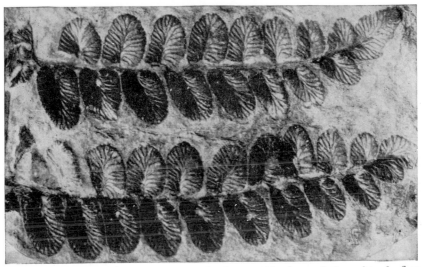

14. Fossil fern showing preservation by carbonization. The form of these fern leaflets (*Neuropteris*, × 3) is clearly shown by the impression in the fine sediment that buried this plant, but, in addition, the original tissue is represented by a thin film of carbon over the area of stem and leaflets. The specimen is from Early Pennsylvanian beds of Alabama. (*Charles Butts, U. S. Geol. Survey.*)

The original form of organic remains is by no means always preserved in fossils. Compaction of sediments by the weight of overlying rocks is likely to produce a flattening of the contained fossils. This is especially noteworthy in shale. Regional metamorphism is likely to distort or even obliterate fossils contained in sediments.

The term *index fossil* is applied to kinds of fossils that are especially restricted in vertical range, widely distributed horizontally, fairly abundant, and sufficiently distinctive in character to permit ready identification. This merely means that some fossils may be differentiated as more useful than others for purposes of correlating the containing rock strata. Abundance makes them more readily found, and if they are distinctive they are less likely to be confused with a somewhat similar fossil. Usefulness as "indicators" of particular zones in which they occur is increased if they are very widespread geographically and is sharpened if they are restricted to a small thickness of beds vertically.

Structural relations.   The age of any sedimentary deposit may be determined relatively by its structural position in respect to associ-

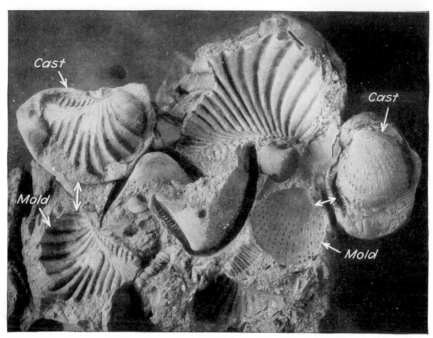

15. Molds and casts of Mesozoic marine shells. The original shell substance has been re-moved by solution from the fine-grained sandstone that bears only the external and internal impressions to show the form of the shells. Replicas of the shells may be made by pouring or pressing a suitable substance into the mold so as to produce a cast. Two such artificially made casts are illustrated. Because the kinds of shells here represented are restricted vertically, but widespread horizontally, they are valuable guide fossils. *(U. S. National Museum.)*

ated rocks. Thus, in a succession of undisturbed beds or only slightly warped strata, relative age is indicated by the order of sequence, the oldest beds occurring at the base and the youngest at the top. This *law of superposition* is a starting point in geologic chronology. By observing the fossil organic remains in a succession of beds, the order of sequence of faunas and floras is established, and once this is learned, the proper age position of isolated occurrences of fossils is indicated. A scale that shows the proper geologic sequence of all assemblages of organisms is built up. Locally, where sedimentary rocks stand vertically or are overturned, relative age is indicated by fossils and also in many instances by physical evidence such as cross-bedding, ripple marks, and the attitude of joints and shear lines.

16. Fossil trail of a four-legged animal in sandstone of Permian age. The impressions on a bedding plane of the Coconino sandstone in the Grand Canyon area of Arizona prove that the maker of the tracks, doubtless a reptile, had sharp-pointed toes. Even though no skeletal remains are found, different kinds of creatures may be identified by distinctive characters of their tracks. *(U. S. National Museum.)*

17. A fossil fish from Early Tertiary lake beds in southwestern Wyoming. The outline and various structural features of this fish are well preserved in the fine mud of a very large fresh-water lake that in Eocene time, about 50 million years ago, extended over parts of Wyoming, Colorado, Utah, and Nevada. The fish lies on a bedding plane of the shale (Green River), the carbonaceous residue differentiating it from adjoining parts of the rock. The body has been greatly flattened by compaction of the sediments. *(American Museum of Natural History.)*

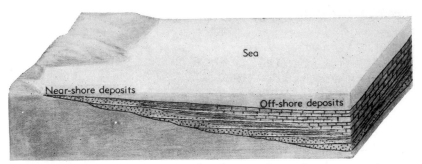

18. Overlap of sedimentary formations. This diagram shows the characteristic structural relations of marine deposits belonging to an uninterrupted succession of beds laid down by a transgressing sea. Each rock layer overlaps in a landward direction the deposits occurring beneath them, so that progressively younger strata come to rest directly on older rocks in the marginal areas of their distribution. It is noteworthy, also, that different types of deposits shift in position as the sea advances on the land. Thus, near-shore deposits are everywhere in contact with older rocks, but they represent successively younger parts of the marine deposits.

When the successions of sedimentary strata are studied throughout a region, special structural relations may be recognized, and these have direct bearing on interpretation of history. *Overlap* consists of the greater extent in some directions of successively younger beds than older ones, so that the more far-reaching or overlapping strata come to rest on older rocks than those they normally overlie. Clearly, this defines an expanding area of sedimentation, as when a sea is slowly transgressing a land area, bringing successively younger marine strata directly into contact with what had been land. The opposite of

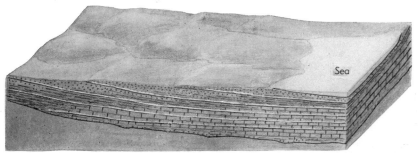

19. Offlap of marine sedimentary formations. The reverse of overlap is offlap, which in marine deposits is produced by a regressing sea. Marginal marine deposits thus come to rest on strata that were laid down in an offshore position.

overlap is *offlap,* in which successively younger beds have more and more restricted distribution. They indicate a retreating area of sedimentation, as when a sea regresses from the land. Study of these structural relations aids in recognizing movements of sea and land.

Sedimentary rock structures in many areas include *folds* and *faults,* especially in mountain belts. Obviously, every such fold and fault is geologically younger than the rocks that are deformed by the fold or fault. How much younger can be learned in those places where undisturbed strata abut or overlie the disturbed beds. If oldest undisturbed rocks in such relations are only slightly younger than the latest formed sediments involved in deformation, geologic date of the deformation may be somewhat narrowly defined. On the other hand, if the gap is large, there is no way to tell reliably whether deformation occurred shortly after deposition of the latest rocks involved in the disturbance, or a very long time later but shortly before deposition of the oldest undisturbed beds. The age of mountain building in any area must be attacked in this way.

A structural relation of sedimentary rocks that is especially im-

20. Geologic dating of crustal deformation. The diagram, which represents part of the eastern border of the Rocky Mountains, shows two sequences of stratified rocks having discordant structure. The tilted and folded beds were truncated by erosion before deposition of the horizontal overlying series. Hard rocks of the folded series make hogbacks, and weak strata form monoclinal valleys. The deformed and eroded rocks were buried beneath younger deposits and then subsequently exhumed partly. The geologic date of the folding must be later than the youngest deformed stratum and older than the lowermost horizontal deposit.

21. Nonconformity separating Pre-Cambrian and Paleozoic formations in the Grand Canyon region of Arizona. Rocks of the V-shaped inner gorge of the canyon consist of crystalline igneous and metamorphic rocks of Pre-Cambrian age. They are truncated evenly by the great nonconformity that forms the lower boundary of Paleozoic rocks in this area. The basal Paleozoic deposit, which is a cliff-making sandstone of Cambrian age, is seen at the summit of the V-shaped gorge. The erosion surface buried by this sandstone is a remarkably even peneplain, which bespeaks very prolonged denudation in pre-Paleozoic time. (*R. C. Moore, U. S. Geol. Survey.*)

portant in historical geology is that represented by unconformities. These are discordances in rock successions that denote interruption in the continuity of rock-making processes. At one extreme is a temporary cessation of sedimentation, unaccompanied by any removal of previously formed deposits; such a minor unconformity is sometimes known as a *diastem*. An interruption in the rock succession where planes of stratification above and below the break are essentially parallel is termed a *disconformity*. No account is taken of the magnitude of the hiatus nor of the configuration of the contact that denotes discordance, which may be very even or quite uneven; the parallelism of beds on opposite sides of the break indicates lack of deformation of the older rocks prior to deposition of the younger. Very considerable erosion, as well as absence of sedimentation, is recognized in connection with some disconformities, but in others no proof of erosion can be found. A *nonconformity* is a type of unconformity in which rocks below the break are more or less distinctly tilted or consist of massive crystalline rocks such as granite or metamorphic rocks like schist. The older rocks have been deformed and have suffered erosion that beveled them prior to deposition of the overlying strata.

Metamorphic Rocks

Kind and distribution. Metamorphic rocks comprise meta-igneous types, derived by alteration of igneous rocks, and meta-sedimentary types, formed by alteration of preexisting sedimentary formations. Identification of the nature of rock materials before metamorphism, wherever this is possible, contributes to correct reading of historical geologic features. Distribution of the metamorphic rocks also has significance. Tracts of metamorphosed rocks somewhat narrowly confined to borders of intrusive igneous rocks represent merely contact metamorphism, whereas very extensive distribution denotes regional metamorphism, which typically affects deeper seated crustal zones and is associated with belts of mountain building. The geologic date when metamorphism of rocks in different areas occurred is indicated by structural relations comparable to those which indicate the time of disturbance of sedimentary rocks. Obliteration of organic remains in most metamorphic rocks makes precise age determinations difficult or impossible.

Correlation

Nature and Objectives

As used in historical geology, correlation applies primarily to determining the equivalence in age of rock formations, but it may also relate to geologic events, such as mountain building in different quarters of the globe or times of glaciation occurring in widely separated areas. The purpose of correlation is not simply to compare the geologic record of one region with that in another, although this is necessary in picturing the evolution of any large area. The basic requirement for correlation lies in the fact that no one area on the earth's surface presents anything like a complete record of geologic

A

limestone

shale

limestone

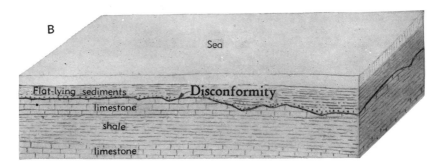

B

Sea

Flat-lying sediments   **Disconformity**

limestone

shale

limestone

C

limestone

shale

sandstone

crystalline rocks

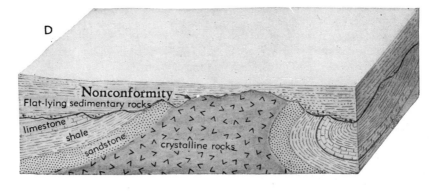

D

Nonconformity

Flat-lying sedimentary rocks

limestone

shale

sandstone   crystalline rocks

history. Sedimentation was interrupted in one region while it proceeded in another. Crustal disturbance, generally accompanied by volcanism, affected crustal belts at certain times, while quiet reigned in other, possibly adjoining, districts. The aim of correlation is to determine the relation of rocks in one area to those in others.

METHODS OF CORRELATION

Continuity.   One of the simplest and most direct means of establishing correlation of sedimentary rock units is that of establishing their continuity. If rock exposures are sufficiently good, equivalence of individual strata a few miles or even some scores of miles apart may be determined by walking along all the intervening outcrops, or perhaps more quickly and painlessly by observing outcrops from a car or tracing them on aerial photographs. By means of borings spaced at reasonably short intervals, beds may be traced reliably underground, and especially by use of techniques such as microscopic examination of well cuttings and correlation of electrical or radioactive well logs, continuity of strata may be established for long distances. Correlation by such means, however, is obviously limited to the sedimentary basin or province in which the formations occur; they have no value for establishing relations between provinces or between different continents.

Lithologic similarity.   Where absence of continuous outcrops and lack of intervening wells give no basis for correlation between two areas, or where sedimentary strata are widely separated by older rocks, as on opposite sides of a broad anticline or mountain belt, similarity of lithology may support correlation. Unless very distinctive peculiarities are duplicated in the two areas, however, correlation on

---

22. Types of unconformities. The diagram at the top (*A*) depicts an erosion surface developed on horizontal limestone that is locally rough but elsewhere smooth. Diagram *B* shows on the sides of the block traces of the disconformity produced by burial of the erosion surface beneath younger sediments. The strata on opposite sides of the disconformity are parallel. Although evidence of this break, as studied throughout the region, is clearly marked, there may be large areas (as that at the left of the diagram) in which contact between the two series is very even. Diagram *C* shows a land surface eroded on deformed crystalline and sedimentary rocks. Where such a land surface is buried by younger strata (block *D*), the nonconformity separating them is readily identified and its historical implication is clear.

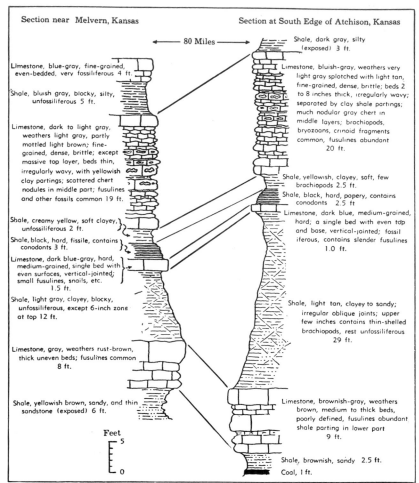

Section near Melvern, Kansas

Section at South Edge of Atchison, Kansas

◄——— 80 Miles ———►

Shale, dark gray, silty
(exposed) 3 ft.

Limestone, blue-gray, fine-grained,
even-bedded, very fossiliferous 4 ft.

Shale, bluish gray, blocky, silty,
unfossiliferous 5 ft.

Limestone, dark to light gray,
weathers light gray, partly
mottled light brown; fine-
grained, dense, brittle; except
massive top layer, beds thin,
irregularly wavy, with yellowish
clay partings; scattered chert
nodules in middle part; fusulines
and other fossils common 19 ft.

Shale, creamy yellow, soft clayey,
unfossiliferous 2 ft.

Shale, black, hard, fissile, contains
conodonts 3 ft.

Limestone, dark blue-gray, hard,
medium-grained, single bed with
even surfaces, vertical-jointed;
small fusulines, snails, etc.
1.5 ft.

Shale, light gray, clayey, blocky,
unfossiliferous, except 6-inch zone
at top 12 ft.

Limestone, gray, weathers rust-brown,
thick uneven beds; fusulines common
8 ft.

Shale, yellowish brown, sandy, and thin
sandstone (exposed) 6 ft.

Feet
5

0

Limestone, bluish-gray, weathers very
light gray splotched with light tan,
fine-grained, dense, brittle; beds 2
to 8 inches thick, irregularly wavy;
separated by clay shale partings;
much nodular gray chert in
middle layers; brachiopods,
bryozoans, crinoid fragments
common, fusulines abundant
20 ft.

Shale, yellowish, clayey, soft, few
brachiopods 2.5 ft.
Shale, black, hard, popery, contains
conodonts 2.5 ft.
Limestone, dark blue, medium-grained,
hard; a single bed with even top
and base, vertical-jointed; fossil
iferous, contains slender fusulines
1.0 ft.

Shale, light tan, clayey to sandy;
irregular oblique joints; upper
few inches contains thin-shelled
brachiopods, rest unfossiliferous
29 ft.

Limestone, brownish-gray, weathers
brown, medium to thick beds,
poorly defined, fusulines abundant
shale parting in lower part
9 ft.

Shale, brownish, sandy 2.5 ft.
Coal, 1 ft.

23. Correlation on the basis of lithologic similarities and identity of sequence. The two successions of stratified rocks in eastern Kansas, shown here plotted to scale, may be correlated on the basis of close correspondence of the nature of the rocks, supplemented by identity in the sequence of the strata. The occurrence of many intermediate outcrops of these rocks between Melvern and Atchison permits confirmation of the accuracy of the correlation shown.

this means alone is very insecure. Observation shows that almost every type of sedimentary deposit occurs somewhere among deposits belonging to each part of past earth history. White sandstone representing a given age at one place is not necessarily represented by white sandstone at another locality 100 miles or even 10 miles distant. On the contrary, we have noted that some sediments, where continuously traceable, show marked lateral variation in lithologic characters.

Structural relations. Similarity of structural relations has value for correlation, at least within a single sedimentary province. This refers not so much to attitude of the beds, which also may have significance, as to the order of sequence of strata. If a succession of beds having differing lithologics and features of stratification is matched elsewhere by a like sequence—especially if thicknesses of respective units approximately correspond—equivalence of the two sections seems probable. Again, correlation on such grounds is not to be expected outside a single sedimentary province.

Organic remains. Similarity of organic remains is the one basis of correlation that may be applied to comparison of sedimentary deposits belonging to different provinces or different continental areas, and with varying precision it indicates equivalence in age. Some marine organisms of the geologic past had a relatively short geologic life span, for their remains are nowhere found distributed through more than a few feet of sedimentary beds; yet identical forms are known from all the continents. Such short-ranging but widely distributed cosmopolitan types are especially valuable for establishment of tie points between rock successions of different parts of the globe. Many other organisms, including both marine and terrestrial types, are found to occur in two or more separated regions of sedimentation or on different continents, and these, too, are indispensable tools for interregional correlation. Finally, it is not to be overlooked that fossils are among the best materials available to the geologist for establishment of correlation within sedimentary basins.

The Geologic Column and Time Scale

DEFINITION AND NATURE

The term *geologic column* refers to the entire succession of rocks, from oldest to youngest, that is known to occur in a given region or on the earth as a whole. Thus, we may speak of the geologic column of Pennsylvania or of Illinois, meaning all the rock divisions collectively that are known to occur in either of these states. Such a column comprises two types of rock units, as discussed later—one consisting of local rock units defined on a lithologic basis and the other of widely recognized rock divisions defined on a paleontological or time basis (time-rock units). The geologic column of a large area, such as a continent or the whole world, consists of time-rock units solely. It is made up by bringing together in proper order the time-rock divisions recognized in different places so as to represent as completely as possible all known geologic time. It is a composite yardstick.

The geologic time scale consists of major and minor time divisions arranged in proper order, corresponding to segments of the geologic column that are defined on a time basis.

The names applied to main time-rock divisions of the geologic column and to corresponding divisions of the geologic time scale are mostly derived from areas where they were first studied and named in Europe, despite the fact that not all these divisions are best developed on that continent. Accordingly, the span of some divisions is modified by data derived from other parts of the world. The geologic columns of Pennsylvania and Illinois, unlike this general column, entirely lack some divisions, because rocks representing these are not found there.

CLASSIFICATION OF CONSTITUENTS

Rock units. All types of rocks may first be classified in units that are defined primarily by their physical nature—that is, lithology. Usage in North America recognizes as the basic element in this classification what is known as a *geologic formation,* which is defined as an assemblage of rocks—igneous, sedimentary, or metamorphic—having generally like characters of lithology and forming a logically differentiated part of the rock succession for geologic mapping. A formation consists typically of rocks representing uninterrupted processes of origin. Formations bear geographic names combined with a lithologic term, as Tuscarora sandstone, Columbus limestone, Utica shale, Milford granite, or varied rocks may be called "formation," without mention of a lithologic type, as Carbondale formation. Boundaries between adjoining formations should be those that any geologist may identify and trace in the field. They may coincide with an unconformity, or simply mark the contact between one type of rock and another. Neither the span nor the boundaries of a rock formation are defined by concepts of time. For example, sand deposited by a transgressing sea may be classed as belonging to a single formation despite evidence that at

24. Contact of two geological formations. The cliff-making rock, which is hard red sandstone, is very unlike the underlying soft, light blue-gray shaly strata. The contact of
these rock units, which are classed as formations, is a boundary that is traced in
geological mapping. Wingate sandstone (Jurassic) on Chinle shale (Triassic) in
southern Utah. (*R. C. Moore, U. S. Geol. Survey.*)

one locality the sandy deposits may be wholly younger than those at
another (Fig. 18).

An important persistent subdivision of a formation is known as
a *member* and may be given a geographic name. A rather local subdivision may be designated as a *lentil,* and part of a formation that
extends laterally into a different formation, eventually pinching out,
is known as a *tongue.* Two or more adjoining formations having certain important features in common may be assembled together as a
group.

According to custom, the geographic names of rock units are nouns
and the initial letter of the rock unit category is not capitalized, as
Colorado group, Leavenworth limestone member.

Time-rock units. Entirely different from rock units in basis of
recognition are divisions of the geologic column known as time-rock
units. These are differentiated from one another by the span of geologic

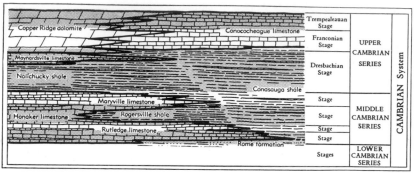

25. Classification of strata in part of the Virginia-Tennessee region according to rock units and rock-time units. The diagram represents a succession of limestone, dolomite, and shale deposits of Cambrian age. The rock units vary in thickness and lateral extent, and in places the different rock units interfinger with one another. The time-rock units shown at the right are determined primarily by characters of fossils; as shown by the alternating light and shaded bands, they do not coincide with lithologic units.

time that they represent and are not defined in any way by lithologic characters.

A basic time-rock unit, termed *stage*, comprises beds representing essentially continuous deposition and containing distinctive organic remains that often may be recognized in widely separated parts of the world. In places such beds may be bounded below and above by hiatuses in sedimentation. Seemingly abrupt changes in the nature of organic remains coincide in position with boundaries between adjoining stages.

Larger in span and composed of two or more stages is the time-rock unit called *series*. Variation in the sedimentary record in different continents, or in different sedimentary basins of the same continent, may lead to definition of series that are only regional in scope.

Major segments of the geologic column, which are deemed to have world-wide application, are known as *systems*. They comprise successive groupings of lesser time-rock units. Each system is broadly characterized by its assemblage of organisms, and in most parts of the world there are discernible breaks between adjacent systems. Owing to continuity of sedimentation in many places, however, problems exist in precise definition of boundaries between the systems in such places.

No generally accepted collective term has been proposed for the rocks of all sorts formed during an era. Accordingly, such units are spoken of simply as Paleozoic rocks, or Mesozoic rocks.

For the purpose of distinguishing time-rock units from rock units, geographic or other definitive names employ an adjectival form, and the initial letter of the time-rock category is capitalized, as in Coloradoan Stage, Cincinnatian Series, Cambrian System.

Time units. Divisions of geologic time are based on the duration of time that corresponds to making of the time-rock units. The time unit corresponding to a stage is designated as *age,* that of a series as an *epoch,* and that of a system as a *period.* An *era* is a long time division comprised of two or more periods and recognized as forming a major chapter in earth history; the eras are partly differentiated and are named from dominant life characters, as Mesozoic, meaning medieval life, the age of dinosaurs.

The names of time units are written like those of corresponding time-rock units, as in Coloradoan Age, Cincinnatian Epoch, Cambrian Period.

MEASUREMENT OF GEOLOGIC TIME

Various attempts to measure geologic time have been undertaken. For example, suppose we knew the average number of years required to make a layer of limestone 1 foot thick and likewise knew data for other sorts of sedimentary rocks; we could then multiply figures representing the total thickness of each rock type by appropriate years-per-foot factors and derive a product representing at least a large part of geologic time. Sedimentation rates are much too variable and little known, however, to put much reliance in such a method of computing geologic time.

During the past few decades, atomic research has led to a new method of measuring geologic time, which within reasonable limitations is reliable and definite. This method depends on the observation that certain radioactive elements—chiefly uranium and thorium— undergo a slow, spontaneous atomic disintegration, unaffected by any surrounding conditions of heat, pressure, chemical association, or the like. Each single atom of uranium (U, atomic weight 238.14) breaks down into one of lead (Pb, atomic weight 206) and in the process liberates 8 atoms of helium (He, atomic weight 4) along with production of heat (0.14). This may be expressed by the equation U $(238.14) = Pb \ (206) + 8 \ He \ (4) + heat \ (0.14)$. The rate of disin-

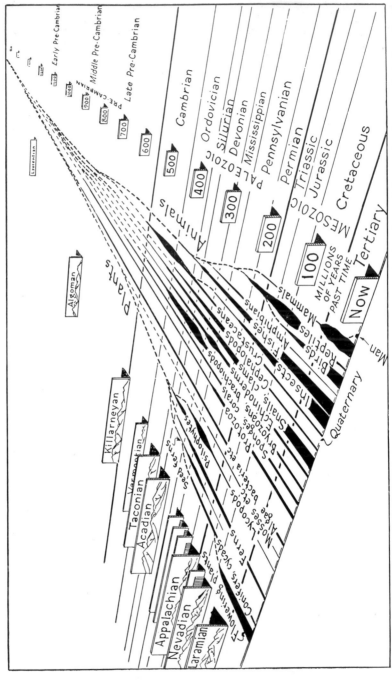

26. Perspective diagram representing geologic time, showing main divisions and indicating the evolutionary development of plants and animals in the course of earth history. Times of important mountain building in North America are posted at the left.

tegration is absolutely constant and can be measured precisely by counting the number of helium atoms given off in a certain space of time by a measured quantity of uranium. Such measurements show that it would require 1,000,000 years for a gram of uranium to yield 1/7,600 gram of lead. Accordingly, the geologic age of a uranium-bearing mineral can be computed using the formula $T = Pb/U \times 7,600$, in which T represents geologic time in millions of years and the ratio of accumulated radiogenic lead (Pb) to remaining uranium (U) is determined and multiplied by the proper factor.

In principle, this radioactive clock may be compared to the old-fashioned hour glass in which time is measured by the slow, steady fall of fine sand through a tiny aperture; a given moment within the hour is marked by the quantity of sand fallen to the bottom part of the glass. Measurement of time by the radioactive method may be based on determining the quantity of helium produced as end product of disintegration, as well as by making a quantitative analysis of lead in a sample. Inasmuch as helium is a very light mobile gas, however, much of it is likely to escape, and age computations based on measurement of helium are likely to yield figures considerably too small, because they cannot measure escaped helium. Erroneous results may be obtained in using the lead method also, if there has been loss of some lead by weathering or if the sample contains primary lead not produced by radioactive disintegration.

The main difficulty in calibrating geologic time with the radioactive clock is the impossibility of precise dating of the uranium- or thorium-bearing minerals in terms of fossil-bearing stratified sedimentary rocks. This is because the radioactive minerals occur in intrusive igneous rocks, and the time of crystallization of these rocks with respect to associated sediments can be determined only indirectly and often incompletely.

The oldest rock yet measured on the basis of reliable radioactive determinations is 1,850 million years old. This rock occurs north of Leningrad in the northwestern part of the U.S.S.R. Studies on lead deposits of many areas indicate that the most probable actual age of the earth is about 3,350 million years (Holmes).

We may better comprehend the immensity of geologic time by changing its scale so as to bring it within mental grasp. Suppose that

1 year of earth history is represented by 1 second on this reduced time scale. Then, 1 minute equals an average human lifetime and barely more than ½ hour corresponds to time from the birth of Christ to the present. If we measure time on this scale starting from Jan. 1, 1950, the date of man's appearance on the earth would be approximately in mid-December, 1949; the beginning of the Mesozoic Era (the age of dinosaurs) would fall in the neighborhood of January, 1946; and the beginning of the Cambrian Period would date back only to early 1933. If the earth is 3 billion years old, it originated—on our reduced scale—in the time of Lincoln, less than 100 years ago.

2. Evolution of Life

Primitive lizardlike reptiles (Casea) from Permian of northern Texas.

Introduction

The observation that organisms preserved as fossils in successive rock layers of the geologic column differ according to relative position of the layers is the essential basis for recognizing that sedimentary deposits at many different places in the world are equivalent in age.

C. R. Knight, Chicago Natural History Museum

This is part of the foundation of historical geology, as discussed in the previous chapter. We need now to extend our introductory study by noting the fact that geologic assemblages of plants and animals show an orderly progression in development from prevailingly simple at the start of the record to highly specialized at its present-day point. The nature of this progressive change and explanation of how it occurs are subjects of great importance and interest.

In the early days of biological science, two centuries ago, no botanist or zoologist conceived that each kind of plant and animal was other than a sharply distinct species having characters given to it when the world began. Each such species, he thought, must have been created individually and separately. The host of extinct species represented by fossil organisms was mostly unknown, and the fact of indefinite boundaries of many species was unrecognized. Some naturalists of the eighteenth and early nineteenth centuries, however, noticed the variation of certain species in seeming response to environment and as a result of experiments in breeding. They suggested that differing forms of life could have evolved by some sort of transformation from preexistent organisms. The concept of organic evolution as the explanation of all variation in plants and animals did not have firm scientific footing, however, until 1859, when Charles Darwin published his epoch-making "Origin of Species." This work contains voluminous incontrovertible documentation of the thesis that all known forms of life are not immutable but on the contrary are subject to evolutionary change. Darwin undertook to explain what he thought was the chief way of producing evolution—unceasing struggle of organisms for existence which leads to varyingly perfect adaptation to their environment and survival of fittest forms. There is need to distinguish between evolution (which Darwin demonstrated and which no competent modern biologist questions) and how evolution is accomplished (which Darwin did not prove and which is not yet adequately known).

Evidence of Evolution

Classification.   The manner in which all known organisms can be arranged in categories based on varying degree of similarities conforms with their origin by evolution, as indicated by the treelike pattern which the categories fit. Related species correspond to twigs growing from a common branchlet (a genus), and related genera comprise branchlets of a single branch (a family); the branches are divergent parts of larger and larger branches (orders, classes, phyla) that in turn spread from main trunks (plant and animal kingdoms). The ascending series of organic groups that show increasing complexity of organization is readily explainable as the product of evolution but not rationally accountable otherwise.

Biochemical relationships. Living matter of whatever sort, as distinguished from nonliving, is characterized by the highly complex chemical structure of its basic constituent molecules, which are mainly formed of carbon, hydrogen, and oxygen. Also, living matter has the properties of growth, response to environmental stimuli, and reproduction. The substance of this matter, called "protoplasm," is not a particular chemical compound but a mixture of interdependent molecular structures, of which some are in process of more complex organization and some are products of decomposition. These common attributes and the continuity in kind and degree of increasing specialization are strong evidence that all organisms are derived from pre-existing living organisms without break. We are ignorant of the conditions of ultimate beginning of the physicochemical chain of life, but that it is an unbroken chain of unnumbered links and directions of branching we cannot doubt.

A biochemical proof of relationship among branches of the tree of life is the close correspondence between quantity of precipitate obtainable from the blood of one animal when tested with that of another and degree of kinship of these animals as inferred from their evolutionary differentiation. For example, the blood of man shows progressively increased precipitate when tested with serum from such animals as a lizard, pig, lemur, ape, and man.

Structural resemblance. The structural organization of plants and animals exhibits similarities in inverse proportion to their evolutionary differentiation. This is seen in structures of the stem, leaf, flower, and seed of various plants, but is most readily apparent in comparative study of the anatomy of many animals. All limb-bearing vertebrates, for example, possess the same basic skeletal plan consisting of skull, backbone, shoulder and pelvic girdles, and four limbs formed of similarly arranged bones. In proportion to their relationship, these animals also show exact correspondence in the nature of their mus-

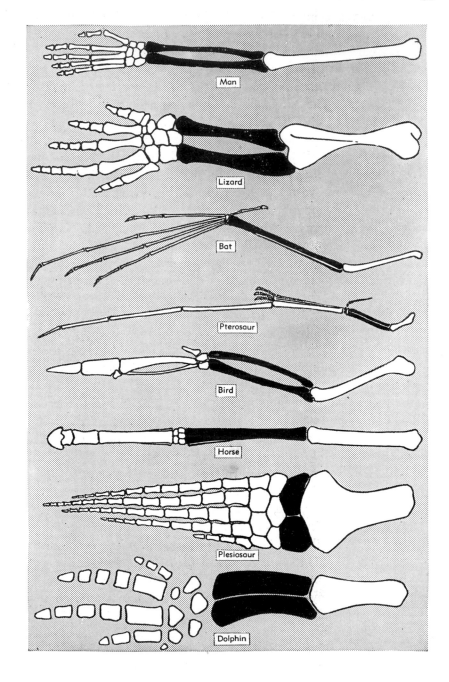

culature, digestive and reproductive organs, circulatory system, and nervous system. Such uniformity of pattern is readily explained as an inheritance of common evolutionary origin but is inexplicable otherwise.

Sequence of growth stages. It is an interesting fact that in varying degree early growth stages of animals reflect adult life forms of the stock from which they are descended. Thus, the human embryo, for example, passes through blastula and gastrula stages characteristic of fully formed primitive invertebrates, and subsequently it has well-defined gill arches like those of a fish; the development of the circulatory system repeats characteristic features seen in fishes, amphibians, and reptiles; the embryo is far advanced before it begins to take on characters that may differentiate it from other mammals. The generalization that the life history of an individual repeats racial history of the group to which the animal belongs is not wholly true because there are many necessary qualifications and variations. This so-called biogenetic law, that "ontogeny recapitulates phylogeny," does agree with many observations on the nature of successive growth stages and supports evolutionary concepts.

Vestigial structures. The organic world contains innumerable examples of once useful organs or other structures that in the course of evolution have become no longer functional. They persist as vestiges, like man's vermiform appendix, hidden little bony tail, ear-moving muscles, and the pineal body in the skull, which is remnant of a third eye that is still well developed in some lizards. Unless such structures become adapted to serve other needs, they are likely to disappear ultimately. These vestiges comprise one type of documentation of evolution because we can recognize them as traces of formerly useful parts.

Experimentation. Man has proved by trial and error, by breeding and selection, that he can change the characters of plant and animal

---

27. Skeletal structure of the front limb of various animals showing correspondence (homology) of component bones. Each has a single upper limb bone (humerus), two bones or remnants of them (radius, ulna) which are represented in black on the diagram, wristbones, and fingers. The arm of man and the lizard is unspecialized, whereas that of the bat, pterosaur, and bird is modified for flight in the air, that of the horse for swift running, and that of the plesiosaur and dolphin for swimming.

species radically. Tulips and other kinds of flowers, hybrid corn, many special types of wheat, vegetables, shrubs, fruit, trees—all these have been modified in various ways because of commercial advantage, aesthetic appeal, or curiosity. Animals, too, have been specialized in divergent ways. Differences between a large draft horse, like a percheron, a race horse, and a shetland pony are greater than between some species, but they are far surpassed by differences of every sort shown by innumerable breeds of dogs. It is hard to imagine that a huge mastiff and tiny pomeranian, a greyhound and a dachshund,

28. Some types of dogs produced by breeding. Dogs well illustrate the range in shape, size, and various aptitudes produced by man under controlled conditions of evolution.

29. Quarry site and some of the bones of extinct mammals excavated from Tertiary strata in western Nebraska. Miocene deposits at Agate Springs, Neb., locally contain well-preserved skeletal remains of thousands of plains animals belonging to species that long ago disappeared from North America. *(American Museum of Natural History.)*

30. A fossil fish of Early Tertiary age. Skeletons of the fishes and many types of higher vertebrates found in the rocks are invaluable paleontological documents that define the actual course of evolutionary development. Comparative study of such remains may lead to conclusions on the ancestral relationships of the organisms.

and many others are artificial derivatives of a common ancestral stock. If nature has done and does what experimentation by man has shown can be accomplished in changing organisms, this is in accord with evolution.

Paleontological evidence. More convincing than any other testimony as to actuality of the evolution of life forms from relatively simple to advanced types is afforded by fossils. These are the incontrovertible records of organisms that formerly lived on the earth. Their structural features, insofar as determinable from hard parts that have been preserved, show the sort of differentiation that had been attained by various plant and animal groups at a given stage in earth history, and comparison of this with earlier and later stages demonstrates the direction of evolutionary modifications.

The fossils may thus be viewed as documents having various degrees of antiquity that are found in the geological archives. They show that forms of life in the comparatively recent past are not greatly different from those living today; on lands the dominant animals are mammals that differ in kind but belong to stocks living today, the plants include abundant flowering trees and shrubs, and marine life includes invertebrates that are closely similar to types represented by shells washed up on modern shore lines. More ancient deposits contain organic remains which differ obviously from living forms and which include only moderately specialized types of plants and animals. Still older rocks yield more primitive organisms, until among the oldest known are only marine plants and a few kinds of invertebrates.

The paleontological record thus furnishes samples of successive populations ranging in age from the distant past down to the present, and these populations show gradual change of many sorts conforming to postulates of the theory of evolution. The forms of life have advanced from the simple to the complex and from the unspecialized to the specialized, but many primitive types of organisms have persisted with little change. So-called missing links in the chain of evolutionary advance are represented by certain fossils, such as the half-lizard half-bird creature that helps define the reptilian ancestry of the birds.

Mode of Evolution

To know why organisms evolve and how evolutionary changes are accomplished is important because one who grasps these things can far better comprehend the history of life and varying physical conditions that make organic ovironments in past geologic periods. However, answers to these questions require appraisal of voluminous, complex data in the fields of genetics, ecology, biogeography, neobiology, and paleontology, and despite much progress, there are still many uncertainties. We confine attention to organic variation, transmittal of variation by heredity, and natural selection.

Organic variation and heredity. No two individuals among plants or animals are precisely identical, however closely they may be related. Offspring differ slightly from parents, and members of any given generation vary among themselves. The bulk of population belonging to a species living at any time has characters, however, that are grouped closely around a mean, and only a small fraction deviates considerably from this average. It is recognized that two sets of factors are expressed in variation within a species or other systematic unit, one being the inherited characters (dependent on features of the germ plasm) and the other being effects of environment. The latter may be repeated in successive generations but, according to tests by experimentation, are not (as postulated by Lamarck) transmissible as acquired characters. Features transmitted by the germ plasm reproduce themselves in successive generations and, if adapted to their surroundings, they tend to persist, thus leading to evolution. Much has been learned of the nature of chromosomes and genes and the mechanism of heredity, but it is not appropriate here to review studies in the field of genetics.

vantage and tend to be weeded out by nature. This natural selection is unquestionably effective, as pointed out by Darwin, in developing and perpetuating differences in plants and animals, whatever may be the germ-plasm mechanism that leads to transmittal of characters. Populations may thus diverge so as to produce distinct species and genera, and such differentiation may be both contemporaneous and sequent in time; also, some systematic groups may exhibit progressive gradual change while maintaining comparative stability in the limit of variation of the successive populations. Fitness for a given mode of life and effective adaptation to environment are important factors in the operation of evolution.

Expression of Evolution

Adaptive divergence.   Both plants and animals of many sorts show remarkable changes in form, structure, growth habits, and even mode of reproduction in becoming adapted to different climatic environment, type of food supply, or mode of living. This divergence in response to evolution is commonly expressed by altering the form and

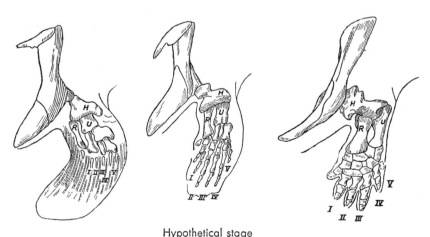

| Devonian lobe-finned fish | Hypothetical stage intermediate between fish and amphibian | Late Paleozoic amphibian |

33. Structural evolution of the limbs of an amphibian. The diagrams indicate that no great change is required to evolve the primitive plan of limb bones belonging to the higher vertebrates out of the ancestral lobe-finned fishes. (*W. K. Gregory, from K. F. Mather, "Sons of the Earth," W. W. Norton and Co., Inc.*)

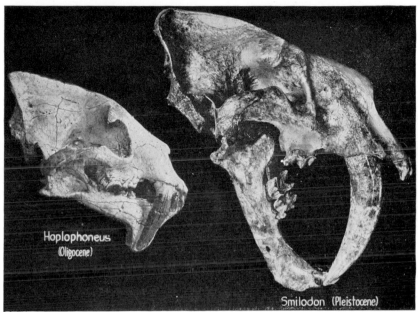

34. Skulls of two types of extinct sabertooth cats from the western United States. The smaller skull belongs to an Oligocene cat *(Hoplophoneus)* and the larger one to a Pleistocene lion *(Smilodon)*. Adaptive specialization is especially shown by characters of the teeth which are suited for grasping and tearing flesh. The teeth of *Smilodon* were notably reduced in number as compared with earlier mammals, for this creature had only 12 to 14 teeth all together. *(American Museum of Natural History.)*

function of some part or parts of the organism, the original identity of which is clearly discernible. For example, the creeping foot of the snail is seen in related marine pteropods to be modified into a flapping organ useful for swimming, and it is changed into prehensile arms that bear suctorial disks in the squids and other cephalopods. The limbs of various mammals are modified according to several different modes of life—for swift running (cursorial) as in the horse and antelope, for swinging in trees (arboreal) as in the monkeys, for digging (fossorial) as in the moles and gophers, for flying (volant) as in the bats, for swimming (aquatic) as in the seals, whales, and dolphins, and for other adaptations. The structures or organs that show main change in connection with this adaptive divergence are commonly identified readily as homologous, in spite of great alterations. Thus, the finger and wristbones of a bat and whale, for instance, have virtually nothing in common except that they are definitely equivalent elements of the mammalian limb.

Adaptive convergence. The opposite of adaptive divergence is an interesting and fairly common expression of evolution. This is adaptive convergence. Whereas related groups of organisms take on widely different characters in becoming adapted to unlike environments in the case of adaptive divergence, we find that unrelated groups of

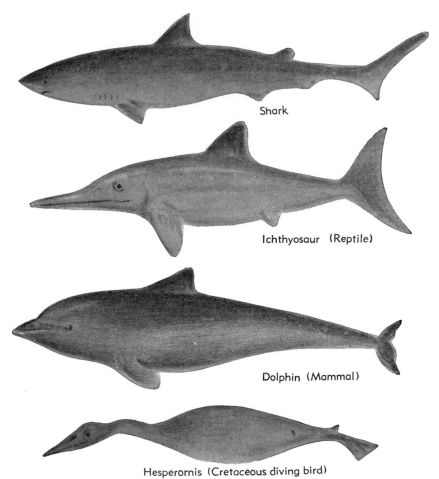

Shark

Ichthyosaur (Reptile)

Dolphin (Mammal)

Hesperornis (Cretaceous diving bird)

35. Adaptive convergence in the form of swimming animals. Fishes and other animals, such as reptiles, mammals, and birds, which have become specially fitted for life in the water, tend to develop a streamlined cigar-shaped form. Except the shark, the animals shown here are air breathers, but none could get around efficiently on land.

organisms exhibit adaptive convergence when they adopt similar modes of life or become suited for special sorts of environments. For example, invertebrate marine animals living firmly attached to the sea bottom or to some foreign object tend to develop a subcylindrical or conical form. This is illustrated by coral individuals, many sponges, and even by the diminutive tubes of bryozoans. Adaptive convergence in taking this coral-like form is shown by some brachiopods and pelecypods that grew in fixed position. More readily appreciated is the streamlined fitness of most fishes for moving swiftly through water; they have no neck, the contour of the body is smoothly curved so as to give minimum resistance, and the chief propelling organ is a powerful tail fin. The fact that some fossil reptiles (ichthyosaurs) and modern mammals (whales, dolphins) are wholly fishlike in form is an expression of adaptive convergence, for these air-breathing reptiles and mammals, which are highly efficient swimmers, are not closely related to fishes. Unrelated or distantly related organisms that develop similarity of form are sometimes designated as homeomorphs (having same form).

Trends of Evolution

Historical geology throws light on the trend of evolutionary changes that characterize both plant and animal groups. The record of life that is preserved in successive sedimentary formations shows how various stocks began as unspecialized offshoots of antecedent organisms, became gradually differentiated, and in general eventually vanished. The factor of time, stretching out through hundred-thousands or millions of years, may be observed in its effects on organic populations. Successful adaptations to the struggle of living under various conditions of physical environment, availability of food supply, interference by competitors and enemies, and abundance in survival of new generations, commonly result in increase in average size of individuals and in a branching that gradually produces new species and genera. As divergent branches become specialized, they tend to be less and less alterable, and after reaching a certain culmination, they die out.

A survey of the record of life permits the following generalizations concerning evolutionary trends. Organisms having simple structures tend to persist; those characterized by complex structures tend to be short-lived. Loss of acquired structures is permanent; for example, air-breathing vertebrates, which are all indirect descendants of fishes, cannot revert to respiration by means of gills. On the whole, plant and animal stocks have advanced progressively in complexity of structure during geological history, but simple forms of life have persisted also. Many specialized branches have prospered for a time and then disappeared. Among most organisms, the life history of the individual recapitulates with varying clearness and completeness the evolutionary changes belonging to its branch of the plant or animal world.

3. The Beginning of the Earth

One of the "island universes" lying far outside of our stellar galaxy.

The Earth in Space

The Earth is a nearly perfect sphere, slightly flattened at the poles and bulging at the equator. It is one of a family of bodies that revolve about the Sun in the same direction and in nearly a common plane. This family comprises nine planets (including the recently discovered, far-distant Pluto) and some 1,300 smaller bodies called "planetoids." The four inner planets (Mercury, Venus, Earth, Mars) are smaller

Lick Observatory

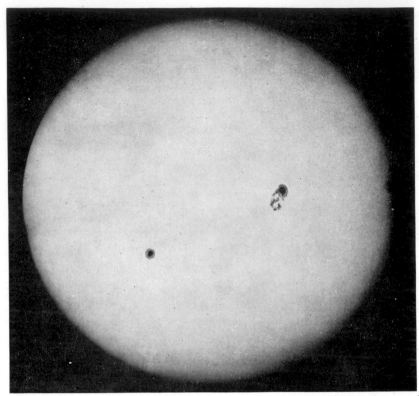

36. The star that we call Sun, which controls movements of the Earth and other planets and which almost surely is their parent. The Sun is composed of materials that are identified also on the Earth, but at the enormously high temperatures prevailing in the Sun, all substances are incandescent gases in turbulent movement. Sun spots, such as the two large ones shown in this photograph, are centers of vortical disturbance in which upwardly projected matter is cooled by sudden expansion, so that it appears dark in comparison to adjacent parts of the Sun's face; they exhibit magnetic properties, and streams of electrons emitted at times of sun-spot activity affect atmospheric conditions on the Earth. *(Mount Wilson Observatory.)*

and denser than the outer ones (Jupiter, Saturn, Uranus, Neptune) except Pluto, which seems to have about the size of the Earth. Most of the planets are accompanied by one or more moons which revolve in nearly circular orbits in the direction of the planet's rotation and nearly in the plane of their equators. The Earth's moon is exceptional

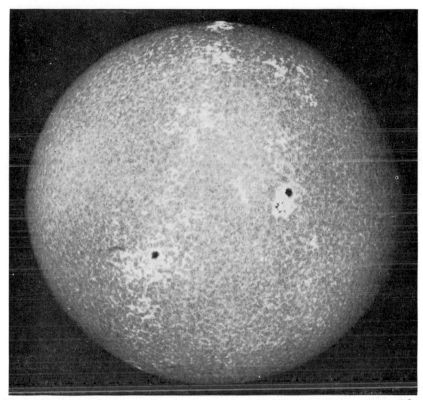

37. Appearance of the Sun as photographed in the light of its incandescent calcium. The mottled aspect of the Sun's disk in this view records the uneven concentration of the element (calcium) in the Sun's atmosphere that furnished the monochromatic light selected for making the photograph. It indicates the agitated condition of matter near the Sun's surface, which is in contrast to the relative stability of the Earth's atmosphere. The same Sun spots that appear in Fig. 36 are seen in this photograph. *(Mount Wilson Observatory.)*

in magnitude as compared to its planet in that its orbital plane is distinctly inclined to the Earth's equator, lying nearly in the common plane of revolution of all the planets.

The dominant body in the part of the universe where the Earth moves through space is the Sun, 93 million miles distant from the Earth. The Sun is one of the lesser stars, a white-hot gaseous sphere having a diameter of 864,000 miles and a mass 332,000 times greater

38. Explosively ejected prominences of Sun substances that reach a height of 140,000 miles.
These eruptions are not visible when the intense sunlight of ordinary daytime is
diffused by the Earth's atmosphere, but they may be seen during a complete solar
eclipse or by artificially blocking out the Sun's disk in a telescope. The small white
disk represents the size of the Earth. *(Mount Wilson Observatory.)*

than that of the Earth. It rotates once in 25 of the Earth's days, turning slowly in the same direction as that in which the planets revolve
about the Sun; the plane of the Sun's equator is inclined about 7 degrees to the mean plane of the planets' orbits. The huge energy and
heat of the Sun's mass and its enormous radiation of energy into
space are its oustanding characters. Measurements of the radiation
show that the temperature near the Sun's surface is about 6000°C.,
but that of its center is estimated at 30 to 60 million degrees C. The
surface heat is sufficient to vaporize any known substance, and on
Earth is matched only momentarily and microscopically on nature's
scale by the explosion of an atom bomb. Explosive energies within

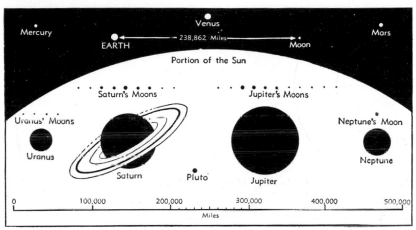

39. The size of planetary bodies compared with a portion of the Sun. The four lesser planets, which are nearest to the Sun, are shown in the upper part of the diagram; they have relatively high density (3.7 to 5.5), whereas the large outer planets are low in density (0.7 to 1.4). The Earth's Moon is unusually large as compared to the planet around which it revolves, but it is matched in size by some of the moons of Jupiter and Saturn and by Neptune's lone moon.

the Sun are judged to represent a splitting and re-forming of atoms with inconceivable rapidity and greatness of scale, explosive disruption of the Sun's mass being prevented only by its enormous gravity. Even so, energy radiated into space corresponds to a loss of mass amounting to more than 4 million tons per second—a radiation of which the Earth receives only one 2-billionth part. Truly, the planets are very minor objects as compared with this star, our Sun, that governs their motions. Also, the largest of the four inner planets, which is the Earth, is very small as compared with Jupiter, which has 318 times its mass and 1,312 times its volume.

The Sun and planets, along with their attendant moons, comprise the main parts of the Solar System. Lesser bodies, such as a great flock of comets and a host of insignificant stony or metallic objects, termed *meteorites,* also belong to the system. The direction of infall of meteorites on the Earth, however, indicates that many of them are foreign to the Solar System. From the standpoint of Earth study, the most significant observation we may make about the Solar System is its essential unity, which is manifested in many features additional to

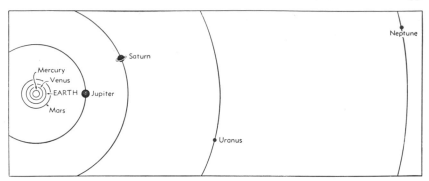

40. Orbits of the planets, showing wide spacing of the outer planets in comparison to the inner ones. The planets revolve around the Sun in nearly circular orbits that lie in almost coincident planes. The size of the planets is exaggerated 100 times with respect to the scale of the orbits.

those mentioned here. It is inconceivable that conditions or events that produced the Earth were not the same as those that made the other planets.

Origin of the Solar System

Two-star hypotheses. A plausible explanation of how our Solar System may have originated is given by two Americans—geologist T. C. Chamberlin, and astronomer F. R. Moulton—and two British scientists —astronomer James Jeans and geophysicist Harold Jeffreys. The basic feature of their hypothesis is that all the planets and lesser bodies of the Solar System that now move around the Sun were formerly parts of the Sun itself. They comprise fragments of Sun matter that have been explosively ejected from it as result of disturbance caused by the passage of another sun—that is, a star—at a distance near enough to affect our Sun's gravitative pull. Such an event must have happened a long time ago, and the subsequent onward flight of this presumed visitor has now carried it so far that it cannot be identified among stars of the heavens.

Known facts about the masses and constitution of stars, including our Sun, indicate that even if the closest approach of star to Sun was several billion miles, the effective inward pull of the Sun's gravity would be so weakened on the side facing the star and opposite to it (after the manner of tides) that explosive eruptions of some material in these directions would be inevitable. Some eruptions would begin

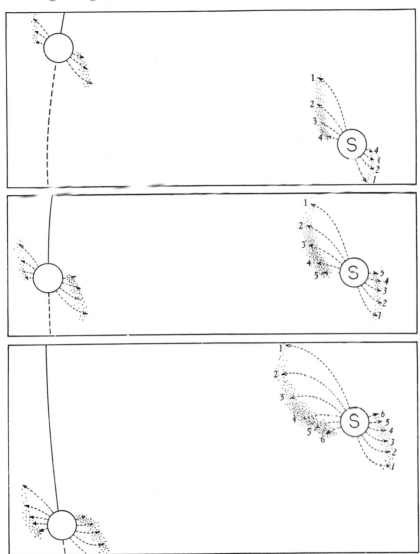

41. Beginning of the planetary system caused by tidal disturbance exerted by a passing star on our Sun *(S)*. Three successive stages in the postulated passage of the star and Sun are shown in the diagrams, and movement of ejected matter from the Sun is represented by dotted lines that are numbered in order of ejection. Curvature of the lines reflects deviation of the ejected matter under influence of differential pull by the passing star. The dispersed Sun matter, consisting of planetesimals (Chamberlin-Moulton) or a gaseous streamer (Jeans-Jeffreys), is thrown into orbital movement around the Sun and segregation into planetary bodies is inaugurated.

as the star approached, reach culminating violence while the star was near it, and diminish as the star receded into space. Changing relative positions of the star with respect to the Sun would cause successive ejections of Sun matter to be thrown out in different directions much as when the nozzle of a hose is rotated sideward. The dispersed material would be distributed essentially in a plane defined by the star's course with respect to the Sun. Undoubtedly, some of the ejected material would fall back into the Sun, but the Sun's own motion, and deflection due to the side pull of the star during its passage, would cause much of the dispersed material to revolve in highly elliptical orbits around the Sun. The planes of these orbits would very nearly coincide.

Organization of the disrupted Sun material into definite planetary bodies and the evolution of near circularity of revolutionary motion are variously explained. According to Chamberlin and Moulton, centers of planetary growth were major masses or nuclei of Sun matter, which by reason of their own gravitative pull served to collect the lesser bodies, which they call *planetesimals*. Infall of planetesimals would gradually add to the mass of planetary nuclei and eventually sweep up most of the independently revolving small bodies. Analysis of the net effect of infalling planetesimals proves that they would tend to throw the nuclei into more and more nearly circular orbits and induce forward rotation of the planets, features that characterize our observed system.

According to Jeans and Jeffreys, however, initiation of the planets is presumed to depend essentially on the breaking into segments of what were originally nearly continuous long streamers of incandescent gaseous matter. On this hypothesis, there is relatively little need for subsequent sweeping up of planetesimals. If, in agreement with the concept of successive solar ejections under the influence of the passing star, the largest volume of ejected matter should have been intermediate between the inner and outer parts, and if lighter elements tended generally to be expelled farthest from the sun, peculiarities in the distribution, size, and specific gravity of the planets would find reasonable explanation.

The Earth and neighboring inner planets are small, relatively heavy, and much more closely spaced than the large, light outer planets, dominated by Jupiter, which are widely spaced. Gradually acquired

42. Part of the Moon's surface. This photograph of the Moon in the first quarter shows the large relatively smooth dark areas called *seas* (although no water exists on the Moon) and lighter areas containing innumerable craters. *(Lick Observatory, University of California.)*

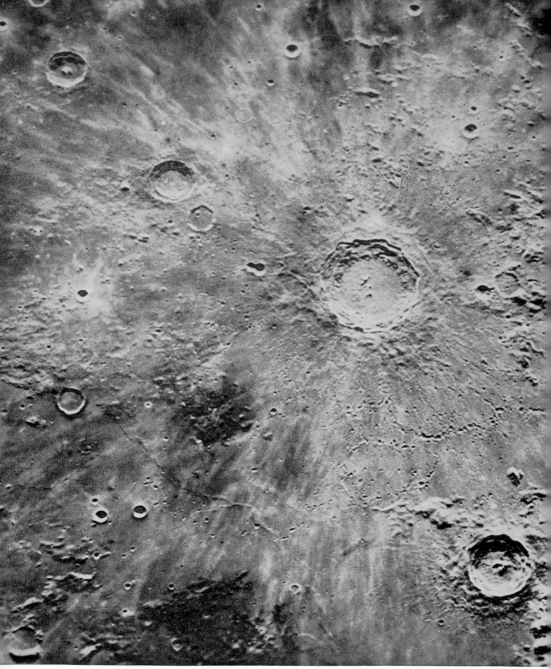

43. Craters of the Moon. The large crater in the center of the view is Copernicus, nearly 100 miles in diameter and having a rim approximately 20,000 feet high. The central peaks in this and other craters and the prominent radiating streaks may reflect infall of planetary bodies; through absence of weathering, surface features on the Moon may be preserved intact indefinitely. *(Lick Observatory, University of California.)*

circularity of the planetary orbits is ascribed by Jeans and Jeffreys to the cumulating resistance effects of a gaseous atmosphere that is supposed to have surrounded the Sun and to have been composed mostly of light materials that leaked away from the bolts of ejected matter.

Satellites of the larger planets represent segregations of originally gaseous materials that were ejected from the planets by tidal disruption. This disruption was induced by the Sun during first passages of the planets in elliptical orbits that brought them relatively near the Sun. Thus, in miniature they represent processes that produced the planets themselves. Certain satellites that depart from rule, as to the plane and direction of their revolution, may be explained as the result of capture by one planet from another during early stages in development of the system.

The Earth's Moon, which has $1/81$ of the mass of the Earth, is unusually great in relative magnitude—in fact, the Earth and Moon may be considered as a double planet, composed of two very unequal parts. Mathematical calculations show that the Moon may have been formed by splitting apart from the Earth as a result of tidal stresses when the combined body was in a liquid or semiliquid state. Reces-

44. A nickel-iron meteorite from Texas weighing 1,630 pounds. Meteorites comprise metallic and stony masses that become incandescent and luminous by reason of friction in their passage through the Earth's atmosphere. Some millions of these bodies are reported to collide with the Earth daily, but a large majority of these disintegrate before reaching the Earth's surface. Some may comprise planetesimals, but the velocity and direction of others indicate origin outside the planetary system. (*Peabody Museum, Yale University.*)

45. Meteor crater near Winslow, Ariz. This air view admirably shows the steep walls and floor of the bowl-shaped cavity, which is 550 feet deep and 4,000 feet across; the elevated rim rises more than 100 feet above the smooth plain that surrounds the crater. Many tons of meteoritic iron have been found in and near the crater. The crater is judged to have been formed by impact and explosion of a large meteorite. *(Spence Air Photos.)*

sion of the Moon to its present distance of 283,000 miles from the Earth and slowing of its rotation until it keeps always the same face toward the Earth are effects of the mutual tidal retardation of the Earth and the Moon. The Moon is too small to hold an atmosphere, and its crater-marked surface and broad lava-like plains are unaffected by weathering. The larger craters have diameters exceeding 100 miles, and they have circular rims up to 20,000 feet in altitude. Radiating streaks extend outward for hundreds of miles from some of them. Perhaps these features denote a former stage of great volcanic activity, but they have been interpreted also as marks due to infall of bodies such as large planetesimals. A buckshot falling on mud may produce an identical pattern.

One-star hypotheses. Explanation of the origin of the Earth and other planets by evolution of a single star—our Sun—without interference or disturbance of another heavenly body was generally accepted by scientists of the nineteenth century. A German philosopher, Kant, in 1755, and a French mathematician, LaPlace, in 1796, published closely similar hypotheses, which postulated that the Solar System was derived from condensation of an enormously dispersed gaseous atmosphere surrounding the Sun. Increased rotational velocity of this atmosphere during condensation was assumed to have produced a discoidal shape, the plane of the disk coinciding with that of the Sun's equator. When velocity at the periphery of the disk reached a critical point, it was judged that centrifugal force would throw off part of the gas as a ring and that breaking up of this ring would produce a planet. The planet would revolve around the Sun in the path of the former ring. Successive rings would make planets nearer to the Sun and ultimately nearly all gas not gathered to make the planets would condense into the Sun. According to this hypothesis, the Sun should possess almost all of the energy of angular motion (moment of momentum) of the System, inasmuch as the Sun's mass is equal to about 99 times that of all planets put together. When it was learned that the planets possess 98 per cent of the total angular momentum of the System—not to mention other difficulties—it seemed necessary to abandon the hypothesis of Kant and LaPlace.

Recently, several European and American scientists (Alfven, 1942; Berlage, 1940; ter Haar, 1948; Weiszacker, 1944; Whipple, 1947) have developed hypotheses based on condensation of gaseous and solid particles in a greatly expanded envelope surrounding the Sun. Utilizing present knowledge of physics in relation to magnetism and condensation of heated vapors of varying composition and temperature, plausible explanations are being developed, not only for the distribution of angular momentum but the spacing and specific gravities of the planets and peculiarities of the satellites. So it may be that origin and evolution of the Solar System again will be judged to follow the general pattern of the hypothesis introduced by Kant and LaPlace.

Molten Earth State

That our Earth passed through a molten state early in its history is a seemingly inescapable conclusion. Initially, its Sun-derived sub-

stance was incandescent and white-hot; probably it was largely gaseous. According to one view, this earliest phase of Earth development
was characterized by a total mass much smaller than that of the Earth
today, and because of such small mass, it is thought to have cooled
rather rapidly to a liquid and finally a solid state. Increase of size
through infall of planetesimal matter, if rapid, would have developed
such heat of impact that the Earth would have remained molten
during most of its growth; on the other hand, if infall of matter was
slow, as postulated by Chamberlin, the Earth may have remained
solid during growth.

If the Earth's share of Sun matter was at outset essentially the same
as its present mass, a molten state must have persisted for a considerable time. Jupiter and the other large planets are still molten, but the
smaller planets have solidified. Strong indication that the Earth was
molten at a time when it had attained about its present mass is found
in the high degree of density stratification within its body, as indicated
by seismic and other observations. The outer Earth crust has an average specific gravity of about 3.0, whereas deeper layers increase progressively in density to about 11.0 in the heavy core. The whole Earth
averages 5.5 in specific gravity. The arrangement of densities is readily
understood if the globe was once molten, for heaviest substances
would come to accumulate below the lighter ones, just as in molten ore
the metal sinks and the rocky slag rises.

Origin of Continents and Ocean Basins

Unevenness in surface configuration of the rock body of the Earth,
or lithosphere, is represented by the differentiation of great land and
water areas of the globe. Continents occupy about one-fourth of the
Earth's surface and oceanic areas roughly three-fourths. The continents
are protuberant parts of the lithosphere, and the oceans occupy relatively depressed parts. The vertical span from the top of the highest
mountain peak (Mt. Everest in the Himalayas) to the bottom of the
ocean's greatest deep is about 13 miles, but the average height of
continents above the average ocean bottom is only 3 miles. This 3-mile
value of average vertical relief is seemingly large and it has far-
reaching importance in Earth history. Yet it is not a very significant
feature in the shape of the Earth as a whole. On a 5-foot globe, the

protuberant continental areas would be represented by a thickness of about $\frac{1}{50}$ inch, which might be represented by a layer of varnish spread over parts of the globe corresponding to areas of the continents. If the distribution of water and land did not serve to differentiate the elevated and relatively depressed parts of the lithosphere, an observer of this 5-foot globe probably would not be able to detect the slightest unevenness in its spherical surface.

The facts just stated do not alter our interest in knowing how and when the continental and oceanic areas of the Earth became differentiated. If we note the values of gravity measurements that have been made at thousands of point on land and at widely distributed though lesser number of points in oceanic areas, it is evident that the protuberant parts (continents) of the lithosphere are light and that relatively depressed parts (ocean basins) are heavy. The respective, average specific gravities are about 2.7 and 3.3. As indicated by the following equation, a relatively light, thick block of continental Earth crust having an area of say 1,000 square miles corresponds in mass to a relatively heavy, thin block of oceanic Earth crust of the same area.

$$\frac{\text{Continental area}}{\text{1,000 square miles}} \times \frac{\text{crustal thickness}}{\textbf{x miles} + 3 \text{ miles}} \times \frac{\text{specific gravity}}{2.7} =$$

$$\frac{\text{oceanic area}}{\text{1,000 square miles}} \times \frac{\text{crustal thickness}}{\textbf{x miles}} \times \frac{\text{specific gravity}}{3.3}$$

Such masses are essentially in weight equilibrium, and accordingly we reason that the continents stand high because they are light. The continents thus represent segregations of relatively light rock material. Some features of their form and distribution suggest their origin in changing rotation rate of the globe, accompanied by slight shrinkage in cooling during a late formative stage in the Earth's early growth, probably in connection with solidification. In any case, it seems evident that no major change from continental to oceanic area, or vice versa, can occur without an accompanying radical shift of mass. Lack of any known mechanism competent to produce such change and evidence supplied by many features of geologic history, outlined in later chapters of this book, indicate that the continents and oceans are essentially permanent features of the Earth's surface.

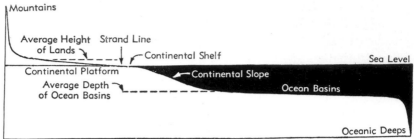

46. Profile showing configuration of the surface of the lithosphere. The relative height of continental areas and depth of ocean basins are shown quantitatively, the width of the diagram representing 100 per cent of the Earth's surface. The small fraction of the surface comprised by mountains and ocean deeps is indicated, and the broad distinction between continental platform and ocean basin areas is emphasized.

They were formed before the time of making any rocks now accessible to the geologist. It is significant that the oldest known rocks are metamorphosed sediments and that no vestige of an original igneous crust of the Earth has been identified.

4. The Pre-Cambrian Era

Pre-Cambrian granite in the Black Hills of South Dakota.

Introduction

The beginning of earth history determinable from rocks exposed at the surface represents time a little less than 2,000 million years ago according to radioactive measurement. There is no way of knowing how much time elapsed between birth of the earth and the making of these oldest known rocks, but it was probably at least 500 million and perhaps more than 1,000 million years. Rocks still older than the oldest now known may be discovered, but that will not appreciably lessen the obscurity of early earth history that man never can remove.

Base of the Cambrian rocks as a historical datum. One of the most important points of reference in the geologic time scale—com-

Chicago and Northwestern Railway

parable to the birth of Christ in reckoning time in years A.D. and B.C.—
is the base of the Cambrian System of rocks. These strata are the oldest
that contain very numerous fossils in many parts of the globe. Older
rock formations, belonging below the Cambrian, are virtually devoid
of organic remains. Whereas fossils occurring in the Cambrian and
younger rocks permit fairly exact correlation of them throughout the
world, and thus give basis for determining equivalence in age, the
Pre-Cambrian rocks cannot be correlated reliably for any great distance. The succession of Pre-Cambrian rocks in one region may be
determined and significant features of early earth history in the
region be interpreted; but absence of fossils, which would indicate
placement in geologic time, means that records of Pre-Cambrian time
on different continents, and even in different regions of the same continent, cannot be fitted together so as to give a connected story.

The unfossiliferous Pre-Cambrian rocks differ broadly from Cambrian and younger formations in physical constitution and structure.
The old rocks are mainly crystalline. Batholithic igneous rocks, such
as granite, are very common, and there is an abundance of highly
metamorphosed rocks. Structure generally is complex. The Cambrian
and later formations are dominantly composed of sedimentary strata
in which well-defined bedding is a conspicuous feature. Except in
mountain belts, where the original horizontal or nearly horizontal
attitude of Cambrian and younger beds has been disturbed by folding and faulting, and locally by metamorphism, structure is simple and
the succession of beds is well defined. It is natural, therefore, to
separate the Pre-Cambrian from other rock formations.

Inasmuch as the base of the Cambrian is dated on the geological
clock as belonging 500 to 550 million years in the past, Pre-Cambrian
time represents at least 1,500 million years. This is time enough for
the building of tremendously thick successions of sedimentary rock,
for uplift and subsequent complete obliteration of great mountain
chains, and for erosion sufficiently profound to cut deeply into the

---

**47. Pre-Cambrian and overlying Paleozoic rocks in the Grand Canyon of the Colorado
River, Ariz.** The contact between Pre-Cambrian and overlying Cambrian strata
is at the base of cliff-forming sandstone (Tapeats), which rests nonconformably on tilted Late Pre-Cambrian stratified rocks (Algonkian). These, in turn,
lie nonconformably on much older Pre-Cambrian schist and granite (Archean)
that are intruded by igneous dikes. (*N. W. Carkhuff, U. S. Geol. Survey.*)

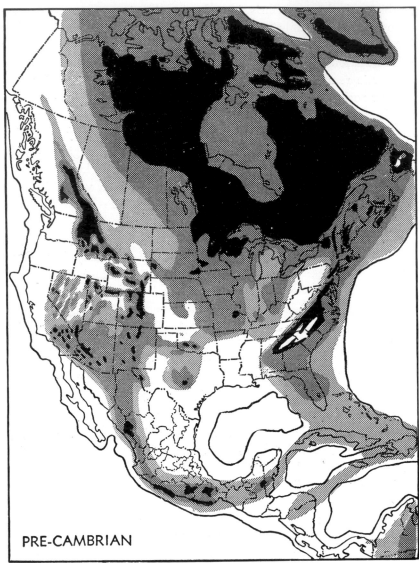

PRE-CAMBRIAN

48. Distribution of Pre-Cambrian rocks in North America. Outcrops of Pre-Cambrian formations are shown in black; the chief area of exposure is the so-called Canadian Shield which flanks Hudson Bay with broad U-shaped outline. Areas in which Pre-Cambrian rocks occur within 5,000 feet of the surface are represented by dark gray, and those in which Pre-Cambrian rocks are covered by 5,000 to 10,000 feet of younger rocks are indicated by light gray. In unshaded areas, Pre-Cambrian rocks are more than 10,000 feet deep.

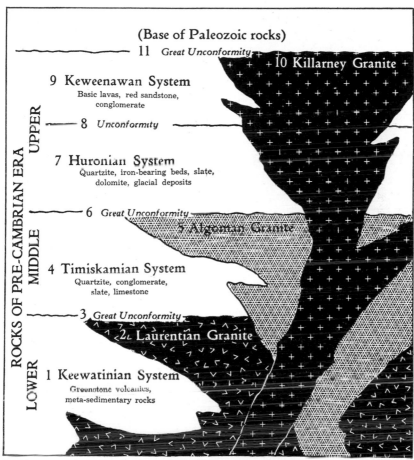

(Base of Paleozoic rocks)

11 *Great Unconformity*

+10 Killarney Granite +

9 Keweenawan System
Basic lavas, red sandstone, conglomerate

8 *Unconformity*

7 Huronian System
Quartzite, iron-bearing beds, slate, dolomite, glacial deposits

6 *Great Unconformity*

5 Algoman Granite

4 Timiskamian System
Quartzite, conglomerate, slate, limestone

3 *Great Unconformity*

2 Laurentian Granite

1 Keewatinian System
Greenstone volcanics, meta-sedimentary rocks

ROCKS OF PRE-CAMBRIAN ERA

UPPER

MIDDLE

LOWER

49. Diagrammatic summary of the classification of Pre-Cambrian rocks in the Canadian Shield region. The numbers associated with parts of this diagram correspond to those used in Figs. 54, 55, and 58.

earth's crust, exposing great areas of granite and metamorphic rocks of the zone of flow. Again and again, prolonged erosion produced widespread peneplains.

The Canadian Region

The most extensive region of Pre-Cambrian rocks exposed in North America comprises about 1,800,000 square miles (Fig. 48). The area surrounds Hudson Bay, its southern fringe extending into the United States, mainly around Lake Superior. Because of its location, shape,

50. Folded Keewatin iron-bearing formation, north of Lake Superior. The oldest known Pre-Cambrian rocks are not part of an original earth crust but consist of sedimentary and extrusive igneous formations that were spread out on still older, but unknown, rocks. (*Canada Geol. Survey.*)

and geologic stability since beginning of the Cambrian Period, the area has been named the Canadian Shield. This region has first importance for study of Pre-Cambrian history, not so much because of its size—for only a small part has been fairly well explored—but because a more complete record has been worked out here than elsewhere on the continent. Also, rocks of this area are extremely important as sources of iron, copper, nickel, gold, silver, cobalt, platinum, and uranium.

A tabular summary showing in diagrammatic form the main divisions of the Pre-Cambrian recognized in the Canadian region is given in Fig. 49. The meaning of this table in terms of geologic history is made clear by accompanying block diagrams (Figs. 54, 55, and 58).

Lower Pre-Cambrian. The oldest rocks (Keewatin) found in the country north of the Great Lakes consist of an enormously thick series of lava flows, ash beds, and sediments that in places occur between the volcanic layers. They have been complexly folded and meta-morphosed and now occur as isolated patches of a few square miles and larger areas up to 10,000 square miles, distributed all the way from Lake Superior to Hudson Bay. Surrounded on all sides by granite, the stratified rocks are like ships frozen in a sea of ice. The granite is younger than the rocks of volcanic and sedimentary origin, for in many places it is seen to cut through and across the layered rocks.

The floor on which the Lower Pre-Cambrian sediments were laid down, and over which the great succession of lava flows spread, is entirely unknown. Nevertheless, it is clear, despite effects of meta-morphism, that the volcanic and sedimentary processes that made these rocks are not different from those of later earth history. Many of the lava sheets are composed of ellipsoidal pillows, which are characteristic of underwater flows. Indeed most, if not all, of this succession was probably formed in a widespread shallow sea. Thick

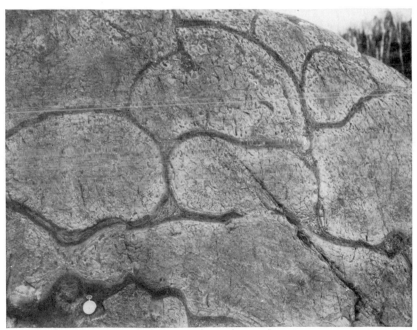

51. Pillow structure in extrusive igneous rock. This outcrop of Pre-Cambrian rocks in Quebec indicates an underwater flow of lava. (*Canada Geol. Survey.*)

52. Folded Pre-Cambrian limestone and gray schist in eastern Ontario. The deformed, metamorphosed sedimentary rocks (Grenville) here shown are part of a succession many thousands of feet thick deposited in a shallow sea. *(Canada Geol. Survey.)*

limestone deposits in southeastern Canada are identified as forming parts of the Lower Pre-Cambrian deposits, although actually these may belong to a younger division.

All the sedimentary and volcanic layers were horizontal or nearly so when they were made. Late in Early Pre-Cambrian time, conditions in the Canadian region changed radically. Accumulation of stratified rocks ceased, and those already formed were profoundly folded and faulted by a crustal disturbance that greatly elevated the land and caused withdrawal of the sea. We infer that stream erosion must have become vigorous in the upraised belts, carving deep valleys amid lofty mountains. Coincident with the disturbance that gave origin to the mountains was a tremendous invasion of the deeper crust by batholiths of granite (Laurentian). As shown by its coarse texture, the granite undoubtedly solidified far below the surface, and it became exposed only after erosion had cut downward profoundly. The Lower Pre-Cambrian granite forms part of the crystalline rocks now exposed in the Canadian region, but we find proof that the granite batholiths were uncovered before the beginning of Middle Pre-Cambrian, because sedimentary deposits of the latter, containing pebbles and boulders of the granite, are found resting on smoothly beveled surfaces of the Lower Pre-Cambrian granite. The interval of erosion was extremely long. We may be confident of this conclusion not only because thousands of cubic miles of rock must have been worn away in broadly exposing the Lower Pre-Cambrian granite, but because the erosion surface ultimately attained characters of a peneplain. Peneplanation, especially in a region of much disturbed hard rocks, is judged to demand very prolonged work of erosive processes during time when the land surface was neither raised nor lowered appreciably by earth deformation. That the Lower Pre-Cambrian rocks were peneplaned is indicated by the smooth surface at the base of the Middle Pre-Cambrian.

Middle Pre-Cambrian. Rocks of the Canadian region that are classed as Middle Pre-Cambrian include thick water-laid sedimentary rocks (Timiskamian), which originally were sandstone, shale and limestone, and intrusive igneous rock, especially granite (Algoman). The history represented by them largely duplicates the record of the Lower

53. Laurentian granite gneiss, eastern Ontario. Granite batholiths of Early Pre-Cambrian age have been regionally metamorphosed in such manner as to produce finely banded structure. *(Canada Geol. Survey.)*

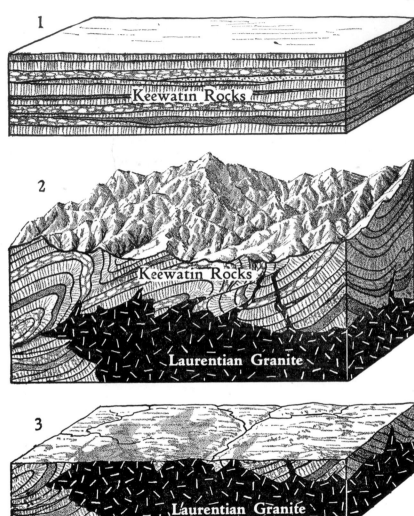

54. Pre-Cambrian geologic history of the Canadian Shield region. The block diagrams depict successive steps in making the rocks and developing structural features. (1) The *Keewatin rocks* originally were laid down as nearly horizontal layers, like modern lava flows and sedimentary deposits. (2) After lavas many thousand feet thick had accumulated in Keewatinian time, *profound deformation* accompanied by deep-seated intrusions of granite made the Laurentian Mountains, which immediately began to be worn down. (3) Prolonged erosion cut deeply into the earth crust, eventually exposing the Laurentian granite and producing a peneplaned land surface; this erosion represents a *great unconformity* in the rock succession.

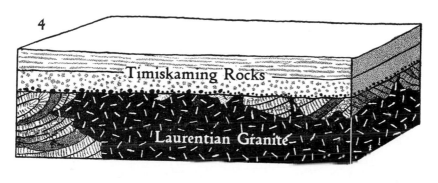

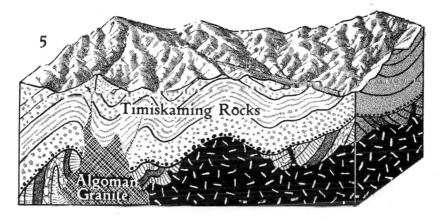

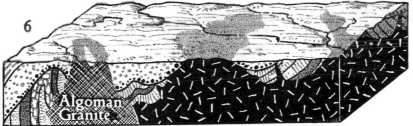

55. Pre-Cambrian geologic history of the Canadian Shield region (continued). (4) *Deposition of the Timiskaming* sediments on the peneplain began when sinking of parts of the land led to submergence by the sea and uplift of adjacent country furnished sediments, which include pebbles worn from the Keewatin lavas and Laurentian granite. (5) Mountain building at the *close of Timiskamian time* profoundly disturbed both the Timiskaming and underlying older rocks, and intrusion of granite, called "Algoman," intersected them. (6) Peneplanation that truncated the rock structure is recorded by another *major unconformity.*

Pre-Cambrian except that here we find no such great accumulation of volcanic rocks.

Sedimentation proceeded without important interruption during many million years. We do not know the source area of these sediments. It may have been another part of the largely unexplored Canadian Shield region, or it may have been territory in which Pre-Cambrian rocks are now concealed by younger formations. The end of sedimentary deposition and the renewal of widespread erosion coincided with another important mountain building and extensive granitic intrusion. The Middle Pre-Cambrian sedimentary rocks were closely folded and partly metamorphosed. The granites belonging to this division closely resemble those of the Lower Pre-Cambrian, which they intersect; the younger granite is clearly identified where it cuts across Middle Pre-Cambrian stratified rocks, and here it is seen to differ from the older granite that lies unconformably below the Middle Pre-Cambrian. Erosion in late Middle Pre-Cambrian time continued long enough to make another important peneplain, thus defining a great unconformity.

Upper Pre-Cambrian.   Aggregate thickness of Upper Pre-Cambrian stratified rocks in Canada exceeds 65,000 feet, including toward the

56. Conglomeratic Late Pre-Cambrian rock. This bouldery deposit (Cobalt), which is widely distributed east of Lake Huron, is inferred to represent glacial till. The outcrop is at Cobalt, Ont. *(Canada Geol. Survey.)*

57. Open-pit iron mine in the Mesabi district, Minn. Hematite formed by oxidation of Pre-Cambrian iron-bearing formations has long been the chief source of iron ore in North America. Huge open cuts are worked by power shovels which load the ore directly into rail cars for shipment to Duluth and thence by lake boats to steel plants in the Chicago and Pittsburgh districts. *(Courtesy of Bucyrus-Erie Company.)*

top thick sandstones and volcanic rocks. Unconformities that occur within this great accumulation of strata represent not only temporary interruption of sedimentation but removal of an unknown thickness of rocks once present. Throughout most of the region, the upper beds lie parallel on the lower, and the unconformities are judged to be smaller in time value than those marking the ends of main divisions of the Pre-Cambrian.

Noteworthy features among the sedimentary rocks of the Upper Pre-Cambrian in the Great Lakes region are occurrence of great iron-bearing formations (Huronian), especially in Minnesota and northern Wisconsin, and the presence, northeast of Lake Huron, of thick boulder conglomerates containing what seem to be well-marked glacial striae and showing the characteristic heterogeneous mixture of materials seen in glacial till. The iron was deposited as a silicate in broad lagoons or a shallow sea. The presumed glacial deposits, which locally are more than 500 feet thick, have been identified in an area extending nearly 1,000 miles from west to east; existence of a considerable ice sheet in southern Canada during part of Late Pre-Cambrian time is thus inferred. This is the oldest known record of glaciation, although it may correspond in age to Pre-Cambrian glacial deposits in China and some other parts of the world.

After prolonged sedimentation in the early part of Late Pre-Cambrian time, southern Canada and the Lake Superior region of the United States were uplifted and became subject to erosion, which in places removed a considerable thickness of previously formed rocks. This is indicated by an unconformity occurring at the base of a great series of basaltic lava flows, associated with conglomerate and red sandstone (Keweenawan), which has a total thickness of at least 25,000 feet. Many of the volcanic sheets were characterized by scoriaceous texture, and filling of the vesicular cavities by minerals has formed amygdaloidal rock.

Mountain building, and a third great epoch of granitic intrusion, mark the close of Late Pre-Cambrian time. The disturbance affected especially the country south of Lake Superior and extending a considerable distance northeastward from Lake Huron. At many places outside the belt of strong folding and metamorphism, the Late Pre-Cambrian strata are only gently tilted or they remain nearly horizontal. Both the little disturbed and the strongly deformed rocks were later beveled by erosion that produced a peneplain, and this erosion surface, which represents a very long time interval, marks the boundary between rocks representing the Pre-Cambrian and Paleozoic Eras. The even sky line, characterizing much of the Canadian Shield region at the present time, is actually this old erosion surface, little modified by subsequent erosion. In a large area, it has been exposed by the stripping away of Paleozoic rocks that buried and preserved it.

Pre-Cambrian Areas in the United States

In contrast to the enormous Pre-Cambrian outcrops in the Canadian Shield region (with which we have included the exposed areas in Minnesota, Wisconsin, and northern New York), Pre-Cambrian outcrops in the United States are relatively small isolated patches, the largest measuring only a few ten-thousand square miles. Some are less than 100 square miles. Perhaps, excepting the Appalachian Pied-

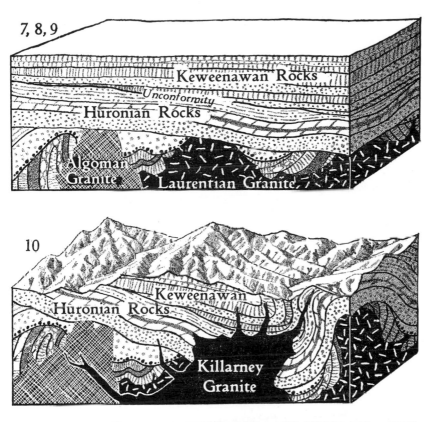

58. Pre-Cambrian geologic history of the Canadian Shield region (continued). (7) Submergence by the sea led to accumulation of a considerable thickness of sedimentary rock layers, called *Huronian*. (8) Sedimentation was interrupted by upwarping of the earth crust; this is recorded by an *unconformity* at the top of the Huronian rocks. (9) Deposition of *Keweenawan* red beds and spreading out of many lava flows covered the Huronian. (10) The *Killarneyan mountain building* terminated Keweenawan time; intrusions of granite accompanied this deformation. (11) Very prolonged erosion removed great thicknesses of Keweenawan and older rocks and produced a peneplain. This defines another *great unconformity*. The next submergence of the land is recorded by Cambrian deposits that contain numerous fossils.

mont area, all of them have been buried under Cambrian or younger rock formations, and the present-day outcrops are due to removal of this former cover by erosion. As we might expect, this stripping away of younger deposits so as to expose the old crystalline rocks, has occurred at places where the substructure of the continent has been most strongly pushed upward during deformative earth movements, some of which represent mountain folding and others only upwarped bulges.

It is noteworthy that the rock successions observed in different Pre-Cambrian areas of the United States cannot be correlated in a reliable manner, even approximately, with one another or with main divisions of the Canadian Shield area. Age determinations by radioactive methods, however, indicate that some—as in the Black Hills of South Dakota, for example—are very ancient, corresponding to Lower Pre-Cambrian, rather than later divisions recognized in the Canadian region.

Appalachian region. New York City, Philadelphia, Baltimore, Washington, and several other important eastern cities of the United States are located on or near Pre-Cambrian rocks belonging to the Appalachian Piedmont, lying east of the Appalachian Mountains proper. The area is a low plateau that rises toward the west, culminating in the Blue Ridge. The chief types of rocks are banded granite (gneiss) and highly metamorphosed sedimentary and igneous rocks (schist). In Maryland and Virginia, there are strongly folded beds of marble, and toward the south, very thick deposits of dark-colored slate. In spite of great alteration, owing to compressive forces and heat within the earth's crust, that has almost destroyed original characters of these rocks, they were once normal types of flat-lying sediments, volcanics, and igneous rocks intruded into them. Details of the record cannot be deciphered clearly or completely; yet in kind, they denote a history corresponding to part of that read in the Canadian region.

Central States. Widely scattered small outcrops of Pre-Cambrian rocks occur near Sioux City; St. Louis; in the Wichita and Arbuckle Mountains of southern Oklahoma; and in the Llano Uplift near Austin and San Antonio. Outcrops occur also in the Black Hills of southwestern South Dakota. Thick red quartzite (originally sandstone), schist, and various sorts of igneous rock, especially granite, are the chief lithologic types observed. The contact of the Pre-Cambrian

59. Eastern part of the Grand Canyon of the Colorado River, Ariz. This photograph shows cliffs of Paleozoic strata lying nonconformably on tilted Pre-Cambrian formations. (*Spence Air Photos.*)

with overlying formations, is mostly that of a smooth erosion surface, which indicates peneplanation of the Pre-Cambrian prior to its burial. Locally, however, as in the Ozark region south of St. Louis, Pre-Cambrian hills, 1,500 to 2,000 feet high, have been revealed by the stripping away of the unconformably overlying younger strata.

Western States. Along the axes of uplifts in the Rocky Mountains from New Mexico to Montana, are many square miles of exposed Pre-Cambrian, mostly granite. Some of the loftiest mountains, including Pikes Peak and Longs Peak in Colorado, form parts of the ancient floor of the continent that have been lifted high by crustal deformation. That this granite was formed millions of years before the Cambrian Period is proved by the fact that Cambrian deposits lie unconformably on the granite and are in part composed of materials derived from the granite.

One of the classic sections of Pre-Cambrian rocks in the south-western United States is that of the Grand Canyon of the Colorado River in Arizona. The inner gorge of this canyon presents a natural section scores of miles long, in which the Pre-Cambrian formations are continuously well exposed. Two main divisions are clearly recognized: an older, highly complex part, consisting of schist and granite, and a younger part composed of little altered sedimentary rocks and some volcanics, tilted at a moderate angle and faulted. That very prolonged erosion preceded and followed the making of the younger division is shown by the smoothness of erosion surfaces, representing unconformities, that truncate structures of the rocks undergoing erosion (Figs. 21 and 59). Locally, however, there are hills formed by hard rock that was not worn down to the general level of the peneplain.

Lastly, we may note the very thick succession of Pre-Cambrian sedimentary deposits in Montana, Idaho, Washington, and extending northward into British Columbia. These rocks are rather evenly bedded and little disturbed. Because of the striking scenery in such regions as Glacier National Park and Jasper Park (Alberta), where streams and ice have carved them deeply, they are objects of interest to many travelers. The tourist, however, is generally unaware of their great antiquity and their origin in a shallow sea. An important part of the succession consists of limestone. Probably the whole succession is Late Pre-Cambrian in age.

Pre-Cambrian Rocks Outside of North America

All the continents, and undoubtedly the ocean basins also, are underlaid by Pre-Cambrian rocks. We may be sure of this because the solid rock lithosphere must have been formed beneath the entire surface of the globe many hundred million years before the beginning of Cambrian time.

On land areas, the outcrops of Pre-Cambrian rocks are comparable to those observed in North America. That is to say, we find in each continent very broad areas of Pre-Cambrian exposures that resemble the Canadian Shield, and there are also numerous smaller areas of outcrop that commonly are found along the axes of mountain uplifts, just as in the Rocky Mountains and other uplifts of North America where the crust has been strongly elevated. The broad lowland outcrop areas constitute so-called "shields," which are the nuclear parts of the con-

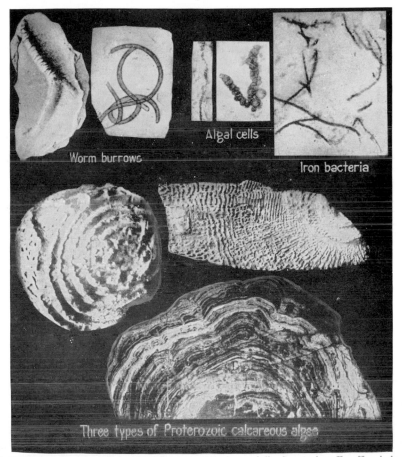

Worm burrows

Algal cells

Iron bacteria

Three types of Proterozoic calcareous algae

60. Fossils from Pre-Cambrian rocks. The term "Proterozoic" refers to late Pre-Cambrian.

tinents; these are bordered by nearly flat-lying sedimentary formations. In Europe, an extensive Pre-Cambrian area lying north of the Baltic is known as the Baltic Shield. Similar shields occur in north central Siberia, the peninsula of India, west central Australia, Southern and Northern Africa, and in west central Brazil.

Pre-Cambrian outcrops in belts of mountain folding are associated with the Alps, Himalayas, Andes, Urals, and many other chains.

Granite and various other igneous rocks, together with highly complex metamorphic rocks of many sorts, are characteristic of the Pre-Cambrian outcrops wherever seen. In addition, some areas include extensive exposures of less metamorphosed rocks of sedimentary origin, but almost universally these ancient rocks are strongly folded and faulted. The Pre-Cambrian rocks generally are characterized by their crystalline texture, complexity of structure, and absence of fossils.

Life of Pre-Cambrian Time

We have noted that Pre-Cambrian rocks everywhere are characterized by absence of fossils. Predominance of igneous rocks in many areas partly accounts for this absence, and the prevalence of metamorphic alteration of sedimentary rocks may well explain lack of organic remains in them. It is a striking fact, however, that many very little altered Pre-Cambrian strata, in which such features as cross-bedding, ripple marks, and mud cracks are well shown, have failed to yield fossils even to skilled and painstaking searchers in the field. If life existed, certainly not much trace of it has been preserved.

The record of Pre-Cambrian life is not quite all negative. Abundance of carbonaceous matter in many places strongly implies the existence of organisms, for no other agency of carbon fixation, having quantitative importance, is known. In rocks younger than Pre-Cambrian, abundant carbonaceous materials are definitely associated with life processes indicated by an abundance of various sorts of plants and animals. Likewise, the great quantities of sedimentary iron deposits in parts of the Pre-Cambrian succession, very probably comprise the record of work done by iron-depositing bacteria, such as are well known today. Indeed, supposed actual traces of these organisms from Pre-Cambrian rocks of Minnesota have been described and illustrated.

Most common and best preserved among actual remains of Pre-Cambrian organisms, are lime-secreting seaweeds or algae. These built concentrically laminated subspherical or lobed structures, ranging from less than an inch to many inches in diameter; they also form colonial growths of various shapes. Fairly well-preserved fossils, representing creatures allied to sponges and corals, have been found in Pre-Cambrian rocks of the Lake Superior region. We may complete the list by recording the presence of trails and burrows, like those made by worms and other invertebrates, and the finding of a very few traces of shelled invertebrates.

Forms of life abundantly represented in rocks next younger than Pre-Cambrian include relatively advanced, complexly organized forms of invertebrate life. Among these are marine crustaceans having differentiated head, tail, many thoracic segments, jointed legs, and delicate respiratory organs. Inasmuch as the entire record of life, from Cambrian time onward, is marked by steady evolutionary change that includes development of more and more advanced types of animal and plant life, it is wholly illogical to entertain the thought that life on the earth began with such forms as are represented by fossils in Cambrian formations. There must have been an extremely long, and virtually unrecorded, slow evolutionary differentiation of life in Pre-Cambrian times. Why is geologic evidence of this inferred development essentially lacking? The best answer seems to be the guess that the primitive early forms of life nearly all lacked hard parts. If this is so, there would be almost no chance of their being preserved as fossils. When, at length, mineral matter of some sort—calcium carbonate, calcium phosphate, or silica—came to be secreted as part of the body covering or other hard parts of the organisms, these remains, when buried in the sediments, were likely to be preserved. All of Pre-Cambrian time, which is judged to represent roughly three fourths of earth history, had elapsed before most sorts of organisms began to build and utilize a skeletal structure.

Pre-Cambrian Climate

During very early Pre-Cambrian time, climatic conditions must have been very different from anything now known on the earth. After cooling had permitted condensation of water vapor, rains could fall on the still hot surface, but the globe must have been densely cloud-blanketed. This steamy sort of environment, which would permit beginning of weathering and erosion, is a matter of guesswork. Later, we may be sure that climatic conditions approximating those now found on different parts of the earth, made appearance, and persisted for very long periods of time. As judged by the nature of sedimentary deposits formed, the climate of some areas and of some parts of Pre-Cambrian time was prevailingly moist and warm. The existence of aridity, or periodic wetting and drying, is inferred from study of some extensive Pre-Cambrian red-beds formations, like those attributed to desert climates in later geologic history. In Late Pre-Cambrian time, part of southern Canada shows signs of having suffered continental glaciation. This evidence of cold climate very early in earth history is not unique, for glacial deposits dated as belonging to Late Pre-Cambrian time have been found in China, others not younger than Early Cambrian occur in northern Norway and Australia. Glacial deposits of doubtful age, but probably Pre-Cambrian, are reported from west-central Africa.

5. The Cambrian Period

Mount Eisenhower in the Canadian Rockies is formed by Cambrian rocks.

Type Region

The Cambrian rocks derive their name from *Cambria*, the Latin name for Wales, where, a century ago, this division of the Paleozoic succession was defined. Together with outcrops in western England, this region furnishes the classic section with which deposits of equivalent age elsewhere in Europe and on other continents are compared and correlated.

Although the nature of the deposits belonging to the Cambrian in

Royal Canadian Air Force

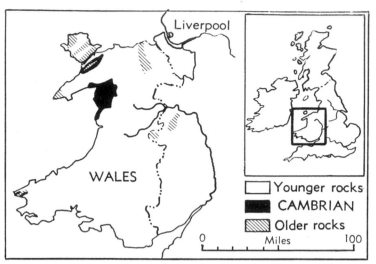

61. Outcrops of Cambrian rocks in Wales. The unconformable contact of Cambrian on Pre-Cambrian rocks is seen both in northwestern and southwestern Wales. The largest outcrop area has a broad anticlinal structure.

different regions differs, definition of boundaries belonging to the Cambrian System is based on the type section. Here, as elsewhere, the fossiliferous Cambrian strata rest on unfossiliferous crystalline rocks belonging to the Pre-Cambrian, from which they are separated by a profound unconformity. The top of the system is also marked by an unconformity in the type region, indicating interruption in sedimentation before deposits belonging to the next younger division of the Paleozoic sequence were laid down in a sea that advanced over the area of eroded Cambrian rocks. The unconformity at the top of the Cambrian indicates a much less important break, however, than that at the base.

Study of the Cambrian System in the type region has led to recognition of three main divisions, called Lower Cambrian Series, Middle Cambrian Series, and Upper Cambrian Series. The boundaries between these parts are marked by unconformities. Even casual examination of large collections of fossils that have been made from each division shows that they differ appreciably one from another. In addition, groups of fossils obtained from successive thin zones likewise can be discriminated and recognized without difficulty. These assemblages of fossils are found to match with collections obtained from lower-most Paleozoic rocks of distant regions, and they furnish the indispensable means of determining age equivalence.

Distribution and Nature of Cambrian Rocks in North America

Rocks identified as belonging to the Cambrian System are widespread in North America (Fig. 63). They are exposed locally in easternmost Canada and eastern New England; in a long, fairly continuous narrow belt in the Appalachian Mountains reaching south to Alabama; in a relatively broad, irregularly shaped tract in the upper Mississippi Valley region; and in small patches scattered through Southwestern and Western States.

Eastern Canada and New England. Deposits of predominantly shaly nature several thousand feet thick in Newfoundland, New Brunswick, Maine, and eastern Massachusetts contain some of the same fossils that distinguish the Lower, Middle, and Upper Cambrian in Wales. Evidently a shallow-water connection between these regions existed in Cambrian time, permitting intermigration of marine invertebrate species that neither in larval stages nor as adults could have crossed wide oceanic deeps. Also, the sea in which these deposits accumulated was evidently not directly joined with Middle and Late Cambrian seas in other parts of North America, because the species of fossils belonging to them are not the same. The eastern Canada-New England area is thus interpreted as a geographically distinct province of Cambrian sedimentation.

Appalachian region. Beginning in Newfoundland and New Brunswick, at the southeast border of the Canadian Shield, outcrops of Cambrian strata are traced almost continuously along the eastern margin of the Appalachian Mountains as far southwest as Georgia and Alabama. Throughout this belt, the rocks have been strongly folded and in

62. Diagrammatic section showing structural relations and divisions of Cambrian rocks in Wales. Important unconformities occur below and above the Cambrian System. In places, however, Ordovician strata lie parallel on Upper Cambrian beds.

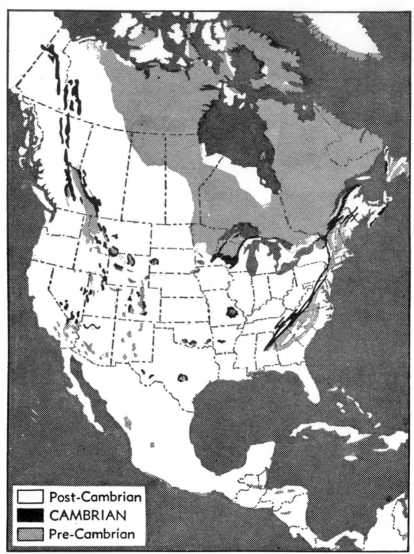

63. Distribution of Cambrian outcrops in North America. Exposures of Cambrian formations adjoin Pre-Cambrian rocks in many places, but some Cambrian outcrops are entirely surrounded by younger formations. Buried Cambrian rocks occur in much of the area shown in white on the map.

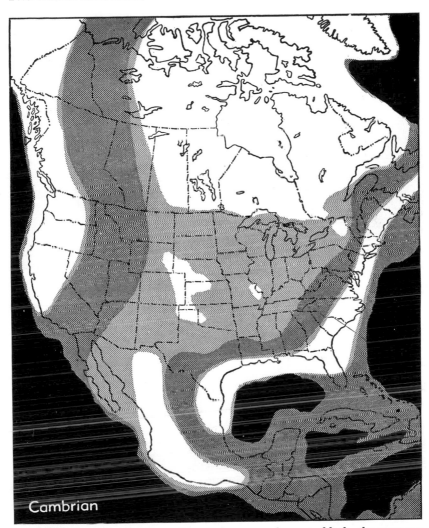

64. Distribution of Cambrian seas. Oceanic areas are shown in black; the most persistent seaways on the continental platform are represented by dark gray, and areas submerged during part of the period (Late Cambrian) only are indicated by light gray. The inferred persistent land areas are white. As indicated by distorted outlines of eastern and western states, the continent is represented as wider than now, so as to compensate for crustal shortening produced by post-Cambrian mountain building.

65. Lower Cambrian quartzite on the Potomac River at Harpers Ferry, Va. The strata are steeply upturned as a result of mountain-making movements in late Paleozoic time. The hard rocks make ridges and the weaker strata form valleys. The view is eastward downstream toward the Blue Ridge. *(Maryland Geol. Survey.)*

66. Ripple-marked limestone in eastern Pennsylvania. The ripple marks prove that this deposit (Conococheague) was made in shallow water. The steeply tilted attitude of the old sea bottom is due to late Paleozoic deformation. *(Pennsylvania Geol. Survey.)*

Series	Stage	Cordilleran Region	Central States			Appalachian Region	Europe
			Missouri	Wisconsin	Minnesota		
UPPER CAMBRIAN (CROIXIAN)	TREMPEALEAUAN	St. Charles form.	Eminence dol.		Madison form.	Copper Ridge dol.	LINGULA FLAGS
					Jordan ss.		
	FRANCONIAN		Potosi dol.		Lodi sh.		
					St. Lawrence form.		
			Doerun dol.		Bad Axe form.	Conococheague ls.	
			Derby dol.		Hudson form.		
			Davis form.		Goodenough form.		
					Ironton ss.		
	DRESBACHIAN	Nounan form.	Bonneterre dol.		Galesville form.	Maynardsville ls.	
					Eau Claire form.	Nolichucky sh.	
			Lamotte ss.		Mount Simon ss.		
MIDDLE CAMBRIAN (ALBERTAN)	STAGES NOT YET DEFINED	Eldon dol.				Maryville ls.	MENEVIAN
		Stephen form.				Elbrook (Conasauga) sh.	Rogersville sh.
		Cathedral dol.					
		Ptarmigan form.				Rutledge ls.	SOLVAN
LOWER CAMBRIAN (WAUCOBIAN)	STAGES NOT YET DEFINED	Pioche sh.				Waynesboro form. / Rome form.	COMLEYAN
						Tomstown dol. / Shady dol.	
		Prospect Mountain qtzt.				Antietam qtzt. / Weisner qtzt.	

67. Time-rock divisions of the Cambrian System and rock units in representative important Cambrian sections of North America. The vertical scale does not represent thickness or time duration, but placement of names indicates correlation in age. Ruled areas denote absence of deposits.

places greatly displaced by thrust faults; yet in many places the unconformable contact of the Cambrian System on the unfossiliferous Pre-Cambrian rocks may be observed. Although these deposits commonly aggregate a mile in thickness, the outcrops do not cover broad areas; because of steep dip, they have the shape of long, narrow strips, running nearly straight for many miles and then changing direction abruptly as they follow the pattern of rock folding. The lower two thirds or three fourths of the section in most places consists of quartzite and sandy shale, whereas the remaining upper part is limestone. Well-preserved marine fossils are found in many places.

The Cambrian rocks are divided into many formations that are defined chiefly by lithologic characters (Fig. 67). Occurrence of uncon-

Significance of Variations

Before we can interpret the history of Cambrian time in North America, we must examine the nature of Cambrian deposition in different parts of the continent more closely, taking note especially of the evidence furnished by fossils. We must learn also, as exactly as possible, the meaning of the great variations in Cambrian deposits that are found from place to place.

Does the greater thickness of Cambrian rocks in the Appalachian and Cordilleran areas, as compared with the Central States, signify a much longer and fuller record of Cambrian time than that found in Wisconsin or Missouri? Not necessarily. Sedimentation rates under varying conditions are by no means constant. If such average rate were ten times slower in Wisconsin than in Nevada during the Cambrian Period, 1,000 feet of Wisconsin Cambrian beds would represent as much geologic time as the making of deposits 10,000 feet thick in Nevada.

Let us postulate that rates of deposition were actually less uneven. Then, the smaller thickness of Cambrian strata in the Central States would mean that a lesser part of Cambrian time is represented by the thinner deposits, because of (1) absence of sedimentation during some portion of the period, (2) erosion that has obliterated part of the record, or (3) both.

Conceivably, the thin Cambrian of the continental interior might represent only the lower part of the whole Cambrian succession, middle and upper parts never having been laid down there; or perhaps Middle and Upper Cambrian, once present in this region, were entirely eroded before deposition of Ordovician rocks. Again, if the thin Cambrian represents some other part of the system, the case is entirely different. We need to know the age relations of the Cambrian sections in each region, and for this we must turn to the fossils and recognize divisions of the Cambrian that are based on fossils.

Cambrian Guide Fossils

Cambrian deposits of eastern Canada and part of New England are found to contain European species of Cambrian fossils associated with others that are restricted to the American side of the Atlantic. Thus, these sections can be divided and correlated. The dominant guide fossils are primitive marine crustaceans called "trilobites," characterized by prominently three-lobed body form. These and all other groups of fossils having importance in historical geology are described in an Appendix and the reader should consult the descriptions as often as needed. Also useful, but secondary in importance, are small, lime-phosphate-shelled brachiopods, which are forerunners of the great group of bilaterally symmetrical two-shelled marine invertebrates, that in later Paleozoic fossil assemblages came to have front rank. Lastly, there are a few snails and the steeply conical shells called "pteropods."

On the basis of these fossils, especially the trilobites, equivalents of Lower, Middle, and Upper Cambrian, as defined in the European section, are identified. For example, the Lower Cambrian is especially characterized by a group of trilobites having a sharp-spiked tail and large, narrowly crescentic eyes (olenellids). This form does not extend upward into Middle Cambrian rocks.

It is important to bear in mind that geographic factors almost universally affect or control distribution of different organic assemblages, and this has been true in the earth's past as it is today. Migration of bottom-dwelling, shallow-water marine invertebrates is completely halted by a land barrier, such as now separates the Atlantic and Pacific waters of North America, and the lateral spread of such organisms may be impeded or prevented by the deep water of ocean basins.

The fact that European guide fossils of Cambrian rocks are found in Newfoundland, southeastern Labrador, New Brunswick, and eastern New England serves to identify the occurrence in eastern North America of Cambrian divisions equivalent to those in Wales. The animals represented by these fossils lived on the bottom of shallow seas, and accordingly we must conclude that in Cambrian time there was a shallow-water pathway of migration between what are today opposite sides of the North Atlantic.

Lower Cambrian spike-tailed trilobites and other guide fossils, equivalent to those of Europe and northeastern North America, occur also in the lower part of the Cambrian throughout the Appalachian belt and in the Far West, but are entirely unknown in the intervening country of the Mississippi Basin. This means that there must have been open shallow-water connections between areas where the faunas occur, passageway to the west probably being located around the

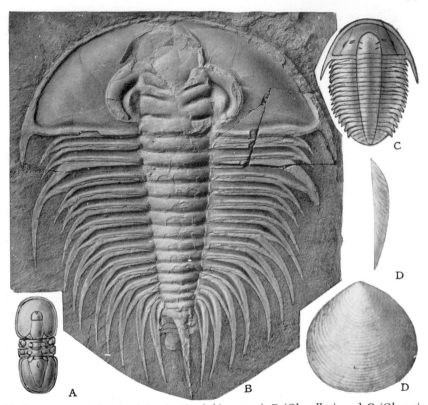

70. Some representative Cambrian fossils. A *(Agnostus)*, B *(Olenellus)*, and C *(Olenus)* are trilobites. The spike-tailed forms having large crescentic eyes are found in Lower Cambrian rocks of the Appalachian and Cordilleran regions of North America and occur also in Europe and Asia. D *(Dicellomus)* is a brachiopod of simple type that occurs in Upper Cambrian deposits of almost all outcrop areas in the United States.

northern margin of the continent. The Lower Cambrian is separated from succeeding strata by an unconformity.

The Middle and Upper Cambrian of Europe and northeastern North America contain fossils that are similar in general type, but almost wholly distinct in particular kinds from those in the higher parts of the Cambrian elsewhere in North America. That these latter deposits are Cambrian, in spite of the difference in their fossils, is shown by their position unconformably below Lower Ordovician. They represent deposits in a shallow sea that was not directly connected with northeastern North America and Europe. Close similarity of the Appalachian and western faunas in the higher Cambrian with those of eastern Asia tells us that these seas were extensions of the Pacific Ocean, rather than the Atlantic. They were laid down in shallow water that spread eastward from the Pacific into the Appalachian area, but this Middle and Late Cambrian seaway did not connect directly with the Atlantic.

The fossils of Middle and Late Cambrian deposits of the Pacific province are readily distinguished one from the other, and they furnish a basis for correlating Cambrian sections from Georgia and Pennsylvania to Nevada and Alberta. The fossils from the Cambrian of the Mississippi Valley area are all proved to be Late Cambrian in age; there are no Middle or Lower Cambrian deposits in this region. This, then, partly accounts for the average thinness of the Cambrian in the Middle States.

Geographic Pattern of North America in Cambrian Time

Geosynclines and borderlands. The Cambrian deposits of the Appalachian and Cordilleran areas are thousands of feet thick, and the areas occupied by these thick deposits are very much greater in a general north-south direction than from east to west. They may be described as belts of thick sediments having trends roughly parallel to the borders of the continent. This concentration of deposition is a very interesting and important feature in the geologic history of our continent, for the pattern of Cambrian sedimentation is closely repeated by that of later Paleozoic periods.

The belts of thick sedimentation define the location of crustal features called "geosynclines." These are elongate, relatively mobile tracts of the earth crust that slowly subside to form trough like depressions, thus inviting inundation by shallow seas that extend from ocean basins, and furnishing natural sites for accumulation of sediment worn

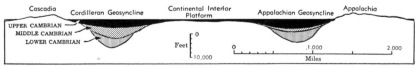

71. Diagrammatic section across the middle part of North America in an east-west direction, showing Cambrian deposits and configuration of the Pre-Cambrian floor. This figure indicates important distinctions between Cambrian deposits of the continental interior platform and of the two adjacent north-south trending geosynclines. Repeated uplift of the borderlands called Cascadia and Appalachia furnished source for most of the sediments carried to the geosynclines. The vertical scale is greatly exaggerated.

Cambrian rocks throughout the region during the time it had been land, were sorted by the sea, and they form parts of the Late Cambrian deposits which now are exposed or lie buried under younger formations in this region. Some sediments also probably were carried into the Mississippi Valley area from the Canadian Shield. Unlike the Late Cambrian deposits in the geosynclines, which are largely limestone, sediments of the interior platform are predominantly mud and sand, and their aggregate thickness is much less than in the geosynclines.

Cambrian Life

The nature of the dominant kinds of Cambrian marine invertebrates has already been noted in reference to guide fossils, and in discussing differentiation of Cambrian seaways, as defined by the assemblages

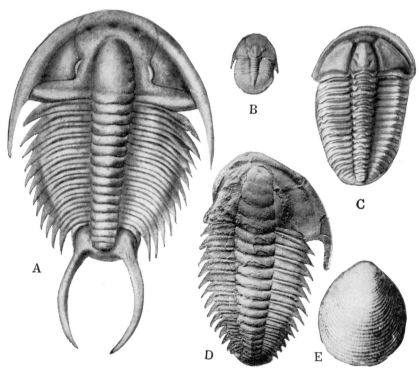

73. Representative Cambrian invertebrate fossils. A *(Crepicephalus)*, B *(Cedaria)*, C *(Conocoryphe)*, and D *(Redlichia)*, are trilobites; E *(Obolella)* is a common type of brachiopod.

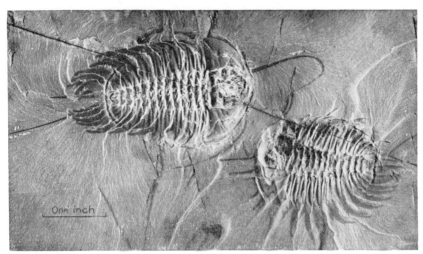

74. Unusually well-preserved Lower Cambrian trilobites. The two specimens (*Wanneria*) on a slab of Lower Cambrian slate are remarkable in having carbonized impressions of the antennae and numerous jointed legs that extend laterally beyond the carapace. (*U. S. National Museum.*)

of life in them. Although several classes of invertebrates that make first appearance in Ordovician rocks are unknown in the Cambrian, the variety of trilobite species, and to a lesser degree that of brachiopods, is amazing.

Plant life is poorly represented among Cambrian fossils. We may be sure that plants were abundant and varied, because they are the source, direct or indirect, of all the food of animals. Therefore, an abundance of animals presupposes an abundance of plants. Most plants, however, are poorly adapted for preservation as fossils. The one type that has left a good paleontological record in Cambrian rocks, comprises lime-secreting seaweeds (calcareous algae) that are marked by fine concentric laminae of calcium carbonate. They form rounded masses a few inches to several feet in diameter and locally are important rock builders.

No fishes or other animals having backbones are known from beds as old as Cambrian. It would not be very surprising, however, if they turned up somewhere in these rocks, inasmuch as Ordovician deposits containing abundant vertebrate remains of primitive type are known. Of course these Ordovician animals had ancestors.

Exceptional fossil assemblage from British Columbia.   An unusual glimpse of marine life that existed in an arm of the Pacific some 500 million years ago is furnished by layers of black Middle Cambrian shale near the town of Field, British Columbia, on the Canadian-Pacific Railway about 100 miles west of Calgary. High on a mountainside have been found thousands of specimens representing upward of 130 species of Cambrian organisms, most of which are entirely unknown elsewhere. They include a strange and varied assortment of crustaceans, soft-bodied worms, jellyfish, sponges, and other invertebrates, in which minute details of structure are imprinted on bedding planes of the shale as tissue-thin films of carbon. Delicate external structures, such as bristles and scales, and even internal parts such as the alimentary tracts of some creatures, are shown (Fig. 77). Ordinarily, the remains of such animals are destroyed by bacteria, or they are devoured by scavengers on the sea bottom, and thus all

75. Rock mass made by lime-secreting seaweeds. Representative of Cambrian plant life is a large calcareous algal mass in Upper Cambrian marine deposits of central Texas. (*A. H. Deen, University of Texas.*)

One Foot

76. A large slab of ripple-marked Upper Cambrian sandstone from New York shows distinctive trails made by an unknown organism. *(U. S. National Museum.)*

traces of them are lost. This local area of Middle Cambrian black shale shows a section of former sea bottom in which bacteria and scavengers evidently could not live, just as today they cannot survive in the stagnant unoxygenated waters on the floor of the Black Sea. The animals preserved as fossils could not have lived in this environment, but evidently they sank into it from above, being buried at length in the soft black ooze. Flattened by the weight of sediments, the carbon of their bodies has been concentrated as the shiny film that now appears on the bedding planes of the shale.

Climate

The nature of climates in Cambrian time is largely a matter of guesswork, especially since inferences have to be made mainly from study of marine deposits. We know that glacial climates prevailed in different parts of the world near the beginning of the Cambrian Period, for deposits of glacial till of Late Pre-Cambrian or Early Cambrian age furnish evidence. However, widespread deposition of pure limestone and dolomite, especially in Middle and Late Cambrian time, and general similarity of the Cambrian marine organisms in high and low latitudes, are interpreted to mean moderately warm equable conditions, without differentiation of prominent climatic belts. Some Cambrian limestones contain thick reef deposits that were built by coral-like organisms, and inasmuch as modern coral reefs are confined to

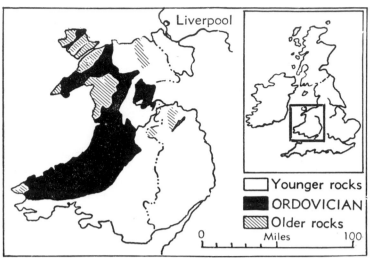

79. Ordovician outcrop areas in the type region of Wales. This classic region contains many fine exposures of fossil-bearing Ordovician strata. On one side, the outcrops adjoin Cambrian or Pre-Cambrian rocks; on the other, they are bordered by younger rocks, mostly Silurian.

and fully recorded elsewhere. The base and the top of the system are marked by important unconformities, denoting somewhat prolonged interruptions in sedimentation, and these boundaries coincide with abrupt changes in the nature of fossil assemblages found in the rocks.

A noteworthy feature of Ordovician deposits in the type region is a decided contrast in the nature of the strata and their contained fossils in one part of the area, as compared with another part that closely adjoins the first. These represent different environments of sedimentation or facies. Ordovician beds in the southeastern part of the outcrop belt are made up almost wholly of thinly stratified limestones, containing abundant trilobites, brachiopods, and many other shell-bearing marine invertebrates of shallow-water type; this is known as the shelly facies, and it is interpreted as having been laid down in offshore clear but shallow water. Contemporaneous deposits in adjacent territory to the northwest consist almost exclusively of carbonaceous dark-colored shale that contains abundant carbonized remains of slender branching invertebrates called "graptolites," but very few other kinds of fossils; these beds are classed as the graptolite facies and are interpreted to represent deposits of a mud-bottom inshore belt where seaweeds grew thickly, furnishing the main source of the carbon.

Occurrence of Ordovician Rocks in North America

Recognition of the system. Deposits of Ordovician age, identified by their fossils, are found in many parts of North America. As in northwestern Europe, they are readily distinguished from the underlying Cambrian, in most places, by the presence of an unconformity separating the systems, and by the abruptness and pronounced nature of changes in the composition of fossil assemblages. Moreover, the same two dominant types of deposits occur on this continent; calcareous beds containing many trilobites, brachiopods, and additional varied kinds of invertebrates, are found in certain areas, and black shale containing few fossils, except abundant graptolites, in other areas. Numerous Ordovician species of North America and Europe are identical or closely similar.

The upper boundary of the Ordovician is marked by a widespread unconformity that separates the system from younger deposits. However, equally pronounced unconformities occur within the Ordovician rocks of North America, and this serves to emphasize the point that definition of the major geologic divisions, called "systems," depends largely on the adoption of a certain type section to serve as a world standard in classification. If the foundations of time-rock classification had been based on early geologic studies in North America, rather than Europe, it is very probable that what we now class as the Lower Ordovician (Canadian) Series would have been defined as

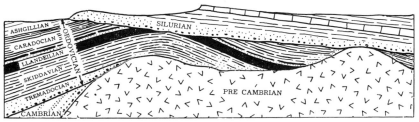

80. Diagrammatic section of Ordovician rocks in Wales. The section shows the presence of Lower Ordovician rocks resting on truncated edges of Cambrian formations; successively younger Ordovician divisions overlap on Pre-Cambrian rocks, also. Deformation and erosion of Ordovician strata, prior to deposition of Silurian sediments, is represented by the nonconformity separating the Ordovician and Silurian rocks.

an independent geologic system. It is delimited below and above by important interruptions in sedimentation, and the rather large group of fossils that it yields is markedly different from those of rocks next older and younger.

General distribution and character. All parts of North America in which Cambrian deposits are found, including the eastern and western geosynclinal troughs and the interior continental platform region, also contain Ordovician deposits (Fig. 81). Like the Cambrian, the Ordovician in the geosynclines is measured in thousands of feet, whereas that of the interior platform aggregates only hundreds of feet. Ordovician seas extended more widely over the interior of North America, however, than those of Cambrian time. We find Ordovician strata resting directly on Pre-Cambrian rocks in territory north of Lake Ontario, in a large area along the southwest shore of Hudson Bay, and on many islands of the Arctic Archipelago west of Greenland.

Divisions. The Ordovician System in North America is clearly

83. Late Middle Ordovician limestone (Trentonian) resting on Pre-Cambrian granite in southeastern Canada. The camera case marks the limestone-granite contact in the center of the view but it is 1 foot or so below the base of the limestone near the left margin. Despite slight unevenness of the Pre-Cambrian surface, there is no basal conglomerate in the Ordovician limestone. Absence of metamorphism of the limestone and other evidence readily prove that the limestone is much younger than the granite, instead of older, as would be the case if the granite intruded the limestone. The structural relations here shown constitute record of the advance of Middle Ordovician seas considerably beyond areas of earlier Paleozoic deposits. (*Canada Geol. Survey.*)

divisible into three main time-rock units that are classed as series. They represent major fluctuations of the seaways that occupied much of the North America continent, and the boundaries between them represent times of general emergence of the continent. During these emergent intervals, of unknown duration, sedimentation ceased, and in some places, previously formed deposits were eroded. Marine organisms underwent accelerated evolutionary changes, which may be correlated with changes in distribution of marine waters. Retreat of shallow seas, from broad areas that had been inundated, inevitably caused migration or extinction of the marine organisms that had been living in the inland seas, those that moved being crowded into peripheral areas of the continental shelf, which already had their own population. Under these conditions, competition for survival would weed out species least able to adapt themselves. Thus, organisms commonly represented among fossils in rocks below such an unconformity may fail to be found in strata belonging above the unconformity. During times of expanding seaways, when large areas of the continent again became suited as habitat for shallow-water marine creatures, the modified old stocks and immigrant new forms of life found maximum play for evolutionary differentiation. The organic assemblage of each main division of the Ordovician rocks accordingly is seen to differ materially from the others. In like manner, subordinate fossil groups characterize lesser time-rock units, classed as stages.

The generally applicable divisions of Ordovician rocks, together with names of formations in representative sections, are indicated in a tabular summary (Fig. 84).

The Lower Ordovician, which is known as the Canadian Series, is defined by type exposures in southern Quebec and northeasternmost New York, along the shores of Lake Champlain, but equally important reference sections are found in the Appalachian region and the Ozark area of Missouri. The break that separates rocks of the Canadian Series from succeeding deposits is the most important boundary within the system, for the change in organisms and general type of sedimentation is markedly greater here than anywhere else in the Ordovician section.

Classic exposures of Middle Ordovician rocks, termed the Mohawkian Series, are found along the Mohawk Valley in central New

Series	Stage	Ozark Region Missouri	Ohio Valley	New York	Appalachian Region	Europe
UPPER ORDOVICIAN (CINCINNATIAN)	RICHMONDIAN	Maquoketa sh. / Fernvale ls.	Richmond group: Elkhorn form. / Whitewater form. / Saluda ls / Liberty form. / Waynesville form. / Arnheim form.	Queenston sh.	Juniata redbeds	ASHGILLIAN
	MAYSVILLIAN		Maysville group: McMillan form. / Fairview form.	Lorraine sh. / Oswego ss.	Reedsville sh. / Martinsburg sh.	CARADOCIAN
	EDENIAN		Eden group: McMicken form. / Southgate form. / Economy Fulton f			
MIDDLE ORDOVICIAN (MOHAWKIAN)	TRENTONIAN	Kimmswick ls.	Cynthiana ls. / Cannon ls. / Lexington ls. / Tyrone-Oregon ls.	Utica sh. / Cobourg ls. / Sherman Falls ls. / Hull ls. / Rockland ls.	Oranda form. / Edinburgh ls.	
	BLACKRIVERAN	Plattin ls.	Stones River gr: Lebanon ls. / Ridley-Pierce ls. / Murfreesboro ls.	Chaumont ls. / Lowville ls. / Pamelia ls.		
	CHAZYAN	St. Peter ss.		Valcour ls. / Crown Point ls.	Lincolnshire ls. / Whistle Creek ls. / New Market ls.	LLANDEILIAN
LOWER ORDOVICIAN (CANADIAN)	BEEKMANTOWNIAN	Black Rock ls. / Smithville ls. / Powell ls. / Cotter dol. / Jefferson City	Knox dol. (subsurface only)	Beekmantown ls. / Tribes Hill ls.	Bellefonte dol. / Axeman ls. / Nittany dol. / Stonehenge ls.	SKIDDAVIAN
	GASCONADIAN	Gasconade dol. / Van Buren dol.			Chepultepec dol.	TREMADOCIAN

84. Time-rock divisions of the Ordovician System and rock units in representative Ordovician sections of North America. The vertical scale is not proportional to thickness or time duration, but the placement of names indicates correlation in age. The ruled areas denote absence of deposits.

York. Highly fossiliferous outcrops are found also in Ontario, the Blue Grass region of Kentucky, near Louisville, and near Nashville, Tenn.

Highly fossiliferous Upper Ordovician strata, comprising the Cincinnatian Series, are nowhere better exposed than in parts of Indiana,

Ohio, and Kentucky, adjacent to Cincinnati. Largely because of the
abundance and fine preservation of the Late Ordovician marine fossils
in this region, a number of leading American invertebrate paleontologists began as boys living in Cincinnati to make fossil collections and
to study them.

Geosynclinal deposits.   During Ordovician time, the Appalachian
and Cordilleran geosynclines continued to sink slowly, the amount of
subsidence being measured approximately by the thickness of Ordovician strata accumulated in these belts. The average thickness is
5,000 feet, and the maximum, in part of the Appalachian trough, is at
least 12,000 feet. Inasmuch as this mile or more of Ordovician deposits
rests on equally thick Cambrian strata, the Pre-Cambrian floor beneath parts of the geosynclines must have been depressed 2 to 3 miles
below sea level by the close of Ordovician time. Even so, since the
geosynclines are estimated to have been upward of 400 miles wide,
the slope of the floor, after combined Cambrian and Ordovician sub-

85. Even-bedded Lower Ordovician dolomite in eastern Pennsylvania. Dolomite and limestone deposits of Ordovician age attain an aggregate thickness of nearly 4,000 feet
in parts of the Appalachian geosyncline. Such deposits denote absence of highlands
in the neighborhood of such marine sedimentation. *(Pennsylvania Geol. Survey.)*

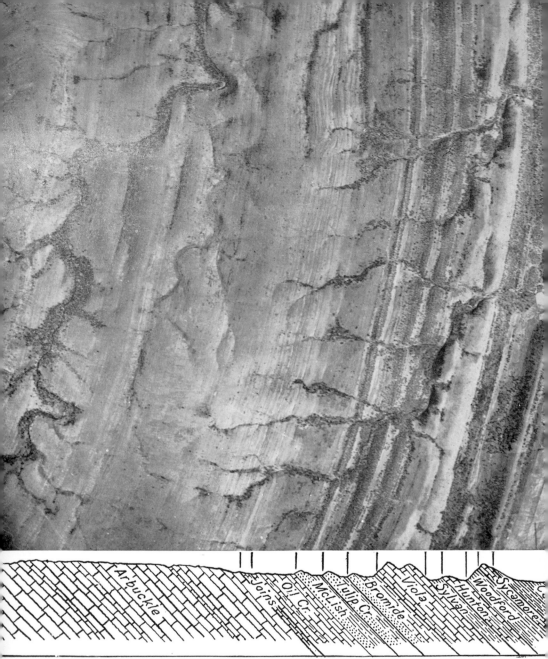

86. Air view of thick Ordovician deposits in the Arbuckle Mountains of southern Oklahoma and geologic section showing classification of rocks. The regularity of features such as topographic expression, variation in color, and distribution of vegetation, associated with the outcrops of these somewhat strongly inclined beds is well shown. *(Soil Conservation Service.)*

sidence, probably did not exceed an average of 60 feet to the mile, and of course, planes of stratification in the upper part of the geosynclinal deposits would be nearly horizontal. The Ouachita and Arbuckle Mountains, in Arkansas and southern Oklahoma, contain Ordovician deposits of geosynclinal type some 10,000 feet thick.

The geosynclines are especially characterized by prominence of calcareous deposits of Ordovician age, which are thickest toward the axis of the troughs. The Lower Ordovician rocks consist mostly of massive dolomite, part of which contains much silica in the form of chert nodules and beds. Younger Ordovician calcareous deposits are mostly limestone. On the side of the geosynclines toward the interior continental platform, the dolomite and limestone formations merge with similar but thinner deposits that extend beyond the troughs.

The parts of the geosynclines adjacent to the outlying borderlands— that is, the eastern part of the Appalachian geosyncline and western part of the Cordilleran geosyncline—were the sites of extensive black-shale accumulation. These belts contain little sandstone (except in the Upper Ordovician of the Appalachian region) and virtually no lime-stone. The black shales are carbon-rich graptolite-bearing deposits. Inasmuch as the varied kinds of invertebrates found in the calcareous deposits are mostly lacking in the black shale and since the graptolite faunas are mainly confined to the black shale, the contrasting environments represented by these deposits evidently exerted a controlling influence on the spread of marine organisms. The shale represents muds derived from the borderlands, as shown by geographic position in the geosynclines, and by interfingering with clear water, calcareous deposits that extend uninterruptedly toward the continental interior. The graptolites did not live in the bottom muds but at or near the water surface, being attached to seaweeds or supported by their own floats. Shallow-water mud and sand, representing very near-shore equivalents of the graptolite-bearing Lower and Middle Ordovician deposits, are unknown, for the original easternmost part of the Appa-lachian geosynclinal deposits and the westernmost part of the Cordil-leran deposits have been eroded away.

Late Ordovician rocks of the Appalachian geosyncline contain some conglomerate, much sandstone, and a considerable thickness of shale representing both marine near-shore and subaerial deposits laid down on land. They denote an important change from types of sedimenta-

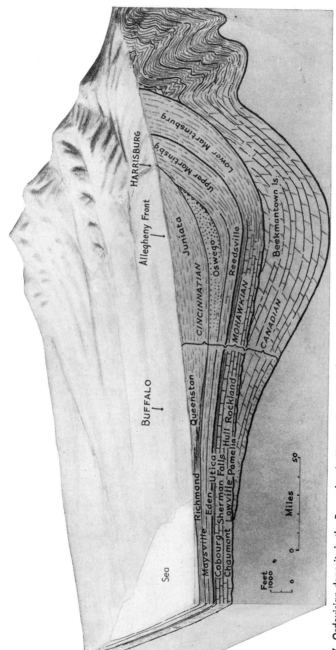

87. Ordovician deposits in the Pennsylvania-New York region. The view across this block diagram is northeastward and the section on the front of the block extends from southern Ontario (at left) to southeastern Pennsylvania beyond Harrisburg. Noteworthy features shown by the diagram are the northwestward thinning of the sedimentary formations, prominence of shale and sandstone deposits toward the southeast, unconformities within the Ordovician sequence, and existence of mountainous highlands near the close of Ordovician time in Appalachia. These are the Taconian Mountains.

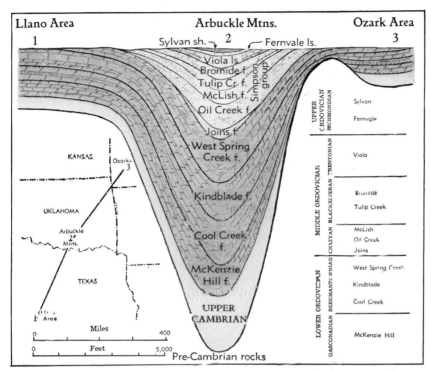

88. Ordovician deposits in the Llano, Arbuckle, and Ozark areas. The diagram emphasizes the greater thickness and completeness of sedimentary records of the geosynclinal area that crosses southern Oklahoma as compared with sections in central Texas and the Ozark region of Missouri.

tion just described. Much of the shale is red. This shale and the coarse sandy deposits lack marine fossils. They are judged to represent stream-borne materials carried westward from Appalachia and laid down above sea level. The conglomerate and coarse sand certainly reflect an uplift of the source country that supplied these sediments and, as noted later, furnish testimony of Late Ordovician mountain building in eastern North America. Upper Ordovician deposits of the eastern part of the continental interior also contain much shale, but this is fine-textured and is associated with many thin beds of limestone, which indicates deposition in muddy, shallow seas distant from the source of the silt and clay.

Continental interior. Throughout the Canadian Shield region and its structural continuation in the interior platform of the Mississippi

89. Cross-bedded shaly Upper Ordovician limestone near Louisville, Ky. These deposits are typical of the very shallow oscillatory seas that transgressed and then retreated from regions of gentle uplifts, such as the Cincinnati arch and Nashville dome. Successive deposits, although parallel, are commonly separated by disconformities. *(Charles Butts, U. S. Geol. Survey.)*

Basin, the comparatively thin Ordovician deposits are made up largely of limestone and dolomite. The sediments making these rocks were laid down in clear, shallow seas. There is one widespread deposit of very pure, even-grained sandstone, and in the upper part of the section a small thickness of shale. The remainder of the deposits is calcareous. There were no nearby lands high enough to be the site of appreciable mechanical weathering, which might have furnished considerable quantities of sand and mud.

That the shallow inland seas of Ordovician time somewhat shifted their position in different epochs, receding and advancing in some areas a number of times, is shown by the presence of minor unconformities in the rock succession. Seemingly, not much change in the relation of land elevation to sea level was required to produce considerable geographic fluctuations of the strand line. The dominantly calcareous nature of the deposits, and the varying distribution pattern of successive formations, accord with the inferred very low-lying, nearly featureless nature of the continental interior during the Ordovician Period.

Especially widespread and uniform in lithologic character are early

Ordovician deposits consisting mainly of dolomite. Silica occurs commonly in many layers, partly in the form of chert nodules and partly as scattered quartz sand grains. The latter indicate the existence during sedimentation of currents sufficiently strong to spread the sand from shore areas far out into the shallow basins. Successive layers mostly lie parallel on one another, or nearly so, but the absence of some deposits over large areas, coupled with evidence of temporary erosion, indicates disconformities. Thus, deposition of sediments was interrupted from time to time.

Outcrops of the older Ordovician dolomitic rocks and records of many thousand deep wells that penetrate these strata show that the formations are distributed from the upper Mississippi Valley southward across Iowa, Missouri, Kansas, and Oklahoma as far as southwestern Texas; they are extensively exposed in the Ozark region of Missouri. Correlation of formations and zonal divisions of formations has been made most reliably by dissolving samples of the rock or drill cuttings in acid and comparing the insoluble residues, which consist mainly of various sorts of silica. Porosity of these buried rocks in many places makes them an excellent reservoir rock for accumulation of oil and gas, some of which may have originated in the Ordovician deposits. The bulk of the oil obtained from the older Ordovician rocks in the mid-continent region, amounting to several hundred thousand barrels annually, probably originated in associated younger strata and migrated into the porous Ordovician strata.

Basins and domes. A structural peculiarity of the broad interior platform of North America is the differentiation of several wide shallow depressions and intervening gentle arches or swells. These features are designated as "basins" and "domes."

The depressions are irregularly saucer-like, being mostly not much wider in one direction than in another. They represent sags of the Pre-Cambrian floor, and they are defined as synclinal basins in the structure of the layered Paleozoic rocks. Examples are the Michigan basin and Illinois basin, in which the beds slope inward from all sides to a low point centrally located in each state. Outcrops of different rock divisions are arranged in concentric belts, the youngest occurring in the middle.

The domes show the reverse of structure characterizing the basins. Rocks dip gently outward in all directions from a central high point,

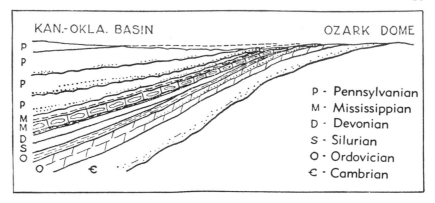

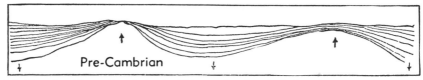

90. Disconformities and variation in thickness of rock units in broad structural basins and domes. Thickness of deposits lying between disconformities commonly diminishes toward the area of a dome, and deposits characteristically overlap in this direction.

and the central outcrop area of old rocks is surrounded by concentric belts of successively younger formations. Typical examples are the Cincinnati dome in Ohio, Indiana, and Kentucky, and the Ozark dome in Missouri.

The gently warped structural pattern, just described, has an important bearing on geologic history of the continental interior region. (1) The basins and domes are possibly very ancient features that persistently have influenced distribution of shallow seas and affected local sedimentation or erosion. (2) Alternatively, they are possibly much more recent features that were produced by deformation confined to time after deposition of the youngest rocks in the areas concerned. In such event the strata throughout most of the interior platform should be fairly uniform in thickness, and should have remained essentially horizontal until the time of deformation that downwarped the basins and uplifted the domes. Prior to this deformation, seas could spread about as easily over one part of the interior as another.

Judgment as to which of these contrasted modes of origin of the basins and domes better accords with actual geological history, requires information derived from field study. Are deposits essentially uniform, or do they differ significantly in distribution, thickness, and lithology? Are some formations confined to basins or thicker in the basins, whereas they are absent or thin in the area of domes? Observations of Ordovician deposits of the continental interior furnish clear answers to these questions and several correlated ones. The basins contain a distinctly thicker and more complete record of Ordovician sedimentation than the upwarped domes, which are characterized by numerous disconformities between Ordovician rock units. Also, there is evidence that during part of Ordovician time, domal areas were subject to erosion, and they supplied sediment to adjacent basins, where it is incorporated in Ordovician deposits. The structural irregularities of the interior platform, such as the Illinois basin and Ozark dome, are therefore ancient features that are expressed in the geological record of Ordovician time, and in part that of the Cambrian Period also.

Volcanic activity. Middle Ordovician deposits of the Appalachian goosyncline and the interior platform, as far west as the Mississippi,

91. Altered volcanic ash (bentonite) bed occurring between layers of Middle Ordovician limestone. This deposit, derived from a volcanic ash fall, is traceable for several miles in southwestern Virginia near Bristol. Ultimately, it may be identified in a much larger area. The bed constitutes an interesting and useful geologic datum since all parts of the bentonite bed are presumed to be closely contemporaneous. (*Charles Butts, U. S. Geol. Survey.*)

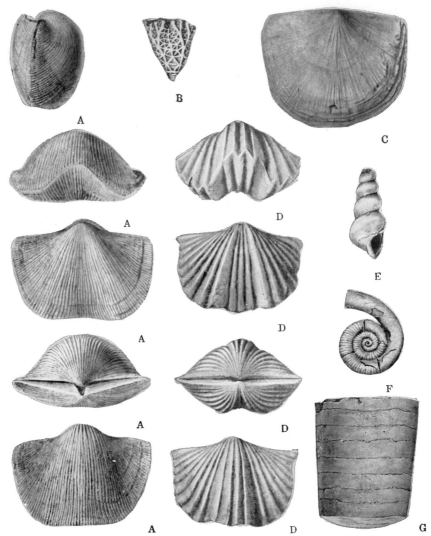

92. Some common Ordovician invertebrate fossils. The fossils illustrated include calcareous brachiopods, having well-developed hinge lines (*A, Hebertella,* five views; *C, Rafinesquina; D, Platystrophia,* four views); a crinoid (*B, Glyptocrinus*) characterized by starlike ridges on the plates; a high-spired snail (*E, Hormotoma*); and two simple-sutured cephalopods (*F, Schroederoceras,* and *G, Orthoceras*). All natural size.

93. Ordovician graptolites. Two specimens of black shale showing the carbonized impressions of graptolite colonies on bedding planes. Natural size.

contain a number of distinctive clayey beds (bentonite) that are identified as altered volcanic ash falls. Commonly, the beds are only 1 or 2 feet thick, but they are especially interesting because each single bed may be interpreted as a rather precisely contemporaneous deposit. Thus, it furnishes a useful datum plane for correlation of associated strata. Some of these altered ash beds have been proved to extend laterally at least scores of miles. The vents from which the explosive eruptions came have not been located, although in Pennsylvania lava flows have been observed in association with an ash bed. Considerable quantities of volcanic tuff, breccia, and submarine lava flows are found associated with Middle Ordovician deposits in eastern Canada and in Newfoundland.

Ordovician Life

Invertebrates. The variety of shallow-water marine life, represented by fossils found in Ordovician strata, considerably exceeds that known from Cambrian rocks. Probably this does not mean that

94. Ordovician shale containing numerous lacy and ribbonlike bryozoans. This specimen, from the Baltic region of Europe, shows the presence of many colonies that are closely similar to forms in American Ordovician strata. *(R. S. Bassler, U. S. National Museum.)*

Ordovician life was correspondingly richer, but that more forms of invertebrates having hard parts adapted for preservation as fossils, existed in Ordovician time. Some beds are literally made up of these organic remains, including especially calcareous-shelled brachiopods, colonies of the so-called moss animals or bryozoans, dismembered pieces or complete carapaces of trilobites, corals, snails, clams, and still other classes of invertebrates. All these groups must have had at least distantly related Cambrian ancestors, but most such inferred antecedents evidently had not acquired the capacity to secrete a protective hard covering. Development of a lime-secreting habit is thus responsible for the seemingly abrupt introduction of rather highly organized invertebrates that subsequently are well represented in the fossil record. The only plausible alternative to conclusions just stated is that these new types of calcareous-shelled invertebrates in the Ordovician rocks, are immigrants descended from Cambrian shell-bearing ancestors, that lived in some wholly unknown area. This is a very improbable explanation.

Trilobites reached the peak of their development during the Ordovician Period. They exhibit a striking variety in shape, and range in size. The largest known trilobite, about 27 inches long, comes from Ordovician rocks.

Among brachiopods, the horny phosphatic-shelled types known from the Cambrian persisted, but they are greatly outweighed in importance by the newly introduced calcareous types, which are mostly much larger, more varied in shape, and more highly organized in structure. They especially distinguish Ordovician from Cambrian deposits, and include many important guide fossils.

Ordovician time is preeminently the age of graptolites; although known from older and younger rocks, they are much more abundant and widespread in Ordovician black shaly deposits than in any other strata, and among them are a large number of guide fossils that occur in widely separated parts of the world. For example, some Ordovician graptolite species that originally were described from Europe have been collected from localities in North and South America, Asia, and Australia.

Approximately 1,000 kinds of bryozoans have already been described from Ordovician rocks, and perhaps an equally large number is yet undescribed. Most Ordovician colonies are branching growths of slender or coarse type, that are made up of innumerable microscopic calcareous tubes which were occupied by the individual organisms.

Along with clams and snails, Ordovician strata contain cephalopods, which are an exclusively marine type of mollusk, represented in modern seas by the pearly nautilus and squids. The shells of some were long, straight, and somewhat tapering; others had loosely or tightly coiled shells; all were divided into chambers of somewhat simple outline. The cephalopods were the largest invertebrates of their time, some having shells that attain nearly 1 foot in diameter and a length of more than 15 feet.

Plants. The calcareous laminated deposits formed by lime-secreting seaweeds are very common fossils in some Ordovician strata. They are the only plant remains definitely known from rocks of this age.

First known vertebrates. Bony plates and miscellaneous skeletal fragments of primitive fishes have been collected from Ordovician deposits in the Rocky Mountain region. Although the remains so far

95. Strongly folded Lower Ordovician limestone in a quarry at Northampton, Pa. Under pressure of mountain-building forces, the limestone here shown has been deformed in almost plastic manner. Ordovician formations along the northeastern border of North America have been affected by two or more epochs of mountain building, and their present structure reflects the sum of these movements. The Taconian orogeny, near the close of the Ordovician Period, was followed by deformations in Devonian and Permian time.

discovered are all fragmentary, there is no question as to their belonging to backboned animals, and for the present, they constitute the earliest record of vertebrates on the earth. The plates and bones occur in marine strata, but their highly localized distribution and fragmentary nature support the suggestion that the fishlike animals to which they belonged actually lived in fresh waters of near-by land, from whence rivers carried them to the sea. If these animals had lived and died in the sea, traces of them ought to be much more widespread. We cannot be sure that vertebrates originated in the fresh waters of continental areas, but we shall observe that the great evolutionary advancement of this group of animals, to which man belongs, is associated with land areas rather than the sea.

Climate

Definite climatic zones, such as characterize the modern world, do not seem to have existed in the Ordovician Period. At any rate, there is hardly any observable difference in the composition of shallow-water marine faunas in Ordovician rocks from Ellesmereland and other parts of Arctic Canada, and those from rocks of similar age in the southern United States. The sea is an equalizing climatic factor; large land areas, especially those having mountains, are characterized by climatic variations, both in temperature and humidity. We may infer that times of extremely widespread shallow seas and low-lying lands, on which mountains were conspicuously absent—and this applies generally to the Ordovician Period—were marked by relatively warm and even climate.

Close of the Period

Mountain building. Two sorts of evidence serve to establish the conclusion that in Ordovician time mountainous areas came into existence in eastern North America. These have been named the *Taconian Mountains,* from an area along the eastern border of New York. One sign of this uplift is the great quantity of gravel, sand, and mud that was furnished by erosion of the elevated terrain; these sediments comprise fluviatile and shallow-water marine Late Ordovician deposits in the Appalachian geosyncline. Some of the hard conglomerate layers now form the resistant core of high mountain ridges, which extend long distances without break. Part of the stream-borne materials consist of reddish alluvial sand and delta deposits.

Another evidence of the mountain building is the folded and faulted structure of Ordovician strata in places where these rocks, beveled by erosion, underlie Silurian deposits. Outcrops showing such relations occur in Pennsylvania, New York, New England, and eastern Canada. They prove that Ordovician and older strata were subjected to mountain-making deformation, which occurred sufficiently long before the time of Silurian sedimentation in the region to permit deep erosion of the Ordovician rocks. Probably, the Taconian mountain building affected the entire length of the Appalachian geosyncline.

Continental emergence.   The end of Ordovician time is signalized by general emergence of the North American continent after the very widespread transgression of the sea in Late Ordovician time. Even the geosynclinal areas were vacated by the shallow seas. Except in areas of mountainous relief in the east, however, elevation of the land seems not to have been enough to permit very much erosion of previously formed deposits. Nevertheless, the hiatus between Ordovician and Silurian strata is clearly defined.

7. The Silurian Period

Silurian strata in the Niagara River gorge below Niagara Falls, N. Y.

Type Region

The Silurian rocks are named from a region in western England and Wales, inhabited by an early tribe known as the Silures. Here, as in many other parts of the world, an important unconformity marks the base of the Silurian System, but the top is less definite, because a transition into overlying continental deposits, known as the Old Red sandstone, occurs at least locally. Elsewhere in the British Isles and

135

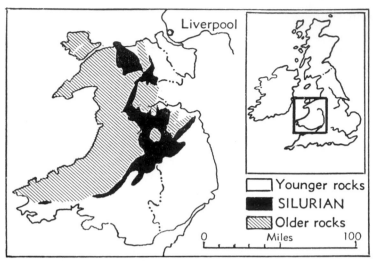

Liverpool

Younger rocks
SILURIAN
Older rocks

0   Miles   100

96. Outcrops of Silurian rocks in Wales and western England where these rocks were named.

northwestern Europe generally, one of the most clearly marked unconformities in the Paleozoic succession defines the upper limit of
Silurian deposits. Toward the close of the Silurian Period, great mountain-making movements, known as the Caledonian orogeny, affected
northwestern Europe and some other parts of the world. Greatly disturbed Silurian and older rocks were then eroded deeply, and the Old
Red sandstone, together with other post-Silurian deposits, was laid
down across the truncated edges of older strata.

Occurrence of Silurian Rocks in North America

Recognition of the system.   The occurrence of Silurian deposits in
North America is proved by finding, at many places in the United
States and Canada, stratified rocks that contain assemblages of marine
shallow-water invertebrates very closely similar to those of the type
region and neighboring parts of Europe. A considerable number of
species found in America seem to be identical with those occurring
in England and richly fossiliferous Silurian rocks of the Baltic region.

The rocks identified as representing Silurian time in North America
lie unconformably on Ordovician strata. In the interior of the continent
and Cordilleran geosyncline, there was no folding or tilting of
Ordovician and older rocks before deposition of Silurian strata, and
accordingly, these rocks lie parallel on older formations. In the

Appalachian geosyncline, however, an angular unconformity is observed at the base of the Silurian in many places, as noted in discussion of the Taconian mountain building given in the preceding chapter.

Distribution and general character of Silurian deposits. Outcrops of Silurian rocks occur mainly in the eastern and northern parts of North America (Fig. 98). In New York, where these rocks were first studied carefully and where the major divisions of the Silurian in North America were named, strata belonging to the system occur in a band, that crosses the state in an east-west direction just south of Lake Ontario. Extensive exposures occur also in the Appalachian geosyncline as far south as Alabama and northeastward to Newfoundland.

The Silurian rocks lie nearly flat in the eastern Mississippi Valley region, where they form the surface of a large area extending from Tennessee across Kentucky, Ohio, Indiana, and Illinois into Wisconsin and Iowa. All of the southern peninsula of Michigan also is underlain by Silurian deposits. That the Silurian seas reached very far to the north in the central part of the continent is shown by the presence of broad outcrop areas of Silurian rocks in Manitoba, on the southwest shore of Hudson Bay, and in islands of the Arctic Archipelago almost to the pole.

In the western United States, Silurian deposits are thin, but they are found at intervals along the trend of the Cordilleran geosyncline from northwestern Canada to the El Paso region of western Texas. Silurian rocks are known also in Alaska.

As we should expect, the nature of Silurian deposits found in dif-

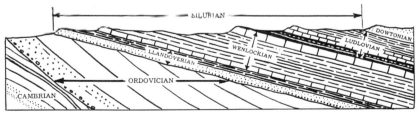

97. Diagrammatic section of the Silurian System in the type region of England and Wales. The Silurian strata dip gently eastward, in general, the harder rocks forming west-facing escarpments. The basal Silurian sandstone rests on various parts of the Ordovician System and in places transgresses on to Pre-Cambrian rocks. The top of the system is less sharply defined, for nearly conformable fish-bearing beds lead up into continental strata of the Old Red sandstone.

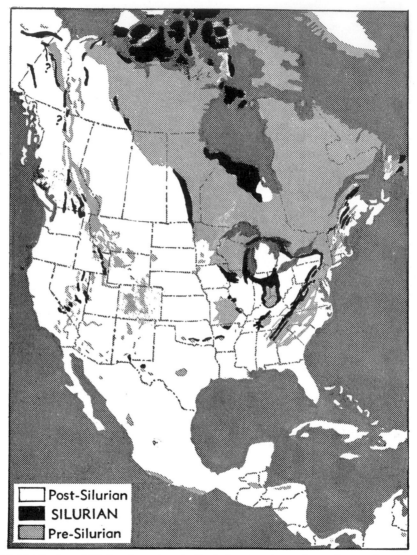

Post-Silurian
SILURIAN
Pre-Silurian

98. Distribution of Silurian formations in North America. A nearly continuous band of Silurian outcrops extends along the Appalachians and around the eastern Great Lakes and Cincinnati region. The northeastern and northern parts of the continent also contain important Silurian areas.

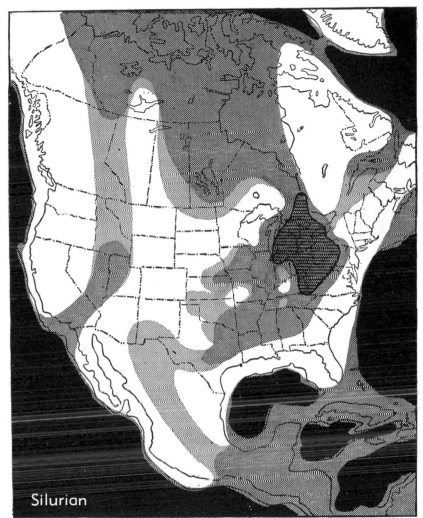

99. Distribution of Silurian seas. Oceanic areas are shown in black; the most persistent seaways on the continental platform are represented by dark gray, and areas submerged during only part of the period are indicated by light gray. Chief areas of inundation were east of the Mississippi River and in the Far North. A restricted seaway of Late Silurian age, in which salt and gypsum were deposited, existed in the eastern Great Lakes region (horizontally ruled). Inferred persistent land areas are white. As indicated by distorted outlines of eastern and western states, the continent is represented as wider than now, so as to compensate for crustal shortening produced by post-Silurian mountain building.

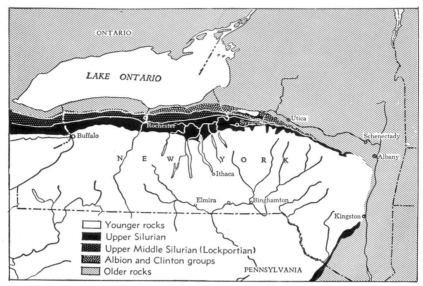

100. Silurian outcrops in the New York region. The chief area of exposure is in an east-west band south of Lake Ontario, but this pinches out near Albany where Devonian rocks overlap the Silurian onto pre-Silurian.

ferent parts of North America differs a good deal, both in kind and thickness. Along the Appalachian trough, where mountains had formed near the close of Ordovician time, Silurian formations are thick and consist largely of coarse materials derived from high land to the east. There is conglomerate, much coarse sandstone, unfossiliferous red sandy shale, and gray silty to clayey shale. Continental sediments in the east grade laterally westward into shallow-water marine deposits, and the interfingered nature of these strata of different origin proves the oscillating position of the shore line during the period.

An interesting and economically important feature of Silurian deposits in this region is occurrence of sedimentary iron ore. The iron oxide is presumed to have been precipitated through action of bacteria in lagoonal areas along the sea borders, but in many places the iron-bearing mineral replaces the original calcareous shell substance of marine fossils and other fragments of calcium carbonate.

Dolomite and dolomitic limestone prevail in Silurian deposits of the Great Lakes and eastern Mississippi Valley area. It is this Silurian dolomite that forms the prominent north-facing escarpment in western

New York over which Niagara River flows, and in which the Falls have been carved. Similar dolomite is widely exposed in Ohio, Indiana, and in the vicinity of Chicago.

Divisions. On the basis of unconformities, denoting interruption in sedimentation, and well-defined differentiation of marine faunas into

Series	Stage	Mississippi and Ohio Valleys	Great Lakes Region	New York	Appalachian Region	Europe
UPPER SILURIAN (CAYUGAN)	KEYSERAN		Raisin River dol.	Manlius ls.	Keyser ls.	LUDLOVIAN
				Rondout ls.		
				Cobleskill ls.		
	TONOLOWAYAN	Kokomo dol.	Put-in-Bay dol.		Tonoloway ls.	
			Tymochtee sh.			
			Greenfield dol.	Bertie waterlime		
	SALINAN		Salina form.	Camillus sh.	Wills Creek sh.	
				Syracuse salt		
				Vernon sh.	Bloomsburg redbeds	
				Pittsford sh.		
MIDDLE SILURIAN (NIAGARAN)	LOCKPORTIAN	Huntington dol.	Guelph dol.	Guelph dol.	McKenzie form.	WENLOCKAN
			Engadine dol. (Racine)	Lockport dol.		
	CLIFTONIAN	Decatur ls.	Cordell dol.			
		Lobelville ls.				
		Bob ls.				
		Beech River ls.				
		Dixon ls.				
		Lego ls.	Schoolcraft dol.			
		Waldron sh.				
		Laurel ls.				
	CLINTONIAN	Osgood form.	Hendricks dol.	Rochester sh. Herkimer ss.	Rochester sh. Keefer ss.	LLANDOVERIAN
				Irondequoit ls. Willowvale sh.		
				Williamson sh. Sauquoit beds	Rose Hill sh.	
			Byron dol.	Wolcott ls.		
				Sodus sh.		
				Reynales ls. Oneida cong.		
				Maplewood sh.		
LOWER SILURIAN (MEDINAN)	ALEXANDRIAN		Mayville dol.	Thorold ss.	Castanea ss.	
				Grimsby ss.		
				Cabot Head sh.		
		Brassfield ls.	Manitoulin dol.	Manitoulin sh.	Tuscarora ss.	
		Edgewood ls.	Whirlpool ss.	Whirlpool ss.		

101. **Time-rock divisions of the Silurian System and rock units in representative important Silurian sections of North America.** The vertical scale does not represent thickness or time duration, but the placement of names indicates correlation. The ruled areas denote absence of deposits.

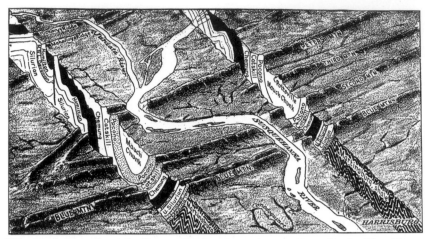

102. Appalachian Mountain ridges and valleys in southeastern Pennsylvania. Blue Mountain, which is made by upturned hard Silurian sandstones, adjoins a plains region that is formed by much-folded, slaty Upper Ordovician rocks (Martinsburg shale). The unconformable contact at the base of the Silurian represents erosion associated with the Taconian mountain building. The folded attitude of Silurian and younger Paleozoic rocks resulted from much later folding that occurred near the close of Paleozoic time. *(Modified from A. K. Lobeck, New York Academy of Science.)*

successive readily distinguishable assemblages, Silurian formations of North America are divided into three series. All are defined and named from sections in the State of New York.

The Early Silurian or Medinan Series comprises sandy and shaly deposits mainly in the east and thin, rather discontinuous limestone in the central states. The Middle Silurian or Niagaran Series is the most widespread division of the system. It contains various clastic formations in the Appalachian trough, but consists mostly of dolomite in the interior region (Fig. 101).

The Upper Silurian or Cayugan Series is the most restricted main division of the system in geographic distribution, being confined mostly to the eastern and northern parts of the continent. It is characterized by evaporites and associated unfossiliferous deposits, but also contains normal marine strata.

Early Silurian Sedimentation

Deposition derived from uplands of Appalachia. In western New York and throughout the Appalachian trough, from Pennsylvania to

Alabama, the Lower Silurian deposits consist chiefly of coarse sandstone and conglomerate. The sand grains or pebbles are held tightly
together in a siliceous cement, and the massively bedded white or
gray rock is extremely resistant; it forms the backbone of many
prominent mountain ridges in the present-day Appalachians. This
deposit rests unconformably on folded Upper Ordovician rocks, and in
its composition furnishes record of
the erosion of elevated country lying east of the Appalachian trough.
The source area of the sediments
is interpreted as belonging to the
Taconian Mountain system, that
had been formed in this region
toward the close of Ordovician
time. The thickness of the sandstone in places is nearly 1,000 feet.
The sandy deposits become thinner
and more fine-grained westward in
the direction away from the Appalachian borderland. The sandstone
is almost entirely barren of any
traces of organisms, and seems
mostly to have been laid down
above sea level. In western New
York and Ontario, however, lateral
gradation and interfingering of the
barren sandstone with marine fossil-bearing shaly deposits may be
observed, and farther west there
are limestone beds laid down in
clear water. Thus, in Early Silurian

103. **Folded Silurian sandstone (Keefer) in
the vicinity of Clifton Forge, Va.** These sandy
deposits belong near the top of the Lower
Silurian section. *(Charles Butts, U. S.
Geol. Survey.)*

time, we may picture somewhat rugged uplands in Appalachia along
the eastern margin of a shallow sea that occupied the geosynclinal belt.
Wearing down of the land was accompanied by alluvial deposition on
a gently sloping coastal plain that merged with the sandy and muddy
bottom of the sea.

Limestone deposition in the continental interior. Lower Silurian
deposits of the continental interior are mostly limestone, but the

maximum thickness is about 300 feet. The beds, which in many places are highly fossiliferous, rest unconformably on various Upper Ordovician formations, but because the contact of the older and younger beds is fairly even and the strata lie parallel, the unconformity is inconspicuous. The clear, shallow waters of Early Silurian time in which these limestone beds were laid down, reached westward at least to Kansas and Oklahoma, and they are also identified far northward in central Canada.

Middle Silurian Marine Transgression

Geosynclinal deposits.   After a time of continental emergence that is indicated by an unconformity above the Lower Silurian rocks, the sea reoccupied virtually all of the previously inundated territory and, in addition, spread widely over the western part of the Canadian Shield and into the Cordilleran geosyncline. In the Appalachian trough, coarse sediments continued to be derived from the highlands of the Taconian belt, and accumulated to a considerable thickness, but in the middle and western parts of the geosyncline, deposition of marine shale was predominant. The shale interfingers eastward with the coarse barren sandstone. Iron-bearing beds occur in this part of the Silurian, and especially in the vicinity of Birmingham, Ala., they are of much economic importance.

Western New York and North Central States.   A classic area for study of the Middle Silurian deposits is the Niagara River gorge, which marks part of the boundary between New York and Ontario. From this section, the name Niagaran, applied to the Middle Silurian Series, is derived. The most prominent formation is the massive dolomite that forms the rim of Niagara Falls, and occurs at the top of the bluffs along the gorge. It is also the resistant rock unit that makes the prominent north-facing escarpment running parallel to the south shore of Lake Ontario. Below the dolomite are fossiliferous shale and thin limestone beds, that comprise the lower part of the Middle Silurian section. Their base approximately coincides with the river level at the foot of the falls, but downstream the beds occur at increasingly high level above the river, so that the entire Lower Silurian and the upper part of Ordovician red-shale deposits are exposed. The sea in which these sediments were laid down extended uninterruptedly westward across the central Great Lakes region to Iowa, as shown

104. Prominent escarpment made by hard Silurian conglomeratic sandstone (Shawangunk) near Kingston, in southeastern New York. These coarse sandy deposits were derived from Appalachia by erosion of the Taconian highlands during Early, Middle, and Late Silurian time. The age of the sandstone varies from place to place. (*N. H. Darton, U. S. Geol. Survey.*)

by nearly continuous outcrops, by lithologic similarity of the deposits, and by occurrence of virtually the same assemblage of marine invertebrates throughout these strata.

Coral reefs. A striking feature of the calcareous Middle Silurian formations, especially in parts of Indiana, Illinois, and Wisconsin, is the local presence of thick unbedded masses of dolomite containing abundant fossil corals. These masses are surrounded by somewhat thinly stratified normal type of dolomite beds, which dip outward

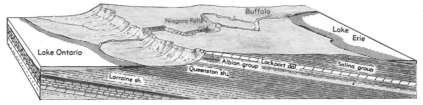

105. North-facing escarpment made by Silurian rocks in western New York and southern Ontario. The diagram shows territory lying between Lake Ontario and Lake Erie, looking slightly south of east. The Silurian (Albion, Lockport, Salina) and underlying Ordovician rocks (Lorraine, Queenston) dip gently southward (toward right). Recession of Niagara Falls has led to formation of the gorge below the falls.

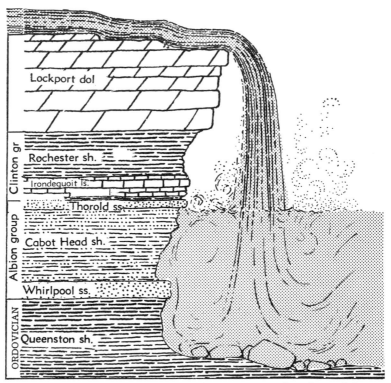

106. Geologic section at Niagara Falls. The Clinton group and Lockport dolomite are exposed above water level at the falls, but all the rocks shown appear above water level downstream. (*Modified from Kindle and Taylor, U. S. Geol. Survey.*)

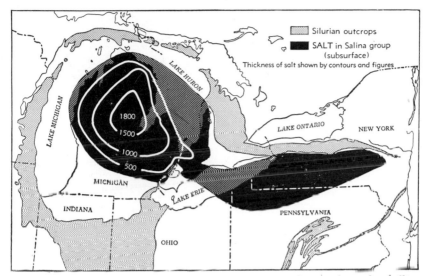

107. Upper Silurian salt deposits in the eastern Great Lakes region. As shown by drilling, the salt deposits are distributed throughout most of the southern peninsula of Michigan, where they attain maximum known thickness of 1,800 feet. Silurian salt underlies a large area in eastern Ohio and northwestern Pennsylvania (beyond limits shown on the map), but in this and the New York region greatest known thickness of salt is about 320 feet.

away from the structureless masses in such manner as to show that the latter were topographic prominences on the Silurian sea floor, just like many modern coral reefs. Whereas corals are found standing in position of growth in the unstratified dolomite masses, specimens found in the adjacent stratified rocks are broken and worn. Unquestionably, these are Middle Silurian coral reefs. They are not very thick—maximum about 75 feet—but some are 2 or 3 miles in diameter. Organisms other than corals contribute to the building of these reef masses, which have come to be termed bioherms (*bios*, life; *herma*, reef).

Because of porosity associated with the reef rock, petroleum may accumulate in bioherms that are covered by impervious beds. At least one good oil field in southern Illinois obtains production from a buried Middle Silurian coral reef, and exploration for others is being undertaken.

Volcanism. Volcanic activity of some importance in Middle Silurian time is recorded by beds of basaltic lava, up to 4,000 feet

thick in eastern Quebec and New Brunswick, and by similarly thick lava and ash beds in Maine.

Late Silurian Restricted Seas

Deposition of evaporites. The latter part of Silurian time is marked by a great restriction of marine waters on the North American continent, and by deposition of much salt and gypsum in isolated Late Silurian basins. Associated with the gypsum, which is the hydrous form of calcium sulphate, is much anhydrite, which is anhydrous calcium sulphate. These deposits indicate concentration of the mineral matter in sea water by evaporation to the point of saturation, at which continued evaporation produces precipitation. The southern peninsula of Michigan and adjacent country eastward to central New York contain thick deposits of Upper Silurian salt, gypsum, and anhydrite, which occur in numerous beds. There is much gypsum and anhydrite also in Upper Silurian deposits of the lower Mackenzie Valley in northwestern Canada.

The aggregate thickness of rock salt near the center of the Michigan basin is at least 1,800 feet, and a few miles south of Syracuse, N. Y., it is 318 feet. Marine deposits associated with the evaporites consist of dolomite and gray to red, unfossiliferous shale. It is probable that some of the shales are subaerial in origin, representing land deposits adjacent to the Late Silurian sea, laid down under a desert climate.

Deposition in unsaturated brines. The top part of the Upper Silurian Series in New York and the Great Lakes region, is characterized by numerous fairly even layers of impure dolomite, called "water lime." These beds contain organisms of specialized type, including a group of large arthropods (eurypterids). The rocks and fossils indi-

---

108. Restoration of Middle Silurian sea bottom in the Niagara region of New York. The stalked organisms are cystoids (at right in upper view) and crinoids, some with outspread arms in position of feeding and others with arms inrolled so that the crown resembled a small football. There are several colonies of corals, distinguished by their circlets of delicate tentacles, and various brachiopods and seaweeds. Four different kinds of trilobites may be seen crawling over the sea bottom and on the coral reef. Straight-shelled cephalopods, and one having a gently curved shell, are identifiable by eyes on the head and the strong tentacles that project from the living chamber. (*Prepared by George and Paul Marchand, under the direction of Irving G. Reimann. Courtesy of Buffalo Museum of Science.*)

migration by which species were interchanged between North America and Europe.

The arthropods called "eurypterids" or "sea scorpions," which characterize Late Silurian deposits in the northeastern United States, were spike- or blade-tailed animals with jointed legs and claws, most of which had an over-all length of only a few inches. The largest attained a length of 9 feet from tip of tail to outstretched pincers, and this Silurian creature is the most gigantic known arthropod, living or extinct.

Vertebrates.   Remains of fishes, which are very scanty and un-

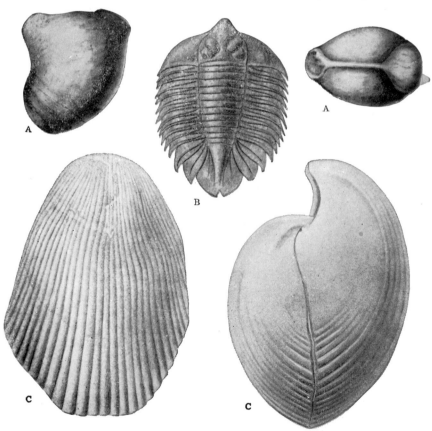

110. Representative Silurian invertebrate fossils. *A.* Two views of a simple-sutured cephalopod *(Phragmoceras)* that is specialized in having a partly closed living chamber. *B.* A characteristic trilobite *(Arctinurus)* with large fluted tail shield. *C.* Two views of a large, ribbed brachiopod *(Conchidium).*

satisfactory, have been described from Silurian deposits, but uppermost Silurian or lowest Devonian (Downtonian) rocks in Europe have yielded nearly complete remains of very primitive fishes. They had a length of about 6 inches and represent a type that lacks well-defined jaws.

Possible land plants and animals. Plant fossils, interpreted somewhat doubtfully to represent primitive land plants, have been reported from Europe and Australia. Also the supposed first air-breathing animals, consisting of scorpions and thousand-leg worms (millipeds), are found in Upper Silurian rocks of Wales. The Silurian scorpions are strikingly like living forms, which suggests, rather than proves, that they breathed air.

Climate

Generally warm, mild, and nearly uniform climatic conditions seem to have prevailed in Early and Middle Silurian times, as throughout most of the Ordovician Period. This is mainly indicated by the near identity of marine faunas of polar areas and those of temperate latitudes in Europe and the United States. Corals are common as far north as the Hudson Bay region.

In the Late Silurian Epoch, desert conditions are indicated by deposits of the northeastern United States and Mackenzie Basin of far northwestern Canada.

Caledonian Mountain Building

One of the major mountain-building deformations of earth history affected northwestern Europe, northern Greenland, Alaska, and much of the Asiatic continent, toward the close of Silurian time. It is known as the Caledonian revolution (from the Roman name for northern Scotland). In most of North America, conditions were very quiet at this time, for there is general absence of crustal disturbance near the boundary between Silurian and Devonian. Throughout the length of Norway and the bordering part of Sweden, however, Silurian and older formations were very strongly folded and pushed eastward along thrust faults; some of the displacements are measured in tens of miles (maximum about 80 miles). In Scotland, northern England, and Ireland, the Caledonian structures trend southwestward, and movement along faults was northwestward. Strongly deformed Silurian and older rocks are seen unconformably beneath the Old Red sandstone (Devonian) or younger Paleozoic rocks, that came to be laid down after erosion had truncated the folded and faulted strata.

Close of the Period

Except for parts of the northern border of the continent, North America was not disturbed by mountain-making movements at the close of Silurian time. Most of the land surface had become emergent at the beginning of the Late Silurian Epoch, but there is no evidence of highland areas. In the Appalachian geosyncline, limestone deposits of latest Silurian age are overlain by very early Devonian limestone, with signs of only a minor interruption of sedimentation to serve in marking the boundary. Thus, in contrast to unrest such as is represented by the Caledonian disturbance elsewhere, the close of the Silurian Period in most of North America was very quiet.

8. The Devonian Period

Lower Devonian escarpment southwest of Albany, N. Y.

Type Region

The name of the Devonian Period is derived from the County of Devon in southwestern England, for it was in this place that fossil-bearing marine deposits belonging between Silurian rocks, below, and Carboniferous formations, above, first were recognized. Continental deposits of equivalent age, known as the Old Red sandstone, unconformably overlie the Silurian in Wales and areas farther north, but such relatively unfossiliferous beds were not deemed suitable as a basis for defining a major division of the geologic column. Actually, the marine Devonian strata of Devon are so folded and faulted that the exact nature of the rock succession is not yet wholly determined, and accordingly, the section of western Germany that comprises

N. H. Darton, U. S. Geological Survey

155

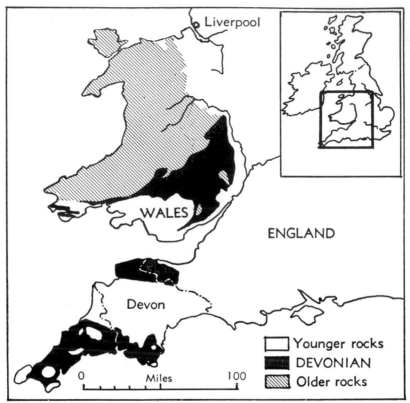

111. Devonian outcrops in Wales and southwestern England where this system was named. The County of Devon contains marine deposits, whereas those in Wales are of continental type.

equivalent highly fossiliferous marine rocks, having somewhat simple structure, has come to be recognized as the European standard. Based on correlation with these deposits, rocks of Devonian age are recognized on all the continents.

Occurrence of Devonian Rocks in North America

Recognition and definition of the system. Characteristic guide fossils of the Devonian System, as represented in western Europe, are found in North America (Fig. 120). These include both various types of marine invertebrates and organisms, such as fishes, that lived in streams and lakes of the land; therefore, essential equivalence in age of both marine and nonmarine deposits representing the Devonian Period is well established on opposite sides of the Atlantic.

Recognition of the lower and upper boundaries of Devonian deposits in most parts of North America, where interruptions in sedimentation defined by unconformities set these deposits apart from adjacent beds, is relatively simple and definite. There are places, however, in which the boundaries are not so fixed. In parts of eastern New York and farther south in the Appalachian geosyncline, sedimentation from Silurian into Early Devonian time seems to have been virtually continuous. Here, the beginning of Devonian time is reckoned by making correlations with near-by sections that record a break and by comparative studies of the fossil faunas. A similar problem in defining the top of the Devonian is encountered in the Ohio and Mississippi Valleys. These questions are not important, however, insofar as the broad features of historical geology of Devonian time in North America are concerned.

Distribution and character of formations. The outcrop areas of Devonian rocks in North America (Fig. 112) and areas inferred to have been covered by Devonian seas, occupy a large part of the continent. In the east, they extend from the shore of the Gulf of St. Lawrence across New England and southward along the Appalachian geosyncline to Alabama. The thickest deposits are found in the classic area of Devonian studies in New York and Pennsylvania. Both marine and nonmarine deposits are exceptionally well developed. The Lower Devonian and part of the Middle Devonian are made up mostly of limestone containing many marine fossils. In New York, these rocks make a north-facing escarpment that trends east-west a few miles south of the Middle Silurian (Niagaran) dolomite scarp; the beds dip southward at a gentle angle. The limestone formations are overlain by highly fossiliferous marine shale, and this in turn by thick sandy continental deposits of predominantly reddish color, that form the Catskill Mountains and cap the northern part of the Allegheny Plateau. In central and eastern Pennsylvania, the Devonian rocks are steeply but not complexly folded, and the beds are excellently exposed in many places. A noteworthy feature of the upper part of the Devonian succession in this area is the great thickness of continental deposits derived from erosion of a highland lying east of the Appalachian geosyncline.

shown by limestone and other rocks of this age in many places in the Cordilleran geosyncline and overlapping on the platform area of the Canadian Shield. Outcrops occur at the south tip of Hudson Bay and extensively in the lower Mackenzie Valley in the far northwest.

Divisions. Devonian rocks of North America have been divided into three parts called Lower Devonian (Ulsterian) Series, Middle Devonian (Erian) Series, and Upper Devonian (Senecan and Chautauquan) Series, but these are not based on the occurrence of widespread unconformities reflecting major oscillations of the Devonian seas. Rather, they define segments of the Devonian column based on comparison of assemblages of fossils with those occurring in the Lower, Middle, and Upper Devonian of Europe. It is convenient, for purposes of description and correlation, to divide the rocks in this manner. In addition, each series is divided into time-rock units called "stages," all of which are based on deposits of the New York area.

Lithologic divisions of Devonian rocks, consisting of groups, formations, and members, are very numerous and most of them are recognized only locally, that is, within 100 miles or less of the type outcrops from which these units are named. Geographic restriction in use of lithologically defined units is imposed mainly by changes in the nature of the Devonian deposits from place to place, but to some extent it reflects uncertainty as to precise equivalence of differently named rocks. The local names tend to become fixed by frequency of using them in geological reports, and thus to persist even when it becomes recognized that they are synonyms of some other rock division.

Devonian History of North America

Early Devonian restricted seaways. At the beginning of Devonian time, the North American continent should be pictured as a land area somewhat larger than now, but, so far as known, lacking mountainous elevations anywhere. There were then no large marine indentations like Hudson Bay. Also, the continent was many miles broader from east to west, for we know that the earth crust included in North America was squeezed and considerably shortened in making the Appalachians, Rockies, Sierra Nevada, and other mountain ranges, all of which were formed after the beginning of Devonian time. The paleogeographic maps in this book show the estimated greater width of the continent in early geologic periods, this added width being all

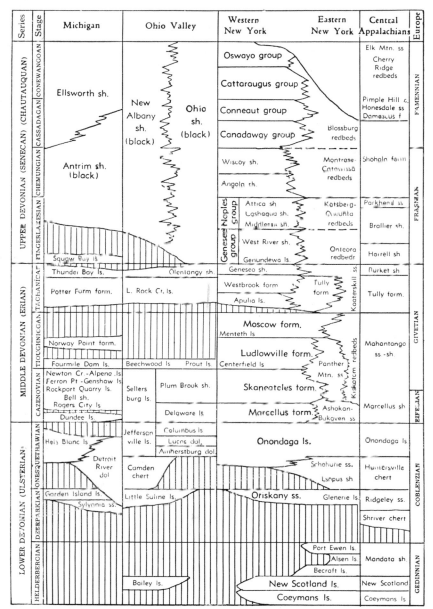

114. Time-rock divisions of the Devonian System and rock units in representative important Devonian sections of North America. The vertical scale is not proportional to the thickness of deposits or time duration, but placement of names indicates correlation of formations. The ruled areas denote absence of deposits.

assigned to the geosynclinal belts, because it is these that have been crumpled by mountain making; the interior lowland platform has not been shortened in width. If seaways like the Appalachian and Cordilleran troughs were plotted on the shortened base represented by their present wrinkled deposits, they would be shown much narrower than they actually were.

In Early Devonian time, an arm of the Atlantic, somewhat resembling the Baltic Sea of Europe, reached southwestward from the present mouth of the St. Lawrence, extending virtually the entire length of the Appalachian geosyncline. Not much sand and mud accumulated on the bottom of this sea, for the deposits found consist

115. Lower Devonian limestone in the Helderberg escarpment southwest of Albany, N. Y. This formation (Coeymans) rests on Upper Silurian beds with little or no break. It is classified as Early Devonian on the basis of comparison of its fossils with those of the basal part of the Devonian System in Europe. *(N. H. Darton, U. S. Geol. Survey.)*

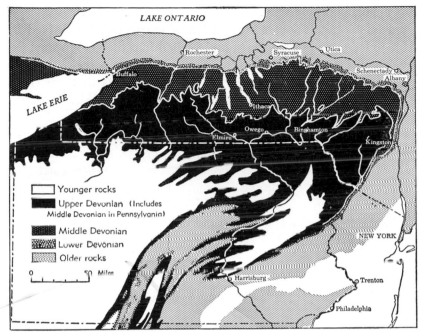

116. The classic area for study of Devonian rocks in North America. The New York and adjacent Pennsylvania region takes first place in study of Devonian historical geology because time-rock classification used in North America is based on this part of the continent. Also, extremely fossiliferous formations and specially important features of Devonian sedimentation are illustrated in this region.

mostly of limestone. A westward extension of this sea, that existed at least temporarily, is recorded by Early Devonian limestones in central Tennessee, eastern Missouri, southern Oklahoma, and central Texas, but no Lower Devonian deposits are known in the northern interior or western parts of the continent.

Middle Devonian mountain building. Toward the close of the Early Devonian Epoch, the northern part of the Appalachian borderland began to undergo profound geographic change. The land, which had been worn low after the Taconian mountain building, was strongly elevated at this time by crustal disturbances that produced new ranges of mountains, which have come to be known as the *Acadian Mountains*. Evidence of this mountain building is seen partly in the folded and faulted structure of Early Devonian and older rocks in eastern Canada; these lie beneath Late Devonian and Mississippian deposits with angular unconformity. Indirect, but more imperfect evidence, is found in the tremendous accumulation of coarse detritus derived by erosion of the mountainous area and carried into the geosynclinal depression to its west. The oldest of these deposits are conglomerates, coarse red and gray sandstones, and finer sediments that are excellently exposed in parts of eastern Canada, the Catskill Mountain region of New York, and in east-central Pennsylvania. The deposits are early Middle Devonian in age, as shown by marine strata farther west into which they grade laterally. This proves that uplift of the source area and initiation of vigorous erosion had occurred not long after the beginning of Middle Devonian time. In part of the region that began then to receive coarse deposits, limestone (Onondaga) was being deposited late in Early Devonian time.

The mountain-derived sediments were laid down partly on land above sea level, and partly in near- and offshore belts of the shallow sea that occupied the Appalachian geosyncline. This inference is supported both by physical characters of the deposits and by their fossil remains. Locally, the nonmarine beds contain stumps of trees standing in the position of growth, and these are associated with fallen logs and leaf impressions; fresh-water clams and fishes have been found in beds that were laid down by streams or in ponds. Adjacent marine deposits of the same age contain the stout shells of bottom-living invertebrates that were adapted to life in the sea not far from shore. Contemporaneous marine deposits several miles farther west consist of fine black muds and thin limestone layers formed in quiet water of somewhat greater depth; these beds contain thin-shelled invertebrates that are adapted to such an offshore environment. The intergrading and interfingering deposits of different types in the Devonian area of New York, Pennsylvania, and other eastern states, constitute unusually interesting examples of sedimentary facies.

The deposits here briefly described permit us to construct a reasonably definite picture of the Acadian Mountains belt, the plain sloping westward from its foothills, and the shallow sea at the margin of the plain. The mountainous country in western New England, and reaching far northeast and south, is judged to have attained elevations of several thousand feet above sea level, possibly comparable to those of the Alps and Rockies. The great alluvial fans and piedmont plain stretching westward from the foothills of this range were constructed

117. Devonian continental deposits in the Catskill Mountains. This view shows Kaaterskill Falls in the Catskill Mountains, one of many places where the irregularly stratified, prevailingly red sandstone and shaly deposits of continental origin compose most of the mass of the Catskill Mountains. These sediments were formed as part of a great delta built westward from the Acadian Mountains formed in Middle and Late Devonian time.

by swift-flowing streams that became gradually sluggish before reaching the coast of the Appalachian seaway. As time elapsed, the sea was gradually filled in and the coastal plain extended farther and

118. Disconformable contact of Middle Devonian on Middle Silurian limestone at Louisville, Ky. This view of a quarry face on Bear Grass Creek shows a perfectly regular, seemingly conformable succession of limestone beds. Fossils establish the Silurian age of lower limestone beds and prove the Devonian age of upper layers. The intersystemic contact occurs just above the white streaks (chert) at mid-height of the photograph. *(Charles Butts, U. S. Geol. Survey.)*

farther west, until in Late Devonian time, land conditions prevailed into western New York and western Pennsylvania.

Middle and Late Devonian seas. The central and western parts of the continent, including areas in the far north, were covered widely by shallow seas during Middle and Late Devonian time. Record of the abundant marine life of these epochs is recorded in the exceptionally well-preserved fossils that are found in many places. The deposits consist mostly of limestone, which is commonly less than 300 feet thick in the interior areas but more than 2,000 feet thick in parts of the western geosyncline.

Devonian Life

The abundance and variety of marine invertebrates formed in Devonian rocks are striking, and in many places the preservation of these fossils is exceptionally perfect. The collection and study of specimens under these conditions are fascinating, not only for trained geologists but for many who lack technical instruction. Localities in western New York, southwestern Ontario, northern Michigan, Indiana, and Iowa are famous for the richness of Devonian fossils.

Invertebrates. All main classes of invertebrates are well represented in Devonian deposits, although dominant groups of earlier Paleozoic times, such as the trilobites, are evidently on the wane. Brachiopods were especially numerous, and among them are many highly useful guide fossils. Slender branching bryozoans and those of delicate lacelike network, are very common in some formations. The variety and beauty of fossil corals in Devonian rocks call for special notice. Also, there are numerous coral reefs, like those in Middle Silurian rocks; they occur chiefly in limestones. Associated with the corals are numerous colonies of lime-secreting coelenterates called "stromatoporoids"; they build laminated calcareous structures, some of which attain a diameter and thickness of several feet. Echinoderms are represented by many kinds of crinoids, including several excep-

119. Middle Devonian limestone largely formed of fossil corals near Louisville, Ky. Coral-filled limestone (Jeffersonville) occurs in the bed of the Ohio River at the so-called Falls of the Ohio. The cylindrical objects weathered out on the limestone surface are horn corals. *(Charles Butts, U. S. Geol. Survey.)*

tionally beautiful forms with ornamented plates; also there are blastoids and a few cystoids. Muddy and sandy deposits contain a host of pelecypods, gastropods, and cephalopods, which include many important guide fossils, especially among the cephalopods; these molluscan groups also occur in limestones. Graptolites are gone, except for a single long-lived, relatively unimportant stock.

A noteworthy feature of some Devonian fossil assemblages, which is by no means confined to the Devonian, however, is differentiation of groups of organisms according to their environment. Thus, we find notable differences between faunas of black muds, clear limestones, gray shales, and other types of sediments.

Rise of fishes. The Devonian Period is sometimes termed the Age of Fishes. This does not mean that fishes are more prevalent as fossils in Devonian rocks than in any other part of geologic time, particularly later systems, for that is not true. Also, certainly it does not mean that the fishes reached the peak of their development thus early in geologic history. This designation signifies rather that, with seeming abruptness, a considerable number and variety of well-developed

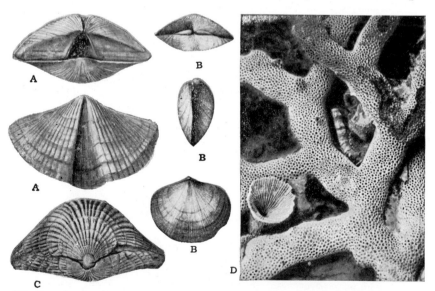

120. Devonian brachiopods and honeycomb coral. Examples of abundant spire-bearing types of calcareous brachiopods are *A (Cyrtospirifer)* and *C (Atrypa)*; a small biconvex, finely ribbed brachiopod *(Dalmanella)* is represented by *B. D* illustrates a branching type of honeycomb coral *(Favosites)* with a small horn coral. Natural size.

121. Devonian trilobites. Although less numerous than in earlier Paleozoic time, trilobites were abundant locally in Devonian shallow seas. The unusual rock fragment here shown contains nearly two dozen specimens of a characteristic Devonian trilobite *(Phacops),* natural size. *(U. S. National Museum.)*

forms of fishes are introduced in the fossil record. A majority of the known forms lived in fresh waters on land, and it seems not improbable that this lowest order of the vertebrates originated in fresh waters of the land. Marine fishes, especially primitive sharks, are also known from Devonian strata, and some reached the respectable size of 20 feet in length. One group of Devonian fishes developed lungs and thus were able to breathe air, and among them we find types having bony supports for front and rear pairs of fins. This bony

122. Restorations of life in a Devonian shallow sea. The most abundant animals are corals, among which there are several sorts of solitary forms known as horn corals and different types of colonial corals; a circle of outstretched tentacles surrounds the mouth of each individual. Coiled cephalopods are seen on the sea bottom at left and

structure closely corresponds to that of leg-bearing vertebrates. Abundant remains of fish begin at the very base of the Devonian in beds (Downtonian) of the British Isles and Norway, that have been classed as uppermost Silurian by some authors. Fossil fishes are treated in the chapter on Paleozoic life.

First amphibians. The Devonian Period is the time when the first definitely known vertebrates higher than the fishes made appearance. These are small amphibians found in Upper Devonian rocks of eastern Greenland. The collected remains of these creatures include numerous skulls and incomplete skeletons. We may note that, by the close of Devonian time, four-legged animals that are the ancestors of reptiles and mammals had made appearance on the earth.

A single three-toed footprint, ascribed to an amphibian, has been

a straight-shelled type at right. Brachiopods cling to the sides of some coral colonies or are partly buried in mud. Small clusters of stalked crinoids may be seen and a half dozen trilobites are crawling about. (*Prepared by George Marchand, under direction of I. G. Reimann. Courtesy of Rochester Museum of Arts and Science.*)

reported from Upper Devonian rocks of Pennsylvania. Whether or not this fossil is indicative of an amphibian, we cannot doubt that one of the most important advances in vertebrate history had been made before the end of Devonian time. This evolutionary advance consisted in the development of limbs capable of being used for walking on land. The limbs of the amphibians were derived from fins of Devonian fishes of a type having the fins supported by a fleshy lobe.

Land plants.   The oldest definitely known land plants occur in the Devonian, and among those of this period are forms ranging from small herblike plants of swamp-living habit to trees having a height of 40 or more feet. The fact that no such remains have been found in Silurian or older rocks indicates that the Devonian is the first part of geologic time in which some of the land surface was forest-covered.

123. Restorations of life in a Devonian shallow sea. A sharklike fish *(Cladoselache)* is swimming toward a large coiled cephalopod that crawls about among the several

The trunks of tree ferns, some of which are 3½ feet in diameter, have been found in Middle Devonian rocks of southeastern New York.

Climate

The similarity of Devonian invertebrate faunas from high- and low-latitude belts indicates that an equable climate of fairly warm and humid type prevailed over much of the globe. No indication of any distinct climatic belts is found. On the other hand, existence of rugged mountain chains—the Caledonian Mountains in Europe, Asia, and Arctic North America, the Acadian Mountains in eastern Canada

sorts of sponges growing on the sea floor. (*Prepared by George and Paul Marchand, under the direction of Irving G. Reimann. Buffalo Museum of Natural Science.*)

and the United States, and mountains in eastern Australia—strongly implies attendant local variations in climate. Mountains cause air currents to move upward, lowering the temperature and causing precipitation. Thus, mountain slopes generally are well watered. In places where winds have a prevailing direction, such as the belts of westerlies in moderately high latitudes and the trade winds in low latitudes, climatic conditions may vary markedly on opposite sides of a mountain range running transverse to such winds. The Acadian Mountains may be presumed to have affected climates in eastern North America in this fashion. The prevailing wind in their latitude presumably was

124. Restorations of Devonian fishes. The large fishes are a primitive armored type *(Coccosteus)*. Ostracoderms are illustrated in the bottom part of the view. *(University of Kansas, Natural History Museum.)*

125. Restoration of Devonian fishes. Spine-bearing sharks are one of the common types. *(University of Kansas, Natural History Museum.)*

126. Restoration of a Middle Devonian forest in eastern New York. Except for the tree fern at right, known Devonian plants were leafless or characterized by short spike-shaped leaves. (*C. R. Knight, Chicago Natural History Museum.*)

from the west, as now; therefore, the side of the range facing the Appalachian seaway should have been well watered, whereas that on the opposite side, toward the Atlantic, may have been fairly arid. No sedimentary deposits laid down on the eastern side of the Acadian chain are known.

Close of the Period

The end of Devonian time is marked by general retreat of seas from the continental areas, so that a well-marked break in sedimentation, in general, separates Late Devonian from succeeding sediments. The Acadian Mountains were still sufficiently elevated to supply much sediment to adjoining areas, but so far as known, there was no renewal of crustal deformation in North America that served to accentuate relief of the land surface. Mountain making (Bretonian) occurred, however, in parts of western Europe at or near the close of the Devonian Period.

Crustal disturbance of local importance occurred toward the close of Devonian time on the east side of the Ozarks in southeastern Missouri. Devonian and older rocks here are found displaced at least 1,000 feet by faulting. After the faulting, the country was smoothed by erosion so that early Mississippian marine strata were laid down evenly across the fault lines, covering Devonian rocks on one side and lower Ordovician strata on the other.

One of the important times of mountain building in eastern Australia occurred at the close of the Devonian Period.

9. The Mississippian Period

Early Mississippian rocks in the Mississippi River bluffs at Hannibal, Mo.

Definition and Type Region

The Mississippian Period and the next following Pennsylvanian Period are the only widely recognized major geologic time divisions that are "made in America." These names have been almost universally adopted by geologists in North America, and to some extent have been used on other continents, but most foreign maps and literature dealing with late Paleozoic deposits employ the term *Carboniferous* for rocks corresponding to Mississippian and Pennsylvanian. This name, which was first applied to coal-bearing rocks in England (1822), embraces two strongly contrasted main parts in almost all areas; rocks called Lower Carboniferous, corresponding closely to the Mississippian, and those classed as Upper Carboniferous, being approximately equivalent to the Pennsylvanian.

177

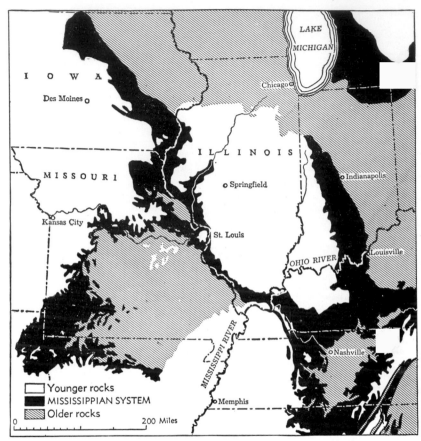

127. Distribution of Mississippian outcrops in the type region along the Mississippi River and in adjacent areas. The older Mississippian formations occur in the north and around the Ozark uplift. Upper beds of the Mississippian System are best exposed along the Mississippi south of St. Louis and in Indiana and Kentucky.

The Mississippian rocks were named from the central Mississippi Valley where splendid exposures show relations of these deposits to beds below and above. Almost all the Mississippian strata of this region are of marine origin, and most of them are abundantly fossiliferous. The rocks are nearly flat-lying, so that the succession of formations can be determined with certainty. Both the base and the top of the Mississippian System are marked by prominent unconformities that indicate widespread interruptions of sedimentation accompanied by erosion. These breaks, together with contrasting features of lithology and fossils, serve to define the Mississippian very clearly as an independent segment of the geologic column having equivalent rank with Devonian, Silurian, and other main time-rock divisions classed as systems.

Guide Fossils

The Mississippian rocks, like older Paleozoic systems, are identifiable throughout North America by means of characteristic fossils, of which a few are illustrated in this book. Many of these organisms are identical with fossils in the Lower Carboniferous rocks of Europe, Asia, and other parts of the globe, and other forms, although distinct, represent the same organic stocks and show the same stage of evolution as are seen in foreign fossil assemblages. Accordingly, close equivalence in age can be determined reliably.

Mississippian sections in widely separated parts of the United States and Canada commonly can be correlated zone by zone by means of invertebrate species having short vertical range, which migrated laterally long distances. Thus, several species of crinoids that are confined to a few feet of beds in central Iowa occur also in a narrow zone in western Montana; bryozoans and brachiopods that characterize a small thickness of beds in Alabama and Kentucky occur also in Arizona and Idaho.

Character and Distribution of Mississippian Deposits

Two contrasting types of Mississippian deposits may be distinguished in North America. The first consists of marine deposits, mostly limestone, that are very widespread west of the Appalachian Mountains. The second comprises thick continental deposits, which occur mostly in the Appalachian region.

The most important outcrop area of Mississippian rocks is that occurring along the Mississippi River from southeastern Iowa to southern Illinois, for the section here displayed embraces all parts of the system from the oldest to youngest and contains the type localities of most formations included in the standard reference section. The marine Mississippian strata of the type section may be traced southeastward as far as northern Alabama and eastward into West Virginia and Pennsylvania. Outcrops are traced westward across Iowa and around the Ozark dome in Missouri and Arkansas. In Oklahoma, Kansas,

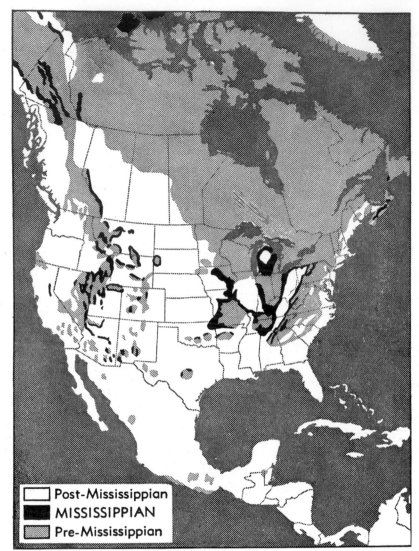

128. Distribution of Mississippian outcrops in North America. The numerous areas of Mississippian outcrops in the western United States, although not prominent on the map, are important and should be noted in comparison with Fig. 129.

Nebraska, thousands of well borings penetrate Mississippian strata, showing that these rocks continue under the Great Plains. Mississippian rocks reappear at the surface on the flanks of the Rocky Moun-

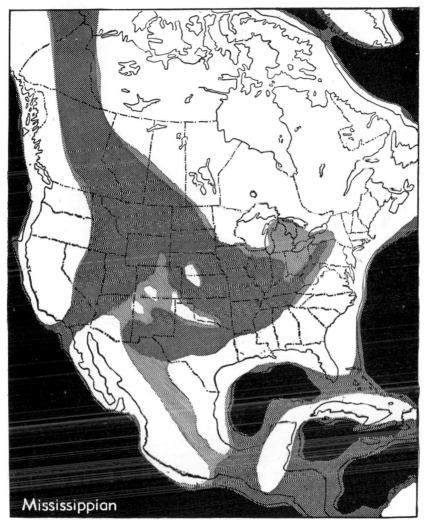

129. Distribution of Mississippian seas. Oceanic areas are shown in black; the most persistent seaways on the continental platform are represented by dark gray; and areas submerged during part of the period only are indicated by light gray. The general pattern of Mississippian seaways resembles that of Devonian time, especially in persistence of a northwestern connection with Eurasia. The inferred persistent land areas are white. As indicated by distorted outlines of eastern and western states, the continent is represented as wider than now, so as to compensate for crustal shortening produced by post-Mississippian mountain building.

tain uplift and in the Black Hills. Thence they extend under cover to other outcrop areas in western states from Arizona and Nevada northward to Alberta and Alaska. Thus, seaways of Mississippian time are seen to have been very extensive.

The continental deposits of Mississippian age in the eastern United States closely resemble the coarse red and gray sandstone and silty redbeds of the underlying nonmarine Middle and Upper Devonian. This offers no surprise, for they have the same origin, consisting of erosion products carried westward from the still rugged Acadian Mountain belt. Aggregate thickness of the Mississippian continental

130. **Lower Mississippian limestone in the bluffs of the Missouri River southwest of Columbia, Mo.** The beds are light-colored, evenly stratified, and, in part, very pure. There is virtually no sandstone and almost no shale in the Mississippian section of this region. (*R. C. Moore, Missouri Geol. Survey.*)

beds in places exceeds 5,000 feet. From Alabama, in the vicinity of Birmingham, they are traced northward to southern New York, and some layers extend westward to southern Illinois. Like the Devonian, the Mississippian nonmarine beds become finer westward and inter-finger with marine deposits.

Divisions. The Mississippian System is divisible into two major parts that are classed as series, and each series contains two main time-rock units that are designated as stages. The successive stages

131. Mississippian limestone resting on Cambrian sandstone in the Black Hills of South Dakota. Mississippian rocks form the light-colored cliff at the top of the slope. The intermediate, dark-colored cliff is Cambrian. In the northern part of the Black Hills, Ordovician limestone intervenes between the Mississippian and Cambrian. *(N. H. Darton, U. S. Geol. Survey.)*

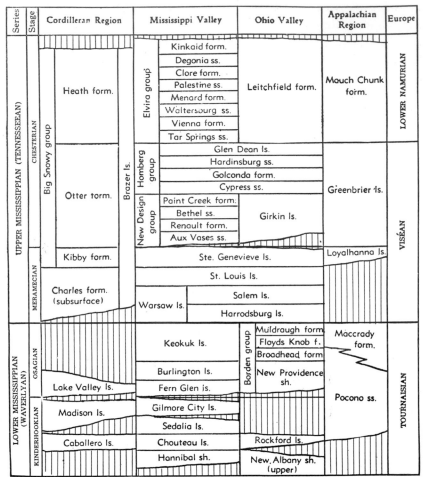

132. Time-rock divisions of the Mississippian System and rock units in representative important sections of North America. The vertical scale is not proportional to thickness of the rocks or time duration, but placement of names indicates correlation of formations. The ruled areas denote absence of deposits.

are delimited in most places by unconformities, and each is characterized by readily distinguished assemblages of fossils. The Lower Mississippian (Waverlyan) Series comprises the Kinderhookian Stage, below, and the Osagian Stage, above. The Upper Mississippian (Tennesseean) Series is made up of the Meramecian and Chesterian Stages, the latter forming the top part of the system.

The dividing line between Osagian and Meramecian deposits, which is the same as that separating Lower from Upper Mississippian, is judged to be more important than the boundaries between other stages, because it marks a more profound change in faunas and is inferred to represent a greater hiatus in sedimentation, generally, than these other boundaries. Recently obtained information, derived partly from studies of outcrops in western Canada and partly from many wells drilled for oil in Montana and adjacent states, indicates that western North America contains widespread thick deposits of Meramecian age that have no equivalents in most other parts of the continent.

The boundary between the Lower and Upper Mississippian Series corresponds to the break in the middle part of the rocks called Lower Carboniferous in Europe, Asia, Africa, and Australia. Thus, Lower Mississippian is equivalent in age to deposits called Tournaisian in other continents, and Upper Mississippian essentially corresponds to those named Viséan abroad.

History of Mississippian Time

Early Mississippian seaways. At the beginning of Mississippian time, the sea that invaded the continental interior transgressed a land that had been thoroughly peneplaned, so that basal Mississippian deposits are found unconformably on not only Devonian but also on Silurian, Ordovician, Cambrian, and Pre-Cambrian. This sea reached westward to the borders of the Cascadian land along the margin of the Cordilleran geosyncline. Probably we should express this in reverse manner, saying that the Cordilleran sea extended eastward into the Mississippi Valley region, for the Early Mississippian marine deposits are far thicker in the west and seemingly they represent a much longer record of limestone deposition than anywhere else on the continent. This thick succession of limestone beds, mostly light-gray massive and in part very cherty, is topographically prominent. It forms the crests of mountains, makes unscalable cliffs and steep canyon walls, and offers striking scenic features in many places.

From Kansas eastward to the Ohio Valley, the Early Mississippian deposits are relatively thin and lithologically somewhat variable. The prevailing lack of coarse sediments, however, indicates that adjacent lands were low. The basal deposit in most of this area consists of black shale, like that of Late Devonian age in the same region and

133. Lower Mississippian limestone resting directly on Lower Ordovician limestone in southwestern Missouri. The Ordovician rocks consist of dolomite, whereas the Mississippian is pure limestone. Middle and Late Ordovician deposits and perhaps Silurian, Devonian, and Early Mississippian (Kinderhookian) beds, once present, are lacking.

farther east. The scanty invertebrate fossils of the black shale are a specialized assemblage, and it is evident that normal types of marine organisms were unable to live in the environment represented by these deposits. Perhaps the blackness of the shale is due largely to occurrence of black, humus-rich soils on land near this sea, the fine carbonaceous material of the soil being the chief source of the shale; such black soils are common today in parts of Russia. Marine deposits overlying this shale, including highly fossiliferous limestone, contain a normal assemblage of bottom-living invertebrates. Local variations in the nature of the deposits surrounding the Ozark Uplift indicate that this area was an island during part of Early Mississippian time.

An unconformity, marking interruption of sedimentation and some erosion of the lowermost stage (Kinderhookian), is found in most places at the base of the second stage (Osagian), which represents the later part of Early Mississippian time. In some areas, Osagian deposits rest directly on pre-Mississippian rocks, which signifies that the sea of the second age invaded territory that had not been covered in the first transgression, or else beds of the first stage, once deposited, were entirely eroded away before deposition of the second.

Two outstanding characteristics of deposits made in the latter part of Early Mississippian time are abundance of chert and a remarkable profusion of crinoid remains.

The chert occurs both as bedded layers and as nodules distributed in the limestone, in places forming nearly half of the rock. Although some chert is undoubtedly a secondary deposit of silica, made by percolating ground water long after deposition of the limestone in which the chert occurs, the siliceous deposits in these Mississippian strata mostly accumulated on the sea bottom along with the calcareous materials. They are primary. The aggregate quantity of this silica that was carried in solution to the Mississippian seas is measured in cubic miles.

The sea in which the Early Mississippian limestones accumulated, extending from Alabama to the Far West, was populated by crinoids in unprecedented numbers and variety. These stalked echinoderms secrete hard parts consisting of crystalline calcite, and their disarticulated fragments are a chief constituent of limestone beds 200 to 1,000 feet thick. That the warm waters were exceptionally clear is indicated

134. Chert nodules in Mississippian limestone. This view of lower Ste. Genevieve limestone at Elizabethtown, in southern Illinois, illustrates the abundance of chert in many Mississippian formations. The chert nodules are dark-colored and, because of their hardness and relative insolubility, they weather in relief. (*Charles Butts, U. S. Geol. Survey.*)

135. Lower Mississippian limestone and shale near Keokuk, Iowa. The limestone contains well-preserved crinoids and other marine fossils; the shale is chiefly noteworthy for its content of crystalline geodes. These strata are part of the type Mississippian section in southeastern Iowa.

by the purity of most of the limestone and almost complete absence of shaly or sandy deposits.

Continental deposits in eastern North America. The highland nature of Appalachia, lying east of the Appalachian geosyncline, has already been stated to characterize Mississippian, as well as Middle and Late Devonian time. There is no proof of renewed folding in the land area, but elevation by strong upwarping is inferred from the nature of subaerial sediments laid down west of Appalachia. Such vertical movements are typical of the history of mountain areas, and they recur at intervals for a long time after initial folding. Whereas Late Devonian deposits in the geosyncline are predominantly red muds, silts, and fine sands, which are indicative of moderate relief in the source area of the sediments, Early Mississippian deposits contain large thicknesses of coarse conglomerates and very widespread, coarse, massive sandstone. These deposits are now tightly cemented and form some of the most prominent Appalachian Mountain ridges.

Late Mississippian continental deposits in the Appalachian geosyn-

cline resemble those of Late Devonian age in showing a predominant
red color and fine texture, but in this part of the period some widespread coarse standstones and conglomerate beds were formed. In
central Virginia, there are Mississippian coal beds of mineable thickness. These indicate existence of swampy areas in which land plants
accumulated in such quantity, unmixed with clay or silt, that carbonaceous material of the plants formed coal. Westward, the continental
deposits graded into marine shale and limestone. The highly oscillatory nature of the sea border is shown by the varying extent to which
marine layers reach eastward and interfinger with the continental
sediments. The record of Mississippian time, from Alabama to New
York, is thus essentially a continuation or repetition of conditions that
had characterized Middle and Late Devonian time in this region, but
plants living on the land and marine organisms inhabiting the sea
serve readily to distinguish the Mississippian formations from those of
Devonian age.

136. Fine-grained cherty limestone of Mississippian age in Virginia. The beds shown here
(St. Louis limestone) belong to the Upper Mississippian Series. The nodules of chert
are characteristic of many Mississippian strata. (*Charles Butts, U. S. Geol. Survey.*)

137. Cross-bedded Mississippian limestone in central Pennsylvania. This limestone (Loyalhanna), of late Meramecian age, differs from most limestone formations, which are evenly bedded, in being strongly cross-bedded. Granules of calcium carbonate were swept along by currents on the shallow sea bottom like sand grains. *(B. L. Miller, Pennsylvania Geol. Survey.)*

Late Mississippian marine oscillations. Less stability in distribution of shallow seas and less uniformity in the nature of sedimentation characterize Late Mississippian geologic history as compared with the early part of the period. Crinoids and many other invertebrates, that had characterized the Early Mississippian marine waters, are conspicuous by their absence or by relatively small numbers. Very fine-grained, dense limestone, largely noncherty, and much oolite are characteristic types of Late Mississippian deposits, which contrast with the coarse crystalline cherty Early Mississippian limestones. Much lateral variation also characterizes some of these deposits, which reflect gentle warping of the sea bottom and establishment of local basins of sedimentation. On the other hand, a few deposits in this part of the column are remarkably uniform and widespread. The limestones in which Mammoth Cave of Kentucky and innumerable smaller caves and sinks are carved are Late Mississippian deposits belonging to the Meramecian and Chesterian Stages. Likewise, the limestone that forms the highland rim surrounding the Nashville Basin of Tennessee is Upper Mississippian. In the Cordilleran geosyncline, the Late Mississippian seas extend far northward into Alberta, and deposits of this age are recognized in Alaska.

The Chesterian Epoch was a time of unusual advance and retreat of the shallow seas in the central Mississippi Valley area. Deposits, which aggregate about 1,000 feet thick in this region, furnish record of regularly rhythmic displacement of the strand line, showing that the sea margin shifted back and forth a distance of some hundreds of miles. There are at least eight such cycles of submergence and emergence, the latter being marked by unconformities and by continental sedimentation that interfingers with the marine deposits. These changes in distribution of sea and land give rise to corresponding changes in the geographic boundaries of different sedimentary facies, so that complex lateral and vertical relationships must be worked out in field studies. Overlap and offlap of rock units are re-

138. Sawed face of Meramecian limestone used for building stone. This view in an Indiana limestone quarry shows part of the so-called Bedford limestone which is sawed into large blocks by machines and then cut to smaller sizes. The irregular marking on the limestone face is a "suture-joint" (stylolite), formed by differential solution and compaction of the rock. (*Carey Croneis, Beloit College.*)

peatedly shown. Rhythmic oscillations, like those recorded in Late Mississippian deposits, are very typical of sedimentation in Pennsylvanian time, also.

Mountain building. Folding of Mississippian strata during this period is not recorded in any part of North America, although strong mountain building near the close of Mississippian time is recorded in parts of northwestern Europe. Existence of mountainous elevations in North America, approximately at this time, is proved indirectly by the enormous quantity of coarse land-derived detritus found in continental deposits of earliest Pennsylvanian time in the Appalachian and Ouachita Mountains. The part of the Appalachian area most affected by this uplift is inferred to have reached from Alabama to northern Virginia. The eastern interior and northern midcontinent areas remained low from the close of Mississippian sedimentation until the beginning of marine deposition in Pennsylvanian time. Erosion was widespread, but where the section is most nearly complete, the unconformity is inconspicuous.

Mississippian Life

Invertebrates. Marine life of the Mississippian Period was richly varied and included numerous representatives of all main classes of invertebrates. Most of the stocks clearly show their derivation from Late Devonian ancestors. Changes consist in the disappearance of many characteristic Devonian genera, in the evolutionary advancement of various persistent old types, and in the appearance of some new elements of unknown origin.

The outstanding group in Early Mississippian time is that of the crinoids, which in the Mississippi Valley region alone include more than 400 described kinds. A very remarkable feature of the record is the abrupt disappearance, at the close of Early Mississippian time, of all but a remnant of this great host. The budlike blastoids, which are close relatives of the crinoids, also culminated in Mississippian time, being especially abundant in the Late Mississippian marine beds.

A large group of spine-bearing brachiopods with concavo-convex shells, called "productids," made appearance and became world-wide in distribution. The brachiopods were a very important constituent of most marine faunas, but less numerous and varied than in the Devonian.

Bryozoans are very abundant in some beds and show a predominance of delicate lacy types, along with small twiglike forms.

Corals are common but not so varied as in Devonian time. Strangely enough, the Mississippian rocks are virtually devoid of coral reef structures, although reefs formed by other organisms are well known in rocks of this system.

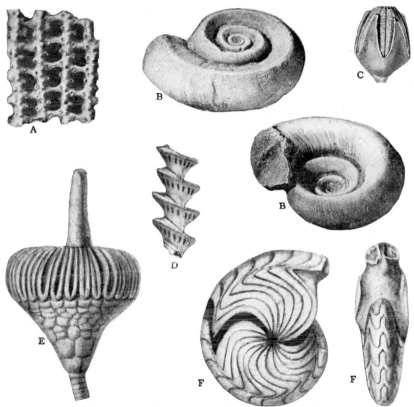

139. Some representative Mississippian invertebrate fossils. Bryozoans include one of the lacy types (*A, Fenestrellina*) characterized by two rows of openings for the individual animals along each branch (enlarged), and part of the screw axis (*D, Archimedes*) of one type of lace bryozoan. Echinoderms are represented by a blastoid (*C, Pentremites*) and a crinoid (*E, Eutrochocrinus*). A broad snail (*B, Euomphalus*) and an Early Mississippian ammonoid cephalopod (*F, Aganides*) are types of mollusks; the outer shell of the ammonoid is broken away so that edges of the chamber walls are exposed, and the space between two of these has been painted dark in order to emphasize the pattern.

140. Upper Mississippian limestone from Kentucky crowded with bryozoans. The observed fossils are mostly of lacy types, including axes of the screwlike *Archimedes*.

Among mollusks, clams and snails are very numerous but not especially noteworthy, whereas the cephalopods are represented by marked advancement in structural complexity as compared with forms known in older Paleozoic rocks. They include several important guide fossils that serve for correlating American Mississippian rocks with those in other parts of the world.

Trilobites persisted but had become a minor element of the fauna. There are only a few Mississippian species as compared with hundreds known from older Paleozoic rocks.

Vertebrates. Remains of fishes are fairly common in Mississippian marine strata. They consist chiefly of the teeth of sharks, especially types having a rounded surface adapted for crushing shells. Because fewer land fishes are known from Mississippian deposits, the variety of these vertebrates is seemingly smaller than that of the Devonian, but it is probable that this simply means a deficiency in preservation of these fossils.

Among leg-bearing animals, there is no question as to abundance of amphibians during Mississippian time, and it is possible that primitive reptiles had made their appearance. Numerous footprints are preserved in some continental Late Mississippian strata, but as yet no skeletal remains have been found in North America. On the other hand, rocks of Mississippian age in Europe have yielded entire skeletons of small salamander-like animals.

Climate

Climatic conditions of Mississippian time, as inferred from widespread distribution and general similarity of marine faunas, were probably fairly warm and uniform over large areas. Existence of coal swamps, at least locally, indicates humidity but not necessarily warmth. Widely distributed red beds of Late Mississippian age, which

141. Evenly layered Mississippian limestone in the Marble Gorge of Grand Canyon, Ariz. The sheer cliff, which rises about 400 feet above the Colorado River, is composed of the Redwall limestone of Early Mississippian age. It is overlain disconformably by Early Permian red shale and sandstone, which form the stepped slope above the limestone cliff.

contain numerous mud-cracked surfaces, are interpreted as indicating alternate drying and wetting, as on a coastal plain in temperate climates of the present day, but occurrence of gypsum and salt deposits in Virginia, Michigan, and Nova Scotia indicates evaporation of basins in a moderately arid climate.

Close of the Period

The end of Mississippian time was marked by withdrawal of the sea from most of the continent and by uplift that was perhaps of mountainous proportions on some of the land bordering geosynclinal troughs, as in the Appalachian and Ouachita belts. In a few places, sedimentation was resumed after only a very short interruption, whereas in most parts of the continent, the hiatus was long and erosion was extensive. On the continental shelf and possibly in parts of geosynclinal belts, sedimentation was uninterrupted from Mississippian into Pennsylvanian time.

10. The Pennsylvanian Period

Evenly bedded Pennsylvanian strata
in southern Utah. (Spence Air Photo).

Definition and Type Region

The Pennsylvanian Period was a time of coal making on the greatest scale in earth history, and it is appropriate that the name of the period is derived from the leading coal-producing state of a country that furnishes nearly one half of the world's annual coal output. Until 1869, coal production from the anthracite district of northeastern Pennsylvania alone exceeded all other coal mined in the United States; but today, output of bituminous coal, both in Pennsylvania and elsewhere, greatly exceeds production of anthracite.

As originally defined, the Pennsylvanian rocks in Pennsylvania included some deposits that are now considered properly to belong in

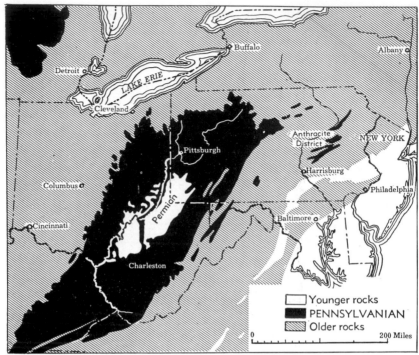

142. Distribution of Pennsylvanian formations in the type region. In western Pennsylvania and adjoining parts of Ohio and West Virginia, the Pennsylvanian formations are nearly flat-lying, and the outcrop area is very broad. Outcrops in the anthracite district of eastern Pennsylvania are elongate patches, owing to the steeply folded attitude of the beds. Pennsylvanian deposits of the Appalachian region are dominantly nonmarine.

the Permian System, and accordingly the upper boundary has been modified so as to exclude these younger beds. A prominent uncon-formity marks the base of the Pennsylvanian rocks in the type region, but no clearly defined break in sedimentation is found at the top. Elsewhere in the United States, folded Late Pennsylvanian beds are found unconformably beneath Lower Permian strata, but in most places, Permian lies parallel on Pennsylvanian and the boundary is an obscure disconformity.

Rocks corresponding to Pennsylvanian in age are commonly called "Upper Carboniferous" in continents other than North America. Generally, the distinctness in character of the Lower and Upper Carboniferous is as strongly marked in Europe and Asia, for example, as that separating Mississippian from Pennsylvanian, but the position of the boundary dividing each pair does not correspond precisely.

Guide Fossils

Deposits of Pennsylvanian age are identified throughout most parts of the world, both by characteristic assemblages of fossil plants and by the nature of marine invertebrates. These organic remains serve not only for correlation of deposits from place to place in the United States, but many of them clearly define equivalence of deposits on different continents. Such widely distributed forms are unusually valuable guide fossils.

Since the plants lived on land and the invertebrates were marine, there is the problem of determining their precise age equivalence. If continental deposits were restricted to one region and marine beds to another, there would be no way of determining these exact relations. Fortunately, there are many places in which plant-bearing continental deposits interfinger or are interbedded with fossiliferous marine strata. For example, the Pennsylvanian sections of Illinois and Kansas contain dozens of such alternations of marine and nonmarine strata, furnishing an ideal record of the time relations of successive floras and faunas. The most important guide fossils among plants are various sorts of ferns, and among invertebrates the leading guides are the protozoans called "fusulines," shaped like large wheat grains.

Distribution and Character of Pennsylvanian Formations

Nature of outcrops. The outcrop areas of Pennsylvanian rocks in the eastern and central parts of the United States are large irregularly shaped patches, some of which extend uninterruptedly across several states. East of the Mississippi, the outer edges of the outcrops mark the contact of Pennsylvanian with older rocks. Except for a small area of Permian beds in the northern part of the Appalachian region, the Pennsylvanian deposits are not overlain by younger rocks, and they have a broadly synclinal structure. West of the Mississippi, however, Pennsylvanian outcrops, although many miles wide in places, are bands lying between older and younger formations, and there are great areas where Pennsylvanian rocks lie buried beneath the surface, concealed by younger rocks.

Distribution. Deposits of Pennsylvanian age in North America are

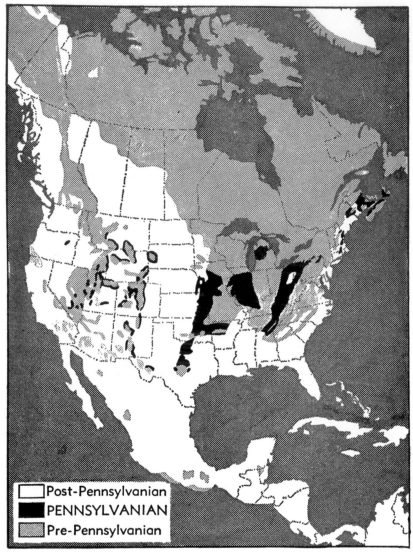

143. Distribution of Pennsylvanian outcrops in North America. Except for exposures in easternmost Canada, known deposits of Pennsylvanian age in North America are confined to the United States. The outcrop areas of greatest extent all lie east of the Rocky Mountains.

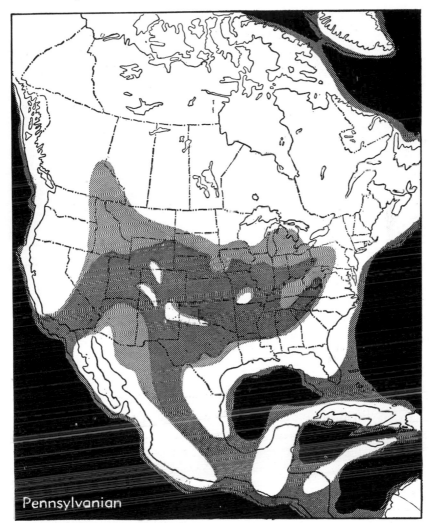

144. Distribution of Pennsylvanian seas. Oceanic areas are shown in black; the most persistent seaways on the continental platform are represented by dark gray; and areas submerged during only part of the period are indicated by light gray. The shallow seas of Pennsylvanian time were most remarkable from the standpoint of their incessant oscillation. Even the areas represented on the map as persistent seaways were actually emergent many times and then submerged again. Inferred persistent land areas are unshaded. As indicated by distorted outlines of eastern and western states, the continent is represented as wider than now, so as to compensate for crustal shortening produced by post-Pennsylvanian mountain building.

145. Appalachian Plateau country, in which uplands are made by thick, hard, nonmarine sandstone beds of Pennsylvanian age. The view shows part of the valley of Blue River in West Virginia. Owing to ruggedness of the topography, the railroads, highways, and settlements are located almost entirely in the valleys. The stratified rocks lie nearly horizontal. (*J. K. Hillers, U. S. Geol. Survey.*)

known from Nova Scotia and New Brunswick, in eastern Canada, to Alabama; in the Central States they are distributed from Michigan to Texas, and in the west they are found from Nevada to Montana. Except in the east, Pennsylvanian rocks are absent in Canada, and deposits of this age are not now known from Mexico or Central America.

Lithologic features.   Outstanding general features of the Pennsylvanian formations are the relative prominence of continental deposits, especially coal, and abundant variation in the nature of beds in vertical succession. The nonmarine stratified rocks include coarse to fine conglomerates, abundant sandstones, sandy to clayey shales, and red beds. They contain remains of land plants in many places, and tracks of land animals less commonly. Most of these deposits are marked by lack of any considerable lateral extent, and they vary in thickness much more irregularly than the marine lithologic units.

Marine deposits become increasingly abundant as one travels away from the geosynclinal belts toward the continental interior. These rocks include some sandstone, but the most persistent and characteristic marine strata consist of limestone and shale. Remains of marine invertebrates are very abundant in a majority of the Pennsylvanian deposits that were formed in shallow inland seas.

An important feature of Pennsylvanian sections in many regions is the repeated occurrence of persistent thin marine layers between continental deposits, and of extensive thin sheets of continental sediments between relatively thick marine strata. This variation in vertical succession is expressed by the occurrence of innumerable alternations of sandstone, shale, coal, fresh-water limestone, and marine limestone. The layers of different sorts of rock range in thickness from less than an inch to tens of feet, but the average thickness of most units is less than 10 feet.

Divisions. Pennsylvanian deposits are divisible into three main

146. Cross-bedded conglomeratic sandstone of Early Pennsylvanian age in Tennessee. This deposit, of probable fluviatile origin, is the Sewanee sandstone, belonging to the Pottsville group. (*Charles Butts, U. S. Geol. Survey.*)

147. Regularly alternating layers of Pennsylvanian limestone, shale, and sandstone in southwestern Colorado. The lower part of mountain slopes above Ouray, Colo., are composed of gently tilted Pennsylvanian deposits, mostly of marine origin. Sandstone beds, which alternate with limestone, contain much feldspar, denoting rapid mechanical weathering of adjacent exposed granite.

parts: Lower Pennsylvanian Series, Middle Pennsylvanian Series, and Upper Pennsylvanian Series. The main coal deposits, but not all, belong in the Lower and Middle Pennsylvanian. On the basis of distinctions in the fossil faunas and floras that are associated with interruptions in sedimentation, the series are each divided into two time-rock units classed as stages. The breaks between successive stages, including those marking the boundaries between series, coincide with times of mountain building in parts of North America or Europe.

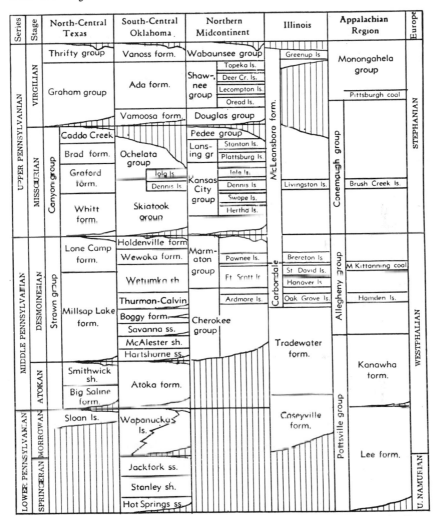

148. Time-rock divisions of the Pennsylvanian System and rock units in representative Pennsylvanian sections of North America. The vertical scale is not proportional to thickness or time duration, but the placement of names indicates correlation in age. The ruled areas denote absence of deposits.

Features of Pennsylvanian History

Making of coal beds. Coal deposits, ranging in age from Devonian to Recent, are known, but the subject of coal making belongs naturally with study of Pennsylvanian history, because at no other time has such quantity of coal been formed in so many parts of the globe.

Everyone knows that coal is a moderately hard black rock, which, when burned, leaves a deposit of ash. Some coals ignite easily and burn with a yellowish flame and much smoke; others are ignited with difficulty, burn with a bluish flame, and give little or no smoke. Some have a low heating capacity, expressed in British thermal units (B.t.u.), and others a high value. These differences are some of the properties of different types of coal, such as lignite, bituminous coal, and anthracite. They denote differences in the coal-making substances or their physical alteration, or both.

Chemical analysis shows that coal consists mainly of carbon associated with varying quantities of oxygen and hydrogen, together with noncombustible mineral matter that produces ash. Low-grade coals contain a large proportion of hydrogen and oxygen in relation to carbon, whereas high-grade or anthracite coals have a relatively low content of hydrogen and oxygen and a large proportion of carbon.

Coal beds are commonly found interbedded with sandy or shaly strata of continental origin. They vary in thickness from a fraction of an inch to several tens of feet locally, and some are known to be con-

149. A chunk of coal from the Pittsburgh bed in western Pennsylvania. The many shiny streaks in this coal consist of altered woody plant tissue. The lighter colored material is made up of other sorts of decomposed plant matter. Natural size. (*R. Thiessen, Illinois Geol. Survey.*)

tinuous laterally over areas of many thousand square miles. Very commonly the bed next beneath a coal is a sticky clay, that may contain traces of roots and that seems to represent an old soil; it is termed "underclay." Also, in many places strata just above a coal bed contain abundant well-preserved leaves of land plants. Microscopic study of the coal proves that it is composed largely of plant remains. Identifiable elements include leaves, flattened twigs or branches, and isolated cell structures of various sorts.

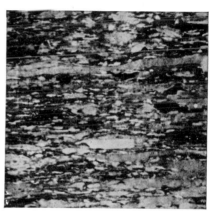

The preservation of coal-making plant remains from the decay that occurs rapidly on dry land is ascribed to the presence of a protecting cover of water, such as in swamps, marshes, or shallow lakes. Even though complete decay is prevented in such environment, there is some decomposition through the agency of bacteria, and the plant materials, pressed together, form an organic deposit termed "peat." The conversion of peat to coal is accomplished by slow chemical and physical

150. Very thin slice of coal cut at right angles to bedding. Viewed by transmitted light, only a small part of a thin section of coal is opaque. The light-colored constituents are various kinds of plant debris. Much magnified. (*R. Thiessen, Illinois Geol. Survey.*)

changes in which compression, heat, and time are the most important factors. Oxygen and hydrogen are progressively driven off, leaving a residual concentration of carbon. Thus is explained the fact that most geologically young coals are lignites, whereas coal of considerable age, like that in the Pennsylvanian System, is bituminous or higher grade. The effect of compression by geologic forces on coal beds is seen in areas such as northeastern Pennsylvania, where coal-bearing deposits have been considerably squeezed and folded. Here the coal beds have been altered to very hard anthracite. Extreme compression may drive off virtually all the volatile hydrocarbons, leaving a residue of nearly pure carbon (graphite). Pennsylvanian rocks in Rhode Island, which have been much more strongly compressed than those in Pennsylvania, contain graphitic coal that can hardly be burned.

153. Pennsylvanian sandstone vertically upturned along the east front of the Rocky Mountains. The view shows the gateway to the Garden of the Gods at Colorado Springs, Colo., with Pikes Peak in the distance. Deformation of the Pennsylvanian sandstone (Lyons) and associated strata occurred in the Laramian orogeny near the close of Cretaceous time.

Geosynclines filled with continental deposits. Continued uplift of lands bordering the Appalachian geosyncline on the east, and the Ouachita geosyncline in Arkansas and Oklahoma on the south, supplied great quantities of stream-borne rock materials that now form Pennsylvanian continental deposits, which in places exceed 15,000 feet in thickness. The sea had access to the geosynclines only temporarily in the early part of the period. In spite of steady subsidence that accompanied deposition of the continental sediments, aggradation exceeded sinking, so that only now and then the shallow sea flooded the inland border of the old geosyncline for a short while.

The many-times repeated coal-forming conditions in parts of the geosynclinal areas, and the equally numerous interruptions represented by the spreading widely over the coals of sand, shale, and other land-derived sediments, point to many recurrent spasmodic uplifts in source areas of the sediments. These movements seem to have been accompanied by a corresponding downward displacement in basins of sedimentation. Thus, surfaces of erosion and deposition were steadily maintained in about the same relation to one another. These conditions, which obliterated the eastern and southern geosynclinal seaways, did not prevail in the Cordilleran geosyncline, although Pennsylvanian deposits, largely marine, attain a thickness of several thousand feet in parts of Utah and Nevada.

Oscillatory seas of the North American interior region. Pennsylvanian deposits of the Illinois-Indiana Basin, Michigan, and the midcontinent region from Iowa to Texas, furnish record of remarkably rhythmic advance and retreat of shallow seas. Dozens of times the sea spread over an area of several hundred thousand square miles, remained long enough to leave record of its existence in deposits of limestone and marine shale, and then retreated from the entire area. Absence of the sea is marked by disconformities, by the spreading of continental deposits containing land-plant remains and, in places, by the tracks of land animals. Coal swamps were established also over large areas during times of emergence. The whole interior platform of the continent must have stood just about at sea level during much of Pennsylvanian time, so that a slight sinking of the land surface (or equivalent rise of mean sea level) permitted the seas to spread very widely, and slight uplift of the land (or depression of mean sea level) caused the seas to retreat from the continent.

The cyclic sedimentation resulting from these oscillatory movements of sea and land is an outstanding feature of Pennsylvanian deposition, and it is observed in Europe as well as in North America. On the whole, subsidence of 2,000 to 4,000 feet took place in the continental interior during Pennsylvanian time; the amount of this sinking is recorded by the total thickness of the deposits formed.

Recurrent mountain building. Major interruptions in the making of Pennsylvanian formations are found to coincide with the building of mountains in some part of the earth, not always in North America. There was moderate crustal deformation in the Oklahoma and Kansas portion of the midcontinent region at the close of Early Pennsylvanian Morrowan time, and strong folding in southern Oklahoma in the middle (post-Missourian) part of Late Pennsylvanian time. Mountain building also occurred in western Texas at the close of Pennsylvanian time. These movements denote crustal instability during

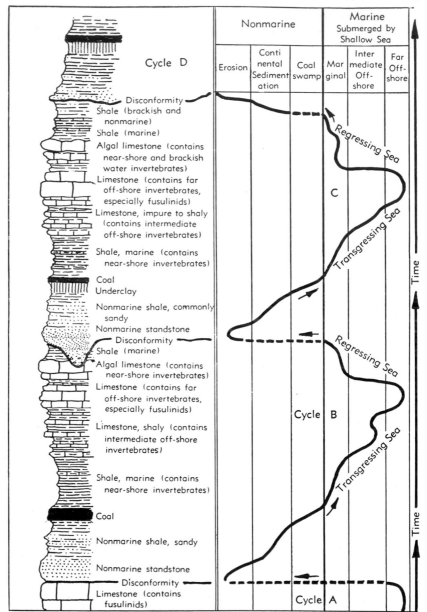

154. Section of Pennsylvanian rock in the midcontinent region, showing cyclic sedimentation.
Repetition of like sequences of nonmarine and marine strata, arranged in groups that
are separated by disconformities, furnish record of repeated advances and retreats
of shallow seas in this region.

the Pennsylvanian Period that seems appreciably greater than in most preceding divisions of the Paleozoic Era. The accumulating stresses led to deformation that culminated in the Appalachian mountain building near the end of Permian time.

Comparable orogenic epochs are recorded in Europe, Asia, and northern Africa during Pennsylvanian time. These deformations were not simultaneous, but occurred at different times. Collectively, they produced mountain ranges that are known as the Paleozoic Alps (or Variscan Mountain system). The Urals are an isolated chain that belongs with the Pennsylvanian mountains.

The boundary that separates the Middle Pennsylvanian Epoch from the later part of the period is marked by a widespread, though somewhat obscure, unconformity and by obvious difference in organisms occurring above and below the boundary. The magnitude of this break leads us to expect that the sea was absent for a much longer time than in ordinary oscillatory withdrawals during the period. We expect such a break to be associated with mountain building, yet none is known at this time in North America. Correlation of Pennsylvanian deposits with Europe, however, indicates that one of the

155. Parallel ridges and furrows formed by lower Paleozoic strata upturned during Late Pennsylvanian mountain building. The view shows Lower Ordovician limestone and shaly beds in the Arbuckle Mountains of southern Oklahoma. The folding of these rocks occurred near the close of Missourian and beginning of Virgilian time.

156. Nonconformity in western Texas separating Cretaceous from upturned Pennsylvanian rocks. Mountain-building movements at the close of Pennsylvanian time disturbed Pennsylvanian and older rocks in the vicinity of Marathon, Tex. (Glass Mountains region). These rocks are evenly truncated beneath overlapping Lower Cretaceous strata. *(C. L. Baker, Texas Bureau of Economic Geology.)*

important mountain buildings of the period in Europe fits the time of the sedimentary break in North America. This interesting observation, and others like it, suggest that sea level throughout the world may be affected by crustal deformation on any continent, and, if this is so, geologic effects may be recorded by simultaneous sea-and-land changes throughout the world. At any rate, it is important to observe that in Europe and Asia at least three distinct epochs of mountain building belong to the Pennsylvanian Period.

Pennsylvanian Life

Although land plants, including forest trees, are definitely known as far back as the Devonian, the luxuriant fast-growing vegetation of the coal swamps and adjacent lands in Pennsylvanian time, which is abundantly represented by well-preserved fossils, gives the first fairly full picture of the earth's early vegetation. As already noted, the close similarity or identity of many of these plants that lived on different continents in Pennsylvanian time greatly aids correlation of the deposits. Very widely distributed organisms of this type are termed "cosmopolitan." Some of the main types of Pennsylvanian plants are included in the review of Paleozoic life development (Chap. 12).

157. Slab of Pennsylvanian nonmarine shale containing a well-preserved fossil fern. This specimen (*Neuropteris*, one-third natural size) is from Lower Pennsylvanian (Pottsville) beds of Alabama. The original plant tissue is preserved as a thin carbonaceous film. (*Charles Butts, Alabama Geol. Survey.*)

Marine invertebrates, although extremely varied and numerous in many Pennsylvanian formations, do not call for special comment here. As a whole, the assemblage is intermediate between those characterizing Mississippian and Permian strata; several of the most common shells collected from Pennsylvanian rocks represent genera that occur also in adjoining systems, although the species are different. The shelled protozoans called "fusulines" are extremely abundant in many Pennsylvanian marine deposits, especially limestones. None of these organisms are known from the Mississippian, but specialized types are numerous in the Permian. Some typical fusulines are shown in Fig. 179 (p. 248).

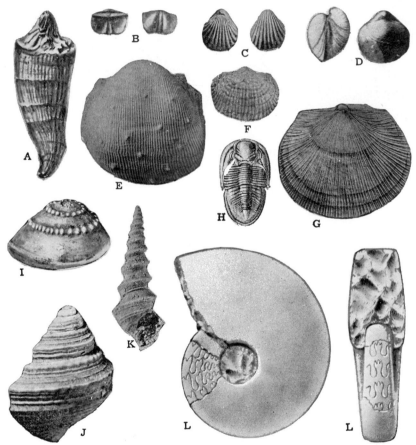

158. Some representative Pennsylvanian invertebrate fossils. A coral *(A, Lophophyllidium)* having a solid axis; several brachiopods *(B, Mesolobus; C, Hustedia; D, Squamularia; E, Linoproductus; F, Marginifera; G, Derbyia)*; gastropods *(I, Trepospira; J, Baylea; K, Goniasma)*; a trilobite *(H, Ameura)*; and an ammonoid cephalopod *(L, Prouddenites)*. All natural size (except *J.* ×6).

159. Restoration of a Pennsylvanian coal swamp. Associated with characteristic types of vegetation are broad-headed early amphibians (stegocephalian) and dragonflies, some of which had a wingspread of 30 inches. *(J. P. Cowan, Courtesy of Hughes Tool Company.)*

Among nonmarine animals, Pennsylvanian fossils include fresh-water clams, air-breathing snails, many sorts of insects, fishes, amphibians, and rarely a few primitive reptiles. The presence of abundant cockroaches, flying insects, such as large dragonflies, and the occurrence of spiders are noteworthy. Richness of the vertebrate record is indicated by the fact that nearly 100 species of amphibians are known from Pennsylvanian rocks of North America. They are mostly small creatures, a few inches long, but a few attained the size of a large crocodile.

Climate

The widespread rich vegetation of the Pennsylvanian Period strongly suggests warm, moist climatic conditions. Absence of growth rings in the woody plants points to lack of seasonal variation in climate, and occurrence of plants of subtropic type in high latitudes indicates mild, equable temperatures in these regions. Arid conditions are shown by occurrence of salt and gypsum in Pennsylvanian deposits of western Colorado and Utah, but this is local and exceptional.

Close of the Period

The boundary between Pennsylvanian and Permian is ill defined in many areas where only slight interruption of sedimentation, if any, occurred at the end of Pennsylvanian time. Elsewhere, a strongly marked unconformity indicates interruption of sedimentation and considerable erosion. Mountain building occurred in western Texas. Coal-forming conditions largely disappeared in Permian time, and climate became increasingly arid, but generally speaking, the changes in these directions were gradual rather than pronounced and abrupt.

11. The Permian Period

Continental Permian deposits in Monument Valley, Ariz.

Type Region

The Permian Period, which comprises the final portion of the Paleozoic Era, derives its name from the province of Perm in northeastern Russia, where highly fossiliferous marine beds and associated continental deposits rest on Carboniferous rocks of Pennsylvanian age. Although the section of this region serves as standard for definition of Permian throughout the world, it is now known that the most richly fossiliferous succession of marine deposits belonging to this period occurs in the western Texas and southeastern New Mexico region of the United States.

Guide Fossils

Identification and correlation of Permian deposits depend mainly on three groups of fossils: first in importance, as defined by general

Santa Fe Railway

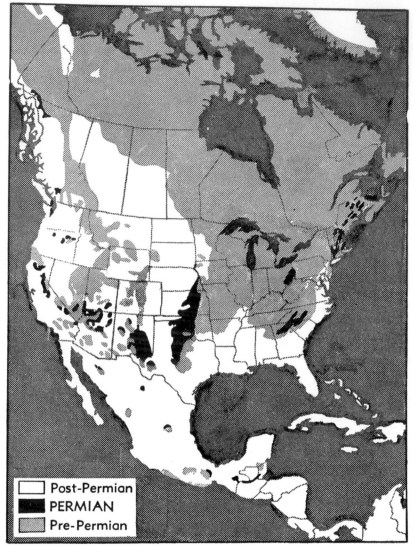

160. Distribution of Permian rocks in North America. The largest outcrop areas, located in the midcontinent and western Texas, represent sedimentary formations. Areas east of the Mississippi indicate deep-seated, intrusive igneous rocks, except sedimentary rock areas near Pittsburgh, Pa., and on Cape Breton Island, eastern Canada.

use, are the marine invertebrates; next are remains of land plants; and third are skeletal remains of land vertebrates. Other organic remains, such as calcareous marine plants, marine vertebrates, and land invertebrates, are known, but these fossils are either too scanty and

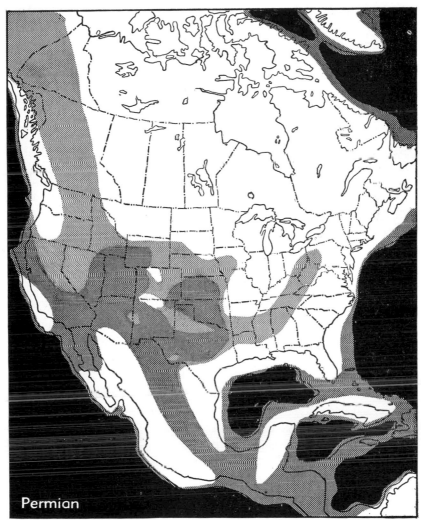

161. Distribution of Permian seas. Oceanic areas are shown in black; the most persistent seaways on the continental platform are represented by dark gray; and areas submerged during only part of the period are indicated by light gray. Chief areas of marine sedimentation are in the southwestern part of the continent. As indicated by distorted outlines of eastern and western states, the continent is represented as wider than now, so as to compensate for crustal shortening produced by post-Permian mountain building.

local in distribution, or insufficiently differentiated as markers of certain zones, to have much practical value for correlation.

One of the most important groups of guide fossils in marine deposits is that of the fusulines, because they include many distinctive short-ranged types and are very widely distributed geographically. Those occurring in Permian rocks are more specialized than forerunners that characterize many Pennsylvanian marine deposits. Complexly sutured cephalopods are also important zone indicators, but are less common fossils. Corals, brachiopods, bryozoans, and, in restricted areas, crinoid remains are also valuable.

Continental deposits of Permian age are distinguished especially by certain types of ferns and conifers that are lacking in Pennsylvanian strata, and wherever land vertebrates are found, these fossils are especially valuable as guides.

Distribution and Character of Permian Deposits in North America

Midcontinent and southwestern regions. The most complete and important Permian deposits on this continent, for purposes of historical study, occur in the midcontinent and southwestern regions. Permian outcrops are continuous from Nebraska to central Texas, occupying an area many thousand square miles in extent (Fig. 160). Exposures in western Texas and southeastern New Mexico, which also are very large, are separated from the midcontinent outcrops by intervening younger formations, but records furnished by many thousand deep borings show that the Permian strata are continuous from one region to the other. In this central portion of the continent, highly fossiliferous marine strata compose an important part of the Permian section. There are also unfossiliferous marine deposits, such as dolomite, anhydrite, and salt, that were formed by chemical precipitation in supersaline waters, and extensive continental deposits consisting mainly of red sand and shale. The aggregate thickness of Permian strata in the region extending from Nebraska to western Texas ranges from about 3,000 to 7,000 feet. Nowhere have the beds been much disturbed from their original near-horizontal attitude.

Western States. Marine Permian formations cap a large part of the Colorado Plateau country in northern Arizona, and are known in Nevada, California, Utah, Idaho, Wyoming, Montana, British Columbia, and Alaska. Their fossils are closely similar to forms found in Permian rocks of the midcontinent and western Texas; limestone is the dominant type of deposit. Permian outcrops in Oregon and Wash-

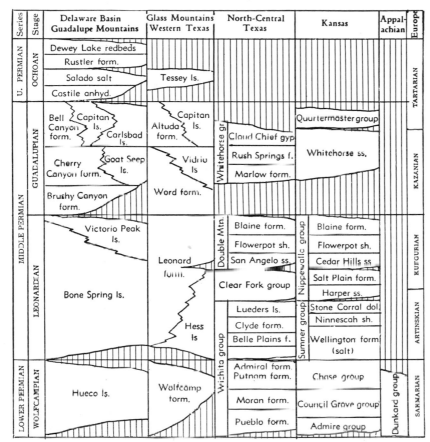

Series	Stage	Delaware Basin Guadalupe Mountains	Glass Mountains Western Texas	North-Central Texas	Kansas	Appalachian	Europe
U. PERMIAN	OCHOAN	Dewey Lake redbeds / Rustler form. / Salado salt / Castile anhyd.	Tessey ls.				TARTARIAN
MIDDLE PERMIAN	GUADALUPIAN	Bell Canyon form. Capitan ls. Carlsbad ls. / Cherry Canyon form. Goat Seep ls. / Brushy Canyon form.	Capitan Altuda ls. form. / Vidrio ls. / Word form.	Whitehorse gr. Cloud Chief gyp / Rush Springs f. / Marlow form.	Quartermaster group / Whitehorse ss.		KAZANIAN
MIDDLE PERMIAN	LEONARDIAN	Victorio Peak ls. / Bone Spring ls.	Leonard form. / Hess ls	Double Mtn. Blaine form. / Flowerpot sh. / San Angelo ss. / Clear Fork group / Nippewalla group Lueders ls. / Clyde form. / Belle Plains f.	Blaine form. / Flowerpot sh. / Cedar Hills ss / Salt Plain form. / Harper ss. / Stone Corral dol. / Ninnescah sh. / Wellington form (salt)		KUFGURIAN / ARTINSKIAN
LOWER PERMIAN	WOLFCAMPIAN	Hueco ls.	Wolfcamp form.	Wichita group Admiral form. Putnam form. / Moran form. / Pueblo form.	Chase group / Council Grove group / Admire group	Dunkard group	SAKMARIAN

162. **Time-rock divisions of the Permian System and rock units in representative Permian sections of North America.** The vertical scale is not proportional to thickness or time duration, but the placement of names indicates correlation in age. The ruled areas denote absence of deposits.

ington, on the other hand, contain fossils of strong Asiatic affinities, belonging to the very late part of the period.

Eastern North America. Eastern North America contains small outcrops of Permian rocks, mostly continental, that are very small remnants of originally widespread deposits. These outcrops occur in an area surrounding Wheeling, W. Va., in northern Nova Scotia, and possibly in the vicinity of Boston. The rocks are mostly red beds.

Divisions. Two main divisions are recognized in the section located in western Texas that is taken as the standard of reference for study of

American Permian formations. These divisions, which are classed as series, are separated from one another by unconformities and each contains two time-rock units classed as stages. Except the uppermost, each stage bears a distinctive assemblage of marine invertebrates. The Lower Permian (Wolfcampian and Leonardian) Series is represented by highly fossiliferous outcrops in the Glass Mountains, 250 miles southeast of El Paso. The Upper Permian (Guadalupian and Ochoan) Series has its typical development about 100 miles east of El Paso. The highest Upper Permian consists of unfossiliferous rocks, which are mainly chemical precipitates.

Features of Permian History

Varied marine sedimentation of the Texas-New Mexico region. The lower boundary of the Permian deposits in western Texas is very sharply defined, for in this region mountains had been formed late in Pennsylvanian time and eroded away before the beginning of Permian sedimentation. Thus, the lowermost Permian strata, in places containing thick basal conglomerates, are found resting on the upturned truncated edges of Pennsylvanian and older rocks, including both lower Paleozoic and Pre-Cambrian formations. The Early Permian seas that spread over this region were clear and warm, as judged by prevalence of limestone deposits and from the nature of bottom-dwelling invertebrates. Reefs were built, some having topographic relief of several hundred feet, but corals played only a minor role in building these reef deposits. The first three stages each contain such structures, associated with thinly and evenly bedded siliceous or dark calcareous sediments laid down in lagoonal areas. Also, in basin areas near the reefs, there was thick accumulation of fine sand. Broad depressions northeast of the reefs, in Late Permian time, became filled, through evaporation, with concentrated brine in which dolomite, anhydrite, and salt were precipitated. Ultimately, the thickness of such deposits amounted to many hundred feet.

End of normal seas in the midcontinent area. Shallow seas, in which invertebrate life was prolific, occupied the northern midcontinent, from northern Oklahoma into Nebraska, during earliest Permian time (Wolfcampian). Cyclic sedimentation, in which fossiliferous limestone and shale are found to alternate in rhythmically regular manner with unfossiliferous red beds, indicate that the sea

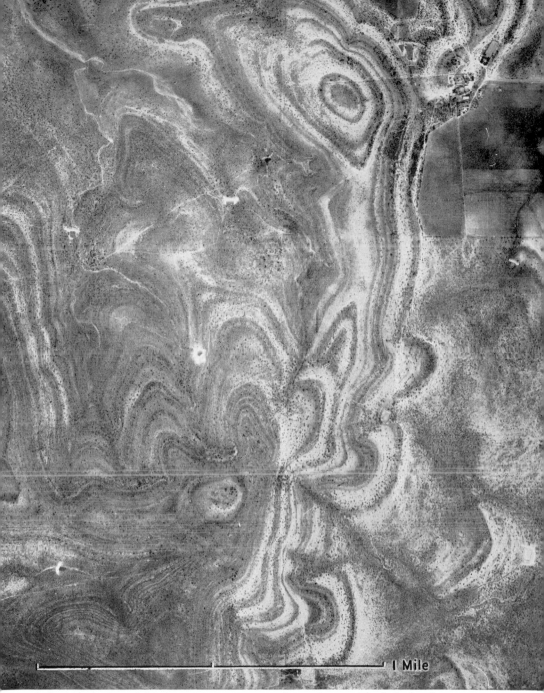

163. Vertical air view of Permian marine strata in north-central Texas. The light bands represent limestone outcrops and intervening dark bands define shaly slopes. This is grassy country used for cattle grazing. *(Soil Conservation Service.)*

advanced and retreated repeatedly, as it had done in Pennsylvanian time.

During the second age (Leonardian) of the Permian, normal marine sedimentation ceased, although a sea continued to occupy the region. Evaporation concentrated the salt in this sea to such extent that most forms of marine life could not survive, and eventually, when gypsum and thick beds of salt began to be deposited, virtually all life in the seas vanished.

The later part of Permian history in this region includes the making of several hundred feet of fine silty and sandy red beds, which in some horizons contain extensive thin beds of dolomite and gypsum. These deposits indicate the work of sluggish streams and the existence of very shallow bodies of saline water that spread over the nearly flat land surface.

End of deposition in the Appalachian geosyncline. Geologic history of the Appalachian geosyncline during Permian time is very incompletely known, inasmuch as deposits belonging to this period now occur only in small areas near Wheeling, W. Va., in northern Nova Scotia, and possibly near Boston. It is probable that Permian deposits originally were widespread in the northern Appalachian region, and possibly also in the southern Appalachians. It is evident

164. Permian limestone in the Flint Hills region of Kansas. This limestone (Cottonwood) is only 6 feet thick or less but is almost continuously exposed from Nebraska southward to Oklahoma.

165. Middle Permian red beds in southwestern Kansas. This view, near the Oklahoma line in Barber County, Kans., shows a typical outcrop of red shale and thin-bedded sandstone capped by a layer of gypsum. These are water-laid sediments, but they are unfossiliferous. Probably they were made by sluggish streams and in shallow saltwater lakes on a nearly flat plain that was alternately subject to wetting and drying.

that if post-Permian erosion had been only a little more extensive, there would now be no record at all of Permian deposits in the eastern United States. The formations that have been preserved belong to the earliest Permian epoch, and they consist almost wholly of continental deposits made by sluggish streams. Thin sandstone beds alternate with reddish and dark-colored shale, and locally there are thin coals.

A single band of strata contains fossils indicating presence of the sea. Although no Permian deposits are now known between southeastern Ohio and the midcontinent region, it is inferred that, at least temporarily in Early Permian time, marine waters were continuous from the midcontinent to the Appalachian region. Whether there were marine advances also later in Permian time, and whether continental sedimentation continued into the later part of the period, are unknown. The Lower Permian land deposits, containing fossil plants and some vertebrate remains, are the last record of Paleozoic deposition in the Appalachian geosyncline. With little doubt, the sediments

Capitan ls.

Cherry Canyon form.

Brushy Canyon form.

Bone Spring ls.

166. Permian marine deposits in western Texas. This northwestward air view of the south end of the Guadalupe Mountains, about 90 miles east of El Paso, shows Leonardian and Guadalupian shale and limestone. The cliff-making cap rock beneath the cloud bank is the Capitan limestone, which is a reef deposit. *(Courtesy Robert Muldrow, III, Kargl Aerial Surveys, Inc.)*

were derived from higher land located hundreds of miles eastward—the same source area that had supplied the coarse detritus of Pennsylvanian deposits.

Marine invasion of the western United States. That shallow seas spread widely across parts of the western United States during differ-

167. **Thin even layers of pure rock salt in a mine at Lyons, Kans.** The salt here being mined is part of a succession about 400 feet thick, occurring 1,000 feet below the surface in central Kansas. (*Courtesy of American Salt Corp.*)

ent epochs of Permian time, is shown by the presence of fossiliferous limestone and shale in Arizona, Nevada, California, and areas farther north reaching to Alaska. In Wyoming and Idaho, these Permian deposits include commercially valuable beds of rock phosphate. The fossils all show some provincial variation of the marine faunas, indicating lack of free intermigration between these areas and the Texas and midcontinent regions; but fusulines and some other guide fossils give basis for correlation with subdivisions of the marine Permian farther east.

Two small areas in Oregon and Washington, recently discovered, contain marine Permian fossils unlike others known from North America, but closely resembling those in very late Permian rocks of eastern Asia. These organisms are evidently Asiatic migrants that reached the western border of North America, but did not penetrate far into this continent, probably because seas in this latest part of the period did not then submerge much of the Western States. Uppermost Permian deposits of the Texas-New Mexico region, which may be equivalent in age, are unfossiliferous beds made up largely of salt and gypsum laid down in an inland sea of very high salinity. This marine remnant

168. Middle Permian limestone on the rim of the Grand Canyon of the Colorado River in Arizona. This formation, composed mostly of limestone, contains some shale and sandy strata near the base. Marine fossils and nodules of silica (chert) are common in some layers. (*J. K. Hillers, U. S. Geol. Survey.*)

certainly was not connected with normal oceanic waters to the west.

Appalachian mountain building. Crustal unrest near the close of the Paleozoic Era is recorded by mountain building during Permian time. In central Europe moderate folding occurred in Middle Permian time, and some mountain-making disturbances may have affected parts of the Western Hemisphere at corresponding date. The main deformation belonging to this part of earth history, however, is that known as the Appalachian revolution, which is inferred to mark the close of Permian and Paleozoic times. Throughout its entire length of more than 2,000 miles, the Appalachian geosyncline was greatly compressed by earth forces, which pushed previously undisturbed Paleozoic deposits northwestward against the rigid interior platform of the continent. The rocks were folded into great anticlines and synclines, and in many places they were broken by thrust faults having the upthrow side on the southeast. Crustal shortening that amounted to 200 miles or more is estimated. Erosion must immediately have begun to attack the uplifted rock strata, carving canyons and making

169. Cross bedded Permian sandstone near Flagstaff, Ariz. This sandstone (Coconino) is a wind-laid deposit ranging to 1,000 feet in thickness. It is preserved in an area of about 32,000 square miles in north-central Arizona. (*N. H. Darton, U. S. Geol. Survey.*)

rugged mountainous topography. By restoration of eroded parts of the folded pattern in the Appalachian Mountains, the structural relief may be determined. Although this cannot be accepted as a measure of topographic relief at any given stage, it supports judgment that, in the early part of their history, the Appalachians may have been as lofty as the present-day Rockies.

The geologic date and duration of the Appalachian revolution actually cannot be determined exactly. They belong somewhere between a late part of Early Permian time and an early part of the Late Triassic. No Late Permian rocks are found in the mountain area, and there are no Early or Middle Triassic deposits. The oldest rocks found resting unconformably on eroded edges of the folded Paleozoic formations are Late Triassic. Of course, the truncated rock structures beneath the Triassic clearly show that profound erosion had occurred after the mountain building and prior to renewal of sedimentation. Such erosion, however, might have been accomplished in a fraction of Early and Middle Triassic time.

A main reason for assigning the mountain revolution to the closing part of Permian time is the change in forms of life represented by fossils found on opposite sides of the Paleozoic-Mesozoic boundary. Comparison of Late Permian and Early Triassic organisms found in various regions shows that marine and nonmarine life assemblages were profoundly altered, and such great, seemingly abrupt biologic change must reflect great physical change in environment. Only as result of unusual alteration of physical surroundings can we account for the extinction of previously well-established, long-enduring plant and animal stocks, and replacement of them by new types. Accentuating the effect of these changes in most places, is a lost time interval of unknown duration. Since the Appalachian revolution surely brought about important geographic changes that include alteration of climate, it is reasonable to conclude that this may be expressed in the nature of the fossil record. All things considered, the close of Permian time seems to have been an unusually critical period in earth history.

Much igneous activity accompanied the deformation of the Appalachian geosyncline during Permian time. This is shown mainly by

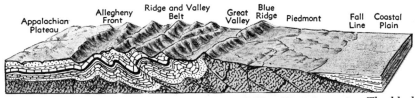

Appalachian Plateau　Allegheny Front　Ridge and Valley Belt　Great Valley　Blue Ridge　Piedmont　Fall Line　Coastal Plain

170. Structural and physiographic units of the Appalachian Mountains region. The block diagrammatically shows relations of structure to characteristic surface features of the Appalachian Mountains and adjoining belts. The folding and faulting occurred near the close of Paleozoic time.

171. Appalachian mountain ridges in Pennsylvania. The curved pattern of subparallel, knife-sharp ridges that rise even to summit level characterizes the entire Appalachian chain and is especially well shown in Pennsylvania. The abrupt bends of ridges at various points are made by plunging of the folds in direction of the mountain trend. (*Pennsylvania Geol. Survey.*)

intrusion of granitic batholiths on a great scale. Large areas of these intrusive masses are now exposed in the area east of the folded stratified rocks—the present-day piedmont belt—where removal by erosion of many thousand feet of originally overlying cover has exposed the deep-seated igneous rocks. The fact that mineral grains of the granite have not been distorted by compressive earth forces proves that intrusion of these rocks did not antedate the Permian folding, for otherwise they would have been much metamorphosed; in places the batholiths unconformably underlie the Triassic.

Volcanism along the Pacific border. No record of Permian folding is found in the western United States, but crustal unrest is indicated by association of fossiliferous Permian strata with volcanic deposits, which in some areas total thousands of feet. Such rocks occur in California, Oregon, and Idaho, and each area includes lava flows, ash beds, and tuff. This evidence of volcanism is noteworthy, inasmuch as Paleozoic rocks older than Permian in the western United States are not associated with volcanic rocks.

Permian Life

Climatic and regional variation of plants. The chief difference between floras of Permian time and those known from the Pennsylvanian Period, is the diminished variety of plant types. This is associated with evidence of climatic variation and regional differentiation of distinct plant groups. Unlike the warm, moist climate of Pennsylvanian time, when identical types of lush vegetation grew thickly in coal swamps and on lands in widely separated parts of the globe, the greater dryness and variability of conditions in Permian time are reflected by plant groups adapted to these changed conditions. Although little coal is associated with Permian continental deposits in North America, mineable coal beds are important in some other parts of the world, such as Australia and Siberia. The flora associated with these deposits most nearly resembles typical Pennsylvanian plant assemblages. Plants in other areas were adapted to drier and probably somewhat cooler climates; these are characterized especially by prominence of conifers and by certain types of ferns and fernlike plants that are not known from the Pennsylvanian.

Permian floras of the Southern Hemisphere are distinguished by a broad-leaved fernlike plant that is not known from North America or western Europe, although in part of Permian time it migrated into the U.S.S.R.

Nonmarine animals. Permian rocks are the oldest in which a fairly abundant representation of land animals is known. Fishes that inhabited streams and ponds are found locally in continental Permian deposits, and they are associated with skeletal remains of amphibians. As described in the following chapter, these amphibians are marked especially by their broad, heavily armored skulls, and they represent considerable advancement over forms known from older rocks.

The most striking and interesting land animals are the reptiles,

172. A connecting link between the amphibians and reptiles. This animal *(Seymouria),* which is represented by fairly abundant skeletal remains from Permian red beds of northcentral Texas, attained a length of about 2 feet and is chiefly interesting because it combines many typical characters of amphibians with those of unspecialized reptiles. Some paleontologists think that *Seymouria* should be ranked among amphibians, but the nest of eggs in a hollow on land, as shown in this restoration, implies that the creature is a reptile, because the eggs of amphibians must be laid in water. *(American Museum of Natural History.)*

which are represented by many complete skeletons collected in Permian rocks of North America—especially Texas—South Africa, Russia, India, and Brazil. All were four-legged creatures of somewhat lizard-like form, that averaged 3 or 4 feet in length. The beginning of successful conquest of the lands by reptiles, which culminated in the great development of this group in Mesozoic time, is shown by skeletal advancement and specialization as compared with their amphibian ancestors.

Although found only very locally, remains of insects in Permian rocks are varied and abundant. The richest known Paleozoic insect locality in the world is a small outcrop of Lower Permian soft limestone in central Kansas, where about 12,000 beautifully preserved specimens have been collected. These fossils prove that most of the main divisions of insects had made appearance on the earth before the close of Paleozoic time.

Marine invertebrates. All main classes of marine invertebrates, except trilobites, are common in marine Permian faunas. Especially important from the standpoint of geologic correlation, are the abundant fusulines, which show complex internal structures. The other most important elements are cephalopods, brachiopods, bryozoans, and corals. Each of these groups includes distinctive forms that are highly characteristic of the Permian System.

Permian deposits on the flanks of the limestone reefs in western Texas contain a great variety of shells, which in the course of fossilization have been changed to silica. By etching away the limestone matrix in dilute acid, the silicified fossils, which are not affected by the acid, are freed from the rock; the majority of these fossils show delicate structural features even more perfectly preserved than average modern shells picked up on a beach. The fauna includes several highly specialized brachiopods, some of which bear long delicate spines, and a great variety of bryozoans, along with corals, clams, snails, ammonoids, crinoids, sponges, echinoids, and fusulines. When paleontologic studies now in progress have been completed, the marine life of Permian time in the western Texas region will be one of the best known among Paleozoic faunas of the world, for knowledge will be based on about 5 million beautifully preserved specimens that have been collected. Besides scientific interest in learning about past forms of life on the earth, this study of Permian fossils has practical

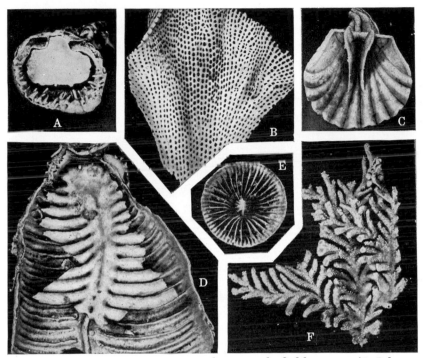

173. Representative Permian invertebrates. These are silicified bryozoans (*B, Polypora; F, Thamniscus*), brachiopods (*A, Prorichtofenia; C, Meekella; D, Leptodus*), and a coral (*E, Lophophyllidium*) etched by acid from Permian limestones of western Texas. Natural size.

value in furnishing accurate means for correlation of the Permian rocks, parts of which are prolific sources of petroleum and natural gas in this region. Beds associated with the great deposits of salt, gypsum, and potash, however, are unfossiliferous.

Climate

The climate of the Permian Period was undoubtedly drier and more varied than in Pennsylvanian or most of preceding Paleozoic time. Conditions favorable to growth of abundant coal-forming plants existed, especially in parts of Asia and Australia. Contemporaneously, in other areas there were warm, alternately wet and dry climates, semiarid climates, true desert climates, and frigid climates. Evidence of these conditions is derived partly from study of fossil organisms and partly from the physical nature of the Permian strata.

Glaciation.   Continental glaciation occurred during Permian time in Australia, India, South Africa, and Brazil. Thick deposits of glacial till belonging to the Permian System are found in all these regions; in some, the glacially eroded surface over which the ice moved is also seen clearly. This glaciated surface shows well-preserved striae and other characteristic marks of ice cutting. The direction of ice movement can be determined in some of the glaciated areas, and it is surprising to learn that the centers of ice accumulation were on the equatorward side of the area of glacial deposition, and that the glaciers moved away from the equator rather than toward it. In eastern Australia, glaciation is recorded in the early part of Permian time by ice deposits interbedded with marine strata; coal-forming conditions were established subsequently and persisted for some time; then there was renewed glaciation, represented by another series of glacial till deposits above the coal-bearing strata. All these deposits belong to the Permian.

Close of the Period

The close of the Permian Period and the end of Paleozoic time were marked by an emergent condition of the continents throughout the world. Shallow seas retreated. Nowhere are transitional marine deposits connecting Late Permian and Early Triassic known, and the hiatus in the record is of unknown duration. Most land areas probably were subject to erosion, but in some regions unbroken continental sedimentation so connects Permian with Trassic, that a satisfactory boundary cannot be determined. South Africa and eastern Russian are regions in which the proper age assignment of some fossil-bearing continental deposits is unsettled, and such deposits are sometimes designated as Permo-Triassic. Nevertheless, the end of Permian time is marked by profound changes in the record of life.

12. Nature and Evolution of Paleozoic Life

Devonian sea bottom in New York.

The Age of Invertebrates

The Paleozoic rocks are the oldest that contain abundant evidence of life. Remains of this life form an essential part of the geologic record,

Rochester Museum of Arts and Science

and the character of the life of these remotely ancient times has much intrinsic interest. Invertebrate marine animals constitute the predominant element in Paleozoic organic assemblage as a whole, and consequently, the era is well designated as the Age of Invertebrates. It is the purpose of this chapter to review the nature and evolution of plants and animals, as recorded by fossils found in the Paleozoic formations.

Plants

That plant life was fairly abundant from the very beginning of Paleozoic time, and doubtless long before, is a safe presumption, because of (1) the prolific fossil remains of animals, all of which are directly or indirectly dependent on plants for food, (2) the appearance of highly organized plant remains in the Devonian and later Paleozoic rocks, and (3) the widespread presence of calcareous algae. Bacteria, which are assigned an important role as precipitating agents of calcium carbonate, may have contributed greatly to accumulation of the thousands of feet of calcareous strata that were made in Paleozoic time.

MARINE PLANTS

The only certainly known plants from the early Paleozoic part of earth history are seaweeds (algae). Some of the most interesting of these are remarkably preserved specimens of gelatinous and membranous algae, that appear as shiny black films on bedding planes of Middle Cambrian shale in British Columbia. On the basis of form and mode of growth, 20 species have been distinguished. Since none of these algae shows a point of attachment, presumably they were floating forms.

Lime-secreting algae are especially abundant and characteristic of some Late Cambrian and Early Ordovician formations. The algal remains consist of calcareous masses that are varied in size and irregularly rounded in shape. They show a finely laminated concentric structure, closely resembling that of some modern blue-green algae. Algal deposits occur in marine later Paleozoic rocks also.

LAND PLANTS

No land plants are known before Devonian time, but it is probable

174. Weathered slab of Lower Ordovician limestone containing abundant calcareous algae. The concentrically banded algae *(Cryptozoon)* are widely distributed in Early Ordovician marine limestones. Other types occur elsewhere in marine Paleozoic strata. *(Amherst College, W. E. Corbin.)*

that the beginning of adaptation to life on land occurred very much earlier. This is indicated especially by the high degree of advancement and specialization of the land plants encountered in the Devonian. When one remembers the unfavorable situation of land vegetation as regards speedy burial, and all the other factors that make preservation unlikely, it is not surprising that the pre-Devonian record of land plants is a blank.

Devonian rocks contain a peculiar group of leafless land plants (psilophytes), which are quite unlike any others, but give evidence in their generalized characters of ancestral relationship to various later forms of vegetation. These strata also show ferns of several types, and scale trees having trunks more than 3 feet in diameter and probably 40 feet tall. The Mississippian and Pennsylvanian Periods mark the culmination of this ancient land flora, when there was greatest variety and when maximum sizes in plants of low orders were attained. Many of the shale deposits near coal beds furnish an extremely rich and beautifully preserved record of these plant growths. Permian time is chiefly characterized by the waning or disappearance of earlier plants, the expansion of early types of conifers, and the development, especially in the Southern Hemisphere, of a cool-climate flora, in which certain rather coarse fernlike plants dominated. This was a time of great change, leading up to the different-looking floras of the Mesozoic Era.

Leafless plants. The first definitely known land flora comes from Devonian rocks of eastern Canada, Maine, Montana, Scotland, and central Europe. A typical representative (*Psilophyton*) of this assemblage was a naked, leafless plant, having a woody stem ½ inch in diameter, and numerous branches rising 2 feet or more (Fig. 175). The tips of young branches twisted in a coil, like new fern leaves, and some bore small, elongate pods, containing the reproductive spores. The stems have breathing pores, such as occur in the leaves of higher plants, and the cell structure shows the presence of a vascular system, which serves for transmitting water and nourishment derived from the underground portion of the plant. The latter did not consist of true roots, but was a horizontal runner bearing small rootlets. Clearly, we find here the adaptation of an originally algal type of aquatic plant to a moist environment on land, and a beginning of the all-important structures that enable land plants to thrive.

Ferns. Ferns (pteridophytes), which are generally distinguished by their numerous branching leaflets and by the presence of spore clusters on the underside of leaves or on specialized fronds, are now represented by some 6,000 species that range from tiny plants to tropical tree ferns 50 feet high. The spores are produced in almost incredible numbers, a single plant sometimes liberating 20 to 50 millions. The ferns made their appearance in Devonian time, and one

175. Restoration of Devonian plants. The tallest plants are tree ferns (*Eospermatopteris*). Others are horsetails (right foreground) and primitive leafless plants (*Psilophyton*). (*C. R. Knight, Chicago Natural History Museum.*)

type (*Archaeopteris*) was world-wide in distribution. Some of the fernlike types of Pennsylvanian time include climbing plants of tropical aspect, many of which suggest lianas. Other climbing forms were of filmy delicacy.

The leaves of many Pennsylvanian ferns were strikingly similar in form to some of the present day, and a few were 12 feet in length. Leaves of this type were borne at the tops of long trunks, which attained diameters of 30 inches or more. These tree ferns were provided with an extremely thick outer zone of protective, water-storing, root-like appendages (Figs. 14, 157, 176).

Seed ferns. A surprising paleobotanical discovery was made some years ago when specimens that looked like ordinary ferns proved to have true seeds, instead of spores. Separated seeds are not uncommon

176. Fossil ferns from Lower Pennsylvanian rocks of Alabama. Well-preserved fossil plant remains are especially common in strata associated with coal beds. The larger leaf here shown is *Pecopteris* and the smaller one, *Alethopteris*. Natural size. *(Charles Butts, Alabama Geol. Survey.)*

in some late Paleozoic beds, but it was not suspected that any of these belonged to ferns. Now, it is clear that many seeds of previously unidentified origin belong to the seed fern, and it is possible that some of the fern species, known at present only by their foliage, may prove ultimately to be seed-bearing, and not true ferns at all.

The oldest known seed ferns come from Middle Devonian rocks of southeastern New York, where fossil tree trunks were found some 65 years ago near the little town of Gilboa. They were recognized as ferns, but not until 1920, when scores of additional specimens with foliage and seeds were unearthed in building a large dam, was it learned that a veritable seed-fern forest existed here. As many as 18 stumps, 4 or 5 feet tall and 1 to 3½ feet in diameter, were found in a space 50 feet square. These seed-fern trees (*Eospermatopteris*) are believed to have grown to a height of about 40 feet, and some of the great leafy fronds at the top were fully 6 feet long (Fig. 175).

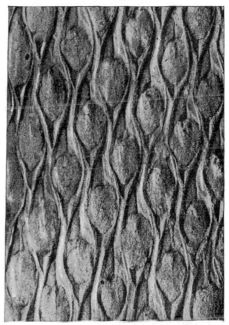

Scale trees. Dominant elements in the late Paleozoic floras were the scale trees (lepidophytes), which are represented by the modern club mosses. In Pennsylvanian time, the group contained splendid trees more than 100 feet high. These plants are distinguished by short, stiff, scaly or needlelike leaves that cover densely all of the trunk and branches, except parts from which the old, dead spines have dropped. The leaves of large fossil spe-

177. **Part of the trunk of a Pennsylvanian scale tree.** The regularly arranged markings on this fossil are the attachment scars of spike-shaped leaves, characteristic of one of the most common Late Paleozoic scale trees (*Lepidodendron*). Natural size. (*Charles Butts, Alabama Geol. Survey.*)

cies not uncommonly attained a length of 6 to 7 inches, and were sometimes nearly ½ inch wide at the base, which was roughly diamond-shaped. The place of attachment of each leaf was marked by a distinctive scar. In some (*Lepidodendron*), the scars were arranged in regularly intersecting oblique rows; in others (*Sigillaria*), they were in vertical series. Some were short, stocky, and unbranched, a trunk 6 feet in diameter at the base tapering to the top less than 20 feet above ground. Others were tall and slender. One unbranched specimen 200 feet long is known. Branches were far less numerous than in modern

178. A Pennsylvanian conifer twig (A, *Walchia*) and leaves of the horsetail (B, *Annularia*). Natural size. *(Kansas Geol. Survey.)*

trees. The scale trees are first known from Devonian rocks, and they are common in later Paleozoic swamp deposits, especially those of Pennsylvanian age.

Horsetails. The so-called "horsetails" are plants having numerous unbranched, hollow, jointed, and ribbed stems. Most modern species are less than 3 feet tall, but one in South America has stems 1 inch in diameter and 30 to 40 feet tall. This group was very well represented in the late Paleozoic floras of all parts of the world. Most of the ancient horsetails were very much larger than their living descendants, some attaining a diameter of 3 feet and a height of fully 100 feet. The upright trunks grew from a prostrate, horizontal stem, and it is evident that they thrived in wet sandy soils. At the nodes along the stem were small branches that bore circlets of leaves. Jungle-like areas of these plants were probably like the dense southern canebrakes on an enlarged scale, and comparable to bamboo thickets of today.

Cordaites. Another conspicuous late Paleozoic plant is an unfamiliar tree known as *Cordaites*, which was distinguished by a tall, slender trunk, rarely 2 feet in diameter but 30 to 100 feet high. Branches occurred only near the top, and they bore a thick mass of leaves up to 3 feet long and as much as 15 inches wide. They are exceedingly widespread in Pennsylvanian and Permian rocks of both hemispheres.

Conifers. The plant group that is represented in modern times by the pines, spruces, and many other cone-bearing trees, contains several primitive Permian types and a few of Pennsylvanian age. One type (*Wulchia*), which was abundant and very widely distributed in Permian time, had numerous slender branchlets growing in the same plane, all densely clothed with short needle-like leaves.

Invertebrates

PROTOZOANS

We might suppose that the oldest fossil-bearing beds would be especially characterized by prominence of protozoans, because these are the most primitive and simply constructed of all animals. On the contrary, fossil protozoans are rare in rocks older than Mississippian. This may be due partly to conditions unfavorable for preservation of their minute delicate structure, but more probably, the scanty fossil records mean that most of the early protozoans lacked hard parts. A few poorly preserved specimens are known from the Upper Cambrian of England and about 50 species of siliceous-shelled simple foraminifers have been discovered by dissolving samples of Ordovician and Silurian limestone in hydrochloric acid.

The delicate siliceous tests of radiolarians have been reported from Pre-Cambrian rocks, but they are not definitely identified in early Paleozoic faunas.

Fusulines. Protozoans are first important as an element in later Paleozoic fossil faunas in Pennsylvanian time, when the "wheatgrain" shells termed "fusulines" occurred in such vast numbers that they form a considerable part of many rock layers. Other kinds of protozoans are present also. The fusuline shells of Pennsylvanian and Permian time are spindle-shaped, some of them long and thin, others nearly spheroidal, and they range in length along the axis from $\frac{1}{16}$ to more than 1 inch, the average being about $\frac{3}{8}$ inch. They are distinguished from microscopic foraminifers by their shape and much greater size, and by their complex internal structure. The Middle Pennsylvanian fusulines (*Fusulina*) have mostly simple, nearly plane walls that divide each spiral turn of the shell into chambers; those of Late Pennsylvanian time (*Triticites*) are distinguished by moderately wrinkled walls, and several belonging to Permian time have highly fluted walls. There is thus a well-marked evolution of this stock during its existence, and most of the very many species are valuable index fossils. The fusulines were bottom-dwelling foraminifers, but they spread very widely over the world, being abundant not only in America but throughout most of the Old World. These fossils are extensively used by paleontologists as an aid in identifying and correlating the Pennsylvanian and Permian formations penetrated by the drill in the midcontinent oil fields. It is interesting to find many perfect, unmutilated specimens of these delicate fossils in well cuttings.

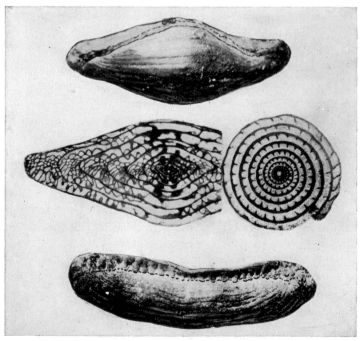

179. **Late Paleozoic wheat-grain-shaped fossils called "fusulines."** These relatively large foraminifers were abundant in Pennsylvanian and Permian marine rocks and are especially important guide fossils. The specimens *(Triticites)* show typical external and internal structural features (enlarged). *(Kansas Geol. Survey.)*

SPONGES

Among Cambrian fossils, siliceous sponges are well represented by several types, including many with a delicate netlike skeleton, that resembles the modern glass sponge known as Venus's-flower-basket.

Sponges were common in Ordovician time, and many of them are valuable index fossils. One of the most important types (*Receptaculites*), which, however, may represent an entirely distinct class of organisms, resembles the large center of a sunflower.

The Silurian rocks contain a somewhat similar genus (*Ischadites*), and there are large numbers of apple-shaped (*Astylospongia*) and saucer-like (*Astraeospongia*) siliceous sponges in some beds. In parts of Tennessee, sponges weather out of the rocks in such profusion that they may be gathered by the bushel.

Sponges of several sorts are known from each of the later Paleozoic periods. Some formations are specially characterized by abundance of sponge spicules, or the presence of certain species of sponges. The massive stony types (lithistids) are much less common than the beautiful, delicate glass sponges (hexactinellids), of which many are found in Devonian rocks.

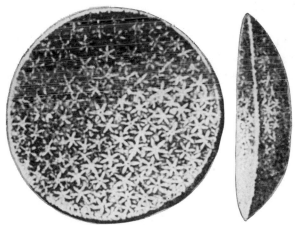

180. A saucer-shaped siliceous sponge from Silurian rocks of Tennessee. The starlike markings on the surface of the fossil (*Astraeospongia*) are large spicules. Top and side views, natural size.

181. Restoration of fossil sponges from Late Devonian rocks of New York. Only sponges in which the skeletal elements (spicules) are knit together are preserved so as to show the form of the animal. *(New York State Museum.)*

COELENTERATES

Stromatoporoids. The lime-secreting hydrozoans, called "stromatoporoids," flourished during parts of Paleozoic time, when they were important as rock builders. The principal representatives of this class in the Ordovician period are columnar growths with external fluting (*Beatricea*), rounded, hemispherical growths (*Stromatocerium*), and flat expanding forms (*Labechia*). The Silurian species are mainly large, irregularly laminated masses, in which the vertical pillars extend only between the layers, rather than continuously across several layers (*Clathrodictyon*). In Devonian time, they reached the peak of their career in numbers and variety. Some colonies were truly gigantic in size, forming calcareous deposits several feet thick and as much as 10 feet across. Locally, they make reefs and may be accounted important as rock builders. The stromatoporoids disappeared suddenly, for they are not found in post-Devonian beds, unless possibly certain Cretaceous fossils belong in this group.

Graptolites. Graptolites are an interesting extinct group of organisms, known only from Paleozoic rocks, and almost entirely restricted to the Ordovician and Silurian. Their remains are extraordinarily abundant in black shales that contain few other kinds of fossils. A few occur in limestone. Accurate correlation of graptolite-bearing deposits, even on opposite sides of the earth, as in England, United States, and Australia, is possible (1) because the animals, attached to seaweeds or supported by a float of their own construction, were transported widely by oceanic currents and (2) because there was comparatively rapid evolution of different species, so that beds only a few feet apart vertically may be characterized by entirely different graptolite assemblages (Fig. 93).

Evolutionary changes among the graptolites are seen in (1) the form of the colonies and (2) the shape and arrangement of the cups. The lower, and therefore older, graptolite zones show species in which numerous branchings are characteristic, while successively appearing later types have branches reduced to 16, 8, 4, 2, and finally 1. Primitively, also, the branches appear to have hung more or less directly downward; in later, more advanced genera, they grew horizontally outward, and, finally, turning upward, the rows of cups were established in a position back to back. There is, therefore, a tendency in colony form to pass from many branches to a single one, and from downward-hanging branches, each with a single row of cups, to those with a double row of cups growing back to back. The simplest cups are short cylindrical tubes growing obliquely outward from the initial cup. In specialized types, these turn at right angles to the stem, or even form an S-shaped bend, and part of the tube may be variously constricted.

The graptolites first appeared in the Middle Cambrian and are widespread in the uppermost Cambrian rocks. The Ordovician marks the heyday of graptolite abundance and differentiation, and in the shale deposits where they occur, they are much the most important among all fossils. There are 67 genera and more than 475 species of graptolites in Ordovician rocks of North America. By Silurian time, they had greatly declined in numbers but are still important. Here occur some of the most peculiar and highly specialized examples. In America, about 35 genera and 175 species of Silurian graptolites are recorded. A few stragglers, consisting of the most long-lived, primitive stocks, lived on into Early Mississippian time.

Corals. Corals are abundantly represented by fossils in Paleozoic formations and they have been very important as rock builders. Many are good index fossils. If the ancient coral polyps were affected by temperature conditions like the modern, the common occurrence of fossil corals in a geologic formation may be interpreted to signify that the deposit was laid down in moderately warm, shallow waters.

Lower Cambrian limestones have yielded specimens of what are probably very primitive corals or possibly sponges (*Archaeocyathus*). These are subcylindrical or conical in shape, and attain a maximum length of nearly a foot. They are specially distinguished by the thick, porous nature of the outer and radial walls, and the presence of a sort of plate that floors the calyx. Locally, they make large reefs, as in Australia, where a limestone 200 feet thick and at least 400 miles in lateral extent, is largely composed of them. The presence of these coral-like forms in Labrador, islands north of Siberia, and in Antarctica, suggests that high latitudes were at least not frigid at this time.

For some reason, corals are rare or lacking in the Middle and Upper Cambrian, but they appear at various horizons in the Ordovician. Characteristic types include both colonial and horn corals. The chain coral (*Halysites*) is typically a Silurian fossil, but has been found in rocks as old as mid-Ordovician. About 35 species of Ordovician corals have been described in North America.

The first really abundant development of corals occurred in Middle Silurian time, when at many places in North America they made reef limestones. About 400 species are recognized. Well-exposed sections of the ancient reefs may be seen in Wisconsin, Iowa, Illinois, and Indiana. Colonial corals are of many types, a few with large individual polyps (*Strombodes*), but the majority with units of small size (*Favosites*, Fig. 120D). Especially interesting are the chain coral and the honeycomb. Horn corals are numerous. A strange coral (*Goniophyllum*), shaped like a four-sided pyramid provided with a cover of four plates, is a characteristic fossil in the Silurian of northern Europe.

At no time in the Paleozoic were horn corals so numerous or varied as in the Devonian Period. They ranged in size from less than $\frac{1}{4}$ inch in length and width to more than 2 feet in length and about 4 inches in width. Some of the very common kinds (*Cyathophyllum, Heliophyllum*) had numerous, evenly spaced radial walls, without a fossular depression in the calyx; others (*Zaphrenthis, Aulacophyllum*) are distinguished by the presence of well-defined fossulae. There are variously specialized forms. For example, one long-ranging genus (*Amplexus*), which is represented by several Devonian species, has extremely short radial walls and very numerous horizontal platforms; another (*Cystiphyllum*), which appeared in the Silurian and died out in the Late Devonian, had almost all of the space inside the outer wall filled by a vesicular growth of curved plates. One of the peculiar and interesting horn corals is a slipper-shaped form (*Calceola*), which is abundant in some of the European Devonian strata but is uncommon in this country.

Compound corals were remarkable in their variety, beauty, and profusion. Two groups are distinguishable, one having relatively large individuals provided with well-developed radial walls, and the other (Tabulata) having small individuals that lack distinct radial walls but have numerous platforms. The first group differs from the solitary or horn corals only in the colonial mode of growth; indeed, there are some genera that include both types of growth. The individuals in many types of colonies are sufficiently separated to permit development of the normal cylindrical form of each coral (*Diphyphyllum*, *Cyathophyllum*). There are also many types in which the individuals were crowded so closely together that the cross section of each coral became polygonal (*Hexagonaria*, *Phillipsastraea*). The tabulate corals include a variety of forms, among which the honeycomb coral (*Favosites*) is most common and generally known.

At many places in the shallow inland seas, the corals grew in profusion and were largely instrumental in building reefs. Some of these are now seen in the Devonian areas of Michigan, Wisconsin, Indiana, Ohio, and Kentucky. One that is famous, because of the beauty and variety of silicified fossil corals that have been collected from it, is located near Louisville, Ky. The coral reef chanced to lie in the river's path and, being harder than the adjacent rocks, it formed an obstruction that made rapids, known as the Falls of the Ohio.

Mississippian formations contain fewer types of corals and, in general, less numerous specimens than the Devonian, but several kinds are restricted to this part of the geologic column.

Pennsylvanian corals are about as common as Mississippian, but the species and most of the genera are different, horn corals being more numerous and widely distributed than the colonial kinds. One of the most common horn corals (*Lophophyllidium*) had a prominent central axis, which forms a spikelike projection in the center of the

calyx (Figs. 158*A* and 173*E*). A colonial form (*Chaetetes*), which is distinguished by the very minute size of the closely packed tubes and by the massive growth of the colonies (to 3 feet in diameter), is an important guide fossil of Lower and Middle Pennsylvanian rocks.

The Permian is noteworthy because of several new kinds of fossil corals, which resemble Paleozoic much more than Mesozoic types.

ECHINODERMS

Varied sorts of echinoderms, which are exclusively marine invertebrates, are abundant in Paleozoic formations, especially from Lower Ordovician upward. The attached forms, which grew fixed by a stem, are the most common and useful as guide fossils. Of the three classes of stemmed echinoderms, cystoids, which are the most primitive, occur in Cambrian rocks; the budlike blastoids and highly organized crinoids make appearance in Ordovician formations.

Cystoids. The cystoids appeared first in the Cambrian and attained maximum numbers and variety in the Ordovician (21 genera, 59 species) and Silurian (28 genera, 113 species). Only a very few cystoids are known from beds younger than Silurian. They are therefore characteristic of the older Paleozoic strata.

Blastoids. Blastoids are distinguished by their five-sided, beautifully symmetrical, budlike form and their generally prominent, finely cross-striated, food grooves. The average size of the calyx is small. These echinoderms were unimportant in early Paleozoic times. They advanced during the Devonian and increased remarkably in numbers and variety in the Mississippian, but after this sudden climax they virtually disappeared. A few blastoids occur in the Early Pennsylvanian rocks of North America, and several species lingered on into the Permian.

One of the commonest Devonian blastoids (*Nucleocrinus*) has about the shape and size of a small hickory nut and is distinguished by very narrow food groove areas. The most important genus in the Mississippian beds (*Pentremites*) is broad at the base, and the sides slope upward toward the top (Figs. 139*C* and 183*B*). Its maximum development in both species and number of individuals is found in the Upper Mississippian rocks. Certain beds of this age in southeastern Missouri, southern Illinois, and western Kentucky contain almost perfect specimens of blastoids that may be collected by thousands.

Crinoids. The structural characters that are of chief importance in classification and in the evolution of the crinoids are (1) the plan of the plates in the dorsal part of the calyx and (2) the number, method of branching, and structure of the arms.

The first definitely known crinoids occur in Lower Ordovician rocks, and are common in some higher portions of the system. Several are distinctive index fossils. Each of the main orders of crinoids, except the articulates, to which most modern crinoids belong, is present in Ordovician faunas, which contain about 125 described crinoid species. Silurian time witnessed a notable advance in the number and variety of crinoids (about 300 species), all of which differ from antecedent forms. Some were very peculiarly specialized. In one (*Eucalyptocrinus*), the arms fitted into partitioned spaces formed by solid calcareous walls raised above the calyx; in another (*Crotalocrinites*), the arms jointed laterally to form a broad flexible network; and in still another (*Petalocrinus*), the arm structures were developed into solid petal-like projections extending outward from the tiny calyx. All these types occur in the Silurian of the central United States and of northern Europe. In some of the Silurian deposits, there are numerous specimens of minute crinoids (*Pisocrinus*) having calices no larger than a pea.

The maximum development of the crinoids clearly belongs to the later part of Paleozoic time, especially the Mississippian Period.

The most specialized and abundant crinoid class in later Paleozoic time was the so-called "camerate crinoid," distinguished by its proportionately large, solidly roofed calyx composed of many plates. In the Early Mississippian Epoch, an almost explosive expansion of the camerates made them the outstanding element in marine invertebrate life. At this time the shallow seas of the central Mississippi Valley were a vast "sea-lily" garden, the remains of crinoid skeletons serving to compose the larger part of limestone strata 200 to 500 feet thick, and covering tens of thousands of square miles. More than 400 different species have been described from this region. Some had small, delicate plates and very slender, feathery arms; others had a large calyx composed of thick heavy plates and were variously ornamented with knobs and spines. A variety of specialized forms is seen. Advanced evolution is indicated in several types by reduction in the number of plates in the basal series, the normal number, five, being reduced to three or even two. Some types had elliptical stem segments and the stem was twisted.

From the standpoint of usefulness of these fossils in identification of the stratigraphic divisions in which they occur, it is interesting to observe that most of the species, and even some genera, are very short-lived. Thus, most of the earliest Mississippian crinoid species disappeared before the beginning of the succeeding stage, and in the latter there are successive zones in which less than 5 per cent of the species persist from one zone to the next. This short vertical range is characteristic of complexly organized, rapidly evolving organisms. The only difficulty in making largest use of the crinoids in correlation

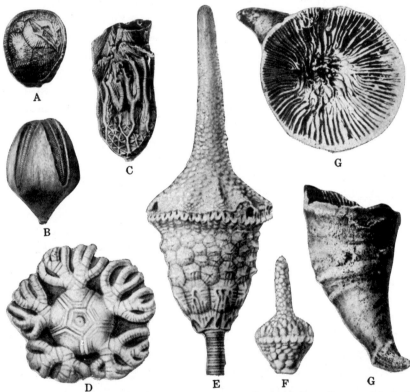

183. Representative Paleozoic echinoderms and corals. The fossils here illustrated include a cystoid (*A, Pseudocrinites*, Devonian), a blastoid (*B, Pentremites*, Mississippian), camerate crinoids (*C, Glyptocrinus*, Ordovician; *D, Platycrinites*, Mississippian; *E, Teleiocrinus*, Mississippian; and *F, Batocrinus*, Mississippian), and a horn coral (*G, Zaphrenthis*, Devonian). Natural size.

of beds is that the calices, which generally are necessary for identification of species, are commonly broken into separate plates and scattered. Except in a few localities, complete crinoid "heads" are uncommon.

North America furnishes some of the most famous crinoid-collecting places in the world. The best Devonian crinoids come from New York, Michigan, and along the Ohio River near Louisville, Ky. A slab of Lower Devonian limestone from eastern New York, in Peabody Museum at Yale University, shows more than 300 complete crinoid calices. Most prolific of all, are some Mississippian localities, especially near Burlington, Iowa, and Crawfordsville, Ind. Many remarkable slabs have been collected in central Iowa, near the little town of Le Grand. Chief foreign areas are in England, Belgium, the Rhineland, and near Moscow, Russia.

Starfishes and echinoids. Starfishes are known as fossils in Paleozoic rocks beginning in Ordovician deposits. Their presence and comparatively high degree of development are interesting, but this group of echinoderms is not important in any of the fossil faunas.

The echinoids or sea urchins were represented in the Ordovician by a single genus (*Bothriocidaris*) having a small globular shell, and in the Silurian by four known genera. The ancient echinoids are characterized chiefly by the large number of columns of plates in the shell. The time of great abundance and differentiation of the echinoids was in the Mesozoic Era.

Plates and spines of sea urchins are commonly found in many formations from Devonian to Permian in age, but complete specimens of the test are generally rare. Worthy of special mention are plates and spines from the Upper Devonian of Iowa, which are perhaps more highly and peculiarly specialized than in any other known echinoid. These plates overlapped one another like shingles on a roof, and the spines, shaped like inverted collar buttons with hexagonal bases, fitted together to form a secondary armor outside the real shell. Some of the Mississippian, Pennsylvanian, and Lower Permian strata contain numerous elongate echinoid spines, with a variety of ornamental spinelets on many of them. The polygonal plates commonly have a large rounded boss in the middle, marking the place of attachment of one of the large movable spines. Smaller spine bases occur on the outer borders of the plates. Occasionally a complete test is found,

Some Silurian formations, especially those belonging to the lower and middle parts of the system, contain very abundant bryozoans, but large massive types are less common. There are numerous delicate branching colonies and the first important development of lacelike fronds. The American Silurian bryozoans number some 95 genera and 336 species.

The bryozoans of Devonian and later Paleozoic time are characterized by the dominance of delicate lacy and slender branching types. The variety is exceedingly great. Though the bryozoans are less conspicuous than most other invertebrate groups, they are by no means the least interesting or valuable in correlation of the rock formations. Some delicate twiglike growths had apertures arranged all around the branches, and some on one side only. A branching form with triangular cross section (*Prismopora*) is an important index fossil in the Upper Mississippian and Lower and Middle Pennsylvanian rocks of the United States.

The lacelike types of bryozoans had the tiny cells of the individual animals arranged in rows along slender branches, which are connected at regular intervals by slender crossbars. Some genera carry two rows of cells to the branch, and others a larger number. The cell apertures all open on the same side of the colony, the opposite side being nonporiferous (Figs. 139A, 173B, F, and 184E).

A peculiarity of some of the late Paleozoic bryozoans (chiefly Mississippian) was the development of special types of solid calcareous supports. The most important one of these is seen in *Archimedes*, which looks very much like a coarsely threaded screw. This screwlike axis supported a spirally arranged lacy bryozoan frond (Figs. 139D and 140).

BRACHIOPODS

Brachiopods are particularly characteristic of Paleozoic rocks, for they were most abundant and varied during this era, whereas in Mesozoic and Cenozoic time, they were represented by only a few surviving stocks of rather simple type. More than 3,500 species are already known from Paleozoic rocks of North America. The evolution of the brachiopods along various lines is shown by (1) composition and structure of the shell, (2) articulation of the valves, (3) nature of the pedicle opening and method of attachment, (4) form and surface ornamentation of the shell, and (5) development of various internal structures.

The Cambrian brachiopods are generally small, mostly less than ½ inch in length and width. The simplest, most primitive shells predominate, for the unhinged shells, composed partly or wholly of lime phosphate, are much more numerous than those with hinged, calcareous valves. Some shells had nearly equal valves with an opening for the pedicle shared by both valves, a feature repeated in the earliest stage of various later brachiopods (Figs. 70D and 73F). Described species of Cambrian brachiopods number at least 59 genera and 536 species, of which 45 genera and 346 species occur in North America.

The succeeding Paleozoic systems also hold a good representation of these simple, unhinged brachiopods. The fact that they occur almost exclusively in the dark shaly formations, indicates that they are specially adapted to this type of environment. They are "facies fossils" and may be expected to occur whenever the proper environment or facies of sedimentation occurs. The insignificant changes shown by these shells, despite existence of the group for scores of millions of years, means that they have little value as indicators of any given geologic horizon. They furnish good examples of an animal stock that is very stable because unspecialized, yet adapted to an environment that always exists somewhere.

All main divisions of brachiopods are represented in Ordovician rocks. A marked advancement over Cambrian species is shown by (1) dominance of hinged calcareous over unhinged phosphatic shells; (2) increase in average size, variety, and numbers; (3) prevalence of strongly striated or plicated shells; (4) development of interlocking anterior margins, with fold and sinus; (5) abundance of concavo-convex shells; and (6) the appearance of specialized internal structures, such as spiral supports for the brachia. Several important groups, which are well represented throughout most of later Paleozoic time, make their appearance.

The group called *orthids* is characteristic of Ordovician rocks in which it reached its peak (Figs. 92A, D and 185B, F). The shells are generally wide-hinged and strongly plicated. Silurian and later Paleozoic strata contain many finely striated orthid shells of rounded outline.

Another very important group is that termed *strophomenids*, in which the shells are generally wide-hinged and flat, or concavo-convex.

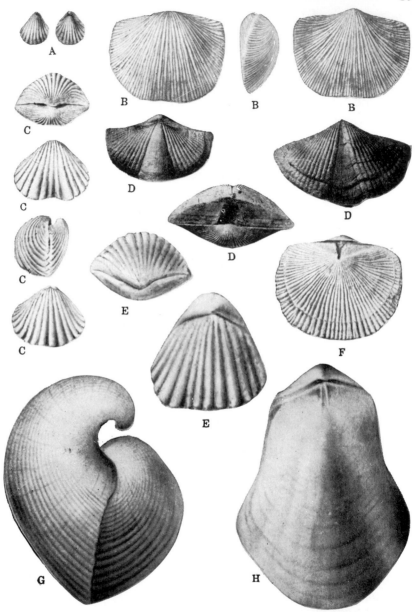

185. Representative Paleozoic brachiopods. The forms shown are all hinged, calcareous shells, natural size; some are figured in two or more different views. Ordovician fossils include *B (Plaesiomys), C (Orthorhynchula),* and *F (Retrorsirostra);* Silurian, *G (Conchidium)* and *H (Pentamerus);* Devonian, *D (Cyrtospirifer)* and *E (Gypidula);* Pennsylvanian, *A (Hustedia).*

The most common Ordovician genera (*Rafinesquina, Leptaena,* and *Sowerbyella*) have a convex pedicle valve and concave brachial valve. This group was very abundant also in Silurian and later Paleozoic rocks (Figs. 92C, 158G, and 173A, C, D).

Closely related *productids* are a dominant element in the Mississippian, Pennsylvanian, and Permian brachiopod faunas of the world. These shells have a very convex pedicle valve and concave brachial valve. Surface ornamentation typically consists of prominent radiating ribs, which may be crossed by concentric wrinkles, and there are commonly numerous long hollow spines, only the bases of which, however, usually appear on the fossils (Figs. 13 and 158B, E, F). The largest known brachiopod (*Gigantella gigantea*), which attains a width of 12 inches or more, belongs to this group.

A third group (*rhynchonellids*), distinguished generally by strongly plicated shells with pointed beaks and no cardinal area, contains numerous representatives (especially *Rhynchotrema*), which are widespread in some formations (Fig. 185C).

A group that includes several important Silurian index fossils is the *pentamerids*. These are mostly smooth, but some are plicated shells in which the interior is divided near the beaks by prominent converging partitions (most important genera, *Pentamerus, Stricklandinia, Conchidium, Gypidula*) (Figs. 110C and 185E, G, H).

The *spire-bearing brachiopods*, which appear first in Ordovician rocks, advanced greatly in the Silurian, and in Devonian and later Paleozoic formations became a dominant type among the brachiopods. The most important genus (*Spirifer*) is a moderate- to very wide-hinged shell with plications radiating from the beaks, and generally with a well-defined median depression (sinus) on the pedicle valve, and a corresponding elevation (fold) on the brachial valve. Internally, there are two spirally coiled brachial supports. The following evolutional changes are discerned: (1) plications in early forms (Silurian and most Devonian species) simple, undivided, absent on fold and sinus; (2) plications in intermediate forms (some Upper Devonian and most Mississippian species) simple, present on fold and sinus; (3) plications in late forms (Pennsylvanian, Permian), branching or arranged in bundles, present on fold and sinus; (4) modifications of shell structure and internal features that are made the basis of separation into distinct genera. The great variety of shape and size in this group and its rapid evolution make many species very good index fossils (Figs. 120*A*, *C*, and 185*A*, *D*).

Two groups of highly specialized, peculiar-looking brachiopods lived in the Permian. One of them (*Prorichtofenia*) resembles a horn coral more than a brachiopod, for it has been strangely modified by its mode of attachment and by thickening of one of the valves. It is found in Texas, eastern and southern Asia, and southern Europe. The other (*Leptodus* and allied genera) has very prominent curving ridges and grooves on the inside of the shell, unlike any other brachiopod (Figs. 173*A*, *D*).

PELECYPODS

The oldest known pelecypods occur in Middle Ordovician beds where several genera suddenly make their appearance. These are rather archaic, generalized types that attained a climax in the later part of Ordovician time. They are characterized mainly by the presence of a large number of simple, similar teeth along the hinge line, which is a primitive type of dentition. Some of the characteristic types were prominently ribbed and had a large winglike expansion on one side of the beak. Others were much like the common living mussel. The Silurian contains fairly numerous fossil clams that differ mostly generically from those of the preceding period.

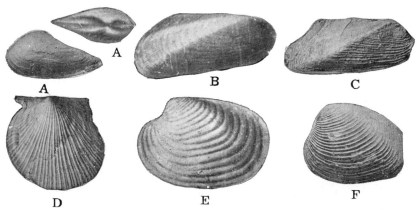

186. Examples of Paleozoic fossil clams. Many Paleozoic pelecypods are much larger than those here illustrated. From the Devonian are *B (Pthonia)* and *E (Grammysia)*; Pennsylvanian forms include *A (Leda), C (Pleurophorus), D (Aviculopecten),* and *F (Astartella).* Natural size.

Pelecypods are abundant in many later Paleozoic formations, especially shales and sandstones. The species are somewhat different in each system, but the main types are very persistent and exhibit little real change. Several are smooth-shelled, rounded, subtriangular, or elongate in outline. Others have prominent concentric lines or plications radiating from the beak, and a few have a combination of these ornamental features. A primitive stage of development is indicated in the majority of shells by unspecialized hinge structures, such as occur in the very youngest growth stages of many modern pelecypods.

Marine Devonian deposits of eastern North America, which are dominantly composed of shale and sandstone, contain a large pelecypod fauna, the description and illustration of which fill two large volumes of the New York Geological Survey. Also, shaly, sandy, and oolitic beds of Mississippian, Pennsylvanian, and Permian age are characterized commonly by abundant clams. The environment that produces oolite is evidently very congenial to the mollusks, as shown by many such limestones that contain especially numerous pelecypods and gastropods, whereas most limestones have more brachiopods, bryozoans, echinoderms, and corals than mollusks.

GASTROPODS

Gastropods are known from earliest Paleozoic time down to the present, their number and variety gradually increasing until they probably now enjoy their maximum vigor. More than 20,000 Recent species are known.

At the base of the Cambrian, the genera are small, archaic forms,

187. A few Paleozoic gastropods. A symmetrically coiled, frilled shell is shown in *A* (*Phragmolites,* Ordovician, X3); the others show common forms of conical spires, natural size (*B, Worthenia,* Pennsylvanian; *C, Gyroma,* Devonian; *D, Clathrospira,* Ordovician).

Ordovician time marks the culmination of trilobites, for their remains are more abundant and varied in rocks of this period than in any others. Among noteworthy forms are small to medium-sized carapaces that have a relatively large head shield bearing a broad pitted brim and long backward-pointing spines (*Cryptolithus*). In one group (*Ampyx*), the head carries a prominent forward or upward projecting spine. Some types are long-bodied and fairly conservative (*Triarthrus*); others are specialized in the development of snoutlike anterior projections of the head (*Megalaspis, Hoplolichas*), or bizarre spinose ornamentation (*Acidaspis, Ceratocephala*); and decadent in the obsolescence or loss of typical features of the head and tail (*Illaenus, Bumastus*). In some genera, there is no trace of segmentation of the central head lobe, which may be indistinct. One form (*Cyclopyge*) shows a remarkable development of the eyes, which are expanded to cover the entire outer thirds of the head shield. Almost all the Ordovician trilobites were able to roll up, so as to conceal the ventral region, and many fossils in this position are found (Fig. 191*E*). The largest known trilobite is from Ordovician strata in Europe. It had a length of about 27 inches. Some American specimens (*Isotelus maximus*) attained a length of nearly 24 inches.

The Silurian history of the trilobites is marked mainly by the disappearance of earlier forms. There were only half as many families in the Silurian as in the Ordovician; the number of genera was reduced about one half (99 to 47) and the number of species from about 390 to 180. One large group was conservative, another carried to an extreme the tendency to overdevelop certain features or to become spinose, and a third lost almost all trace of the fundamental trilobate plan of the shell (Figs. 110*B* and 191*D*).

Among the Devonian and later trilobites, two groups may be differentiated. The general appearance in the one is that of a well-advanced but conservative trilobite, without frills, special ornamentation, or any unusual peculiarities, and without marks of degeneration such as appear in several of the Silurian branches. *Dalmanites* and the abundant *Phacops* illustrate this group. The other is overdecorated and peculiarly specialized in various ways. Extreme development of spines is seen on head, body, and tail, and in one genus the central lobe of the head became very strongly bulbous. These abnormal types did not survive into the Mississippian, when only a few genera of the conservative group, all belonging to a single family, are found. The number is further reduced in the Pennsylvanian, and finally the last of the race is found in the Permian. The overdevelopment, in different ways and specialization that led to extinction, are well illustrated by various branches of the trilobites; and the persistence of the conservative, unspecialized stock is seen in its survival to latest Paleozoic time (Figs. 121, 158*H*, and 191*A*).

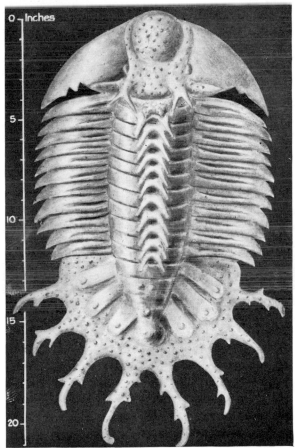

192. The largest known Devonian trilobite. This restoration shows the small eyes and bizarre ornamentation of this trilobite (*Terataspis grandis*), which are characters of specialization.

OSTRACODES AND OTHER CRUSTACEANS

Ostracodes.   The tiny bivalve crustaceans called *ostracodes,* literally swarmed at various times and places in the shallow seas of
Paleozoic time, if we may judge from the abundance of their shells in
certain layers. The number of different kinds is also very large, some
smooth and rounded, some very beautifully and delicately ornamented
with granules or fine-meshed network, some with prominent bulbous
nodes or ridges, and some with projecting comblike frills. Various
Silurian beds of the Appalachian region are mainly identified and correlated on the basis of their ostracode faunas. Also, rock layers of
Pennsylvanian and Permian age in the midcontinent oil fields, as well
as those of the Mississippian and older systems, are commonly identified by means of ostracodes and other microscopic fossils observed in
the drill samples.

Eurypterids.   The eurypterids are an interesting group of extinct
arthropods which include the largest animals of this phylum, measuring up to 9 feet in length. The body was elongate and provided with
a thin chitinous segmented shell. The head region bore on the dorsal
side an outer pair of large compound eyes and an inner pair of simple
eyes; on the ventral side there were six pairs of appendages, some of
which in certain forms were armed with pincers. The tail (*telson*)
was long and pointed, or flat. The presence of gills shows that the
eurypterids were aquatic, and the structure of the appendages indicates that they were mostly mud crawlers, though some were probably good swimmers. They are found associated with marine fossils
in Cambrian, Ordovician, and Silurian rocks, but some became adapted
to a brackish-water environment, and those known from Pennsylvanian
deposits occur with a fresh-water fauna (Fig. 109).

Scorpions and spiders.   A few specimens of scorpions, almost
identical in appearance with modern examples, are found in Silurian
strata of North America and northern Europe. They were aquatic in
habit, but it is clear that scorpions of Pennsylvanian age had become
adapted to life on the lands, breathing air.

From Pennsylvanian rocks in various places come several interesting
fossils that are strikingly like modern crawfishes, but are sufficiently
distinct to make them assignable to different groups. A famous locality
from which some of these and many other less common fossils have

been collected, is on Mazon Creek in Illinois, about 50 miles southwest of Chicago. The fossils, including leaves, shells, crustaceans, insects, spiders, scorpions, myriapods (thousand legs), and rarely skeletal remains of small amphibians and reptiles, occur in nodular concretions embedded in shale.

INSECTS

A development of Paleozoic life that attracts special attention is the first appearance of insects. This group has expanded in later earth history until at present there are more species of insects than of all other kinds of animals put together, and we are told that the only serious competitors of man are the insects. It is perhaps fortunate that the size of modern insects is not that of certain individuals of Pennsylvanian time, when 4-inch cockroaches scurried over the ground and dragonflies with a 30-inch wing spread droned through the air.

The most primitive and one of the most important orders of late Paleozoic insects (Palaeodictyoptera) is characterized by the very archaic structure of the wings, which have a type of venation matching almost exactly the hypothetical ancestral insect wing. To this group belong the first definitely known insects, which occur in rocks of Early Pennsylvanian age. Before the extinction of the primitive insects in Permian time, the order gave rise to several transitional stocks which in turn introduced existing orders.

The cockroaches (Blattoidea) were the most common type of insect in the Pennsylvanian Period (some 800 species) and were numerous in the Permian. The order did not die out at the close of Paleozoic time, but, on the contrary, has persisted to the present day, taking rank as the oldest existing insect group that is represented by fossils. In view of his antiquity of ancestry and once large size and numbers, the despised modern cockroach is entitled to hold his head high among insect associates.

The Pennsylvanian dragonflies are assigned to a more primitive order than that to which the living representatives of this group belong, the difference being mainly in wing structure. About a dozen fossil species are known.

The most remarkable occurrence of Paleozoic insect fossils yet found in the world is in Lower Permian strata a few miles south of Abilene, Kans. More than 12,000 specimens have been collected here, and very

much has been learned from them concerning the early differentiation
and evolution of the insects.

Vertebrates

FISHES

The earliest known fish remains, representing the very primitive
group called *ostracoderms,* occur in Ordovician sandstone (Harding)
of eastern Colorado and Wyoming. The fossils consist of bony fragments that reveal little of the nature of the fishes themselves, but in
later Paleozoic strata, both marine and fresh-water species are represented by fairly complete skeletons. The Silurian rocks contain scattered bony spines that were borne by some of the early sharklike
fishes.

The Devonian Period is often termed the Age of Fishes. This does
not mean that fishes reached the peak of their career at this time
or that they exceeded in number and variety other kinds of life. Rather,
for the first time fishes became well represented in the fossil record,
and, because of their great advancement in the evolutionary scale over
any of the invertebrates, they may properly be termed the dominant
animals of the period. The fishes are the first animals provided with
cartilaginous or bony internal structures, a central nervous system,
and other specialized characters that distinguish the vertebrates. For
this reason and because the higher vertebrates were undoubtedly derived from them, the Paleozoic fishes are of special importance.
Neither paleontologic nor embryologic evidence, however, indicates
the exact mode of transition from invertebrate ancestral stock to fish,
and we are left to infer relationships from similarities of structure
and the geologic order of appearance of the successively higher types
of life. To learn the significant things about the Paleozoic fishes, we
must know the general structural characteristics of this type of animal
(Appendix) and observe the peculiarities shown by fossils.

The oldest fairly complete remains of fishes come from beds (Downtonian) that are variously classed as uppermost Silurian or lowermost Devonian. Since almost all occur in nonmarine or estuarine
deposits, it is reasonable to conclude that the first vertebrates began
their existence in waters of the land and only later entered the seas.
The best fossils have been found in the British Isles, Norway, Spitz-

193. Restoration of an early type of enamel-scaled fish *(Cheirolepis)* from Devonian rocks. *(American Museum of Natural History.)*

bergen, and eastern Greenland. They all belong to the bony-plated group of primitive jawless fishes called "ostracoderms," the largest of which was about 12 inches long. Several types have been discovered, but the most common forms were distinguished by the well-armored head region, behind which was a fishlike trunk and tail covered by bony plates and scales. Formerly, it was supposed that fishes initially had only cartilaginous skeletal parts and acquired bony structures gradually in the course of their evolution. The fact that the most primitive fishes have abundant bone does not agree well with this idea, and modern judgment is that fishes provided with cartilaginous skeletons, like the sharks, have evolved in the direction of losing their

194. Restoration of an Upper Devonian jointed-neck fish *(Dinichthys)*, above, and the modern African lung fish *(Polypterus)*, below. *(American Museum of Natural History.)*

inheritance of bony hard parts. The advanced nature of sharks is shown by their well-developed jaw structure and several other features. Ostracoderms are illustrated in Fig. 124.

Next, we may give attention to the so-called *placoderm fishes*, which had a strong bony armor in the head region but differ from ostracoderms in the well-developed articulation of their jaws. Also, some of this group attained large size, total length being as much as 20 feet. A few possessed very stout bony spines at the front edge of the fins, strengthening them and causing them to project rigidly from the body. The tail was asymmetrical, like that of living sharks. The most peculiarly specialized placoderms were a group of jointed-neck fishes called "arthrodires," in which the front part of the armored head was united by a ball-and-socket joint with the back part; thus the head was freely movable up and down on the trunk. The placoderms seem to have inhabited the sea, for their remains are commonly found in marine Devonian rocks; almost all became extinct before Mississippian time but a few persisted in the Permian Period. *Coccosteus* (Fig. 124) and *Dinichthys* (Fig. 194) are typical arthrodire fishes.

Although fishes belonging in the group of modern *sharks* and *rays* are known from strata as old as Jurassic, none occur in Paleozoic rocks. Forerunners of the true sharks, however, are recognized in

Devonian-to-Permian marine deposits (Figs. 123 and 125). Mostly they are represented by teeth, and it is inferred that the remainder of the skeleton had largely lost its primitive bony structure.

The *bony fishes* (Osteichthyes), which comprise all higher types having advanced jaw structure, bony skeleton, lungs or air bladder, well-developed fins, and a body covering of scales, are important elements of late Paleozoic fish faunas. They include two main groups: (1) the lobe-finned fishes, or crossopterygians, of which the lung fishes are an offshoot, and (2) the ray-finned fishes, or actinopterygians.

The lobe-finned group is distinguished chiefly by the limblike appearance of the pectoral and pelvic fins, which have a fleshy middle portion supported by bones resembling those of the limbs of land vertebrates (Fig. 31). The body is covered by scales, which have a bony lower layer and a superficial layer of shiny enamel (ganoid type). The teeth are conical in shape and commonly show the peculiar complexly folded "labyrinthine" internal structure seen in the Paleozoic amphibians. It is very probable that these fishes, which appeared in Early Devonian time, possessed lungs, like those of the modern lung fishes (Fig. 194), and the firm conclusion is reached that this type of fish is the ancestral stock of the amphibians and higher vertebrates.

The ray-finned fishes are distinguished by structure of the fins, which lack bony supports. The scales are thin and flexible in modern forms. Here belong true bony fishes (teleosts), which comprise more than 90 per cent of existing species of fishes. They are the most highly organized and are equally adapted to life in the seas and in the waters of the land. They are descendants of the Paleozoic ray-finned fishes which first appear in Middle Devonian rocks (Fig. 193).

AMPHIBIANS

The first known land vertebrates appeared in late Paleozoic time, the most ancient fossil indication of this class being footprints of a three-toed animal, doubtless an amphibian, in Upper Devonian rocks of Pennsylvania. The amphibians belong next above fishes in the evolutional scale. Modern amphibians include animals that live in water a good deal or all of the time (salamanders, newts) and also animals that are exclusively air breathers in adult life (frogs, toads).

The Paleozoic amphibians differ especially from those of the present day in the presence of a covering of plates on the head, which in the larger forms was a heavy bony armor. Accordingly, they are commonly called *stegocephalians,* the name meaning "roofed head." All these amphibians had relatively flat, generally broad heads with eyes directed upward, and the mouth very wide. A well-developed tail is invariably present. The early, more primitive types were animals having short, weak legs and laterally flattened tails that functioned as an aid in swimming. Some of the Paleozoic amphibians were only 1 or 2 inches long, but some forms were as large as a crocodile. There was a considerable variety of these animals in Pennsylvanian and Permian times. Some were ponderous and evidently very sluggish, waddling about in a slow, lumbering fashion; others were active, lizard-like creatures with lighter bodies and well-developed limbs; some were probably very capable swimmers; and a few were entirely legless, snakelike forms. The stegocephalians lived in the fresh waters and on the lands. Probably most of them were carnivorous, judging by the nature of the teeth, feeding on invertebrates, small fishes, and other amphibians.

One of the most prominent groups of stegocephalians, called *labyrinthodonts,* show intricately infolded structure of the enamel of the teeth, a peculiarity that is noted in Devonian lobe-finned fishes. The labyrinthodonts attained the maximum known size among amphibians, some having a broad, bony head 4 feet long and a total length of about 15 feet. The skull in these animals was unusually heavy and solid, and the breast was covered by three large, thick bony plates.

An interesting feature that is shown very clearly in Paleozoic amphibians is an opening on the top of the skull behind and midway

195. Restoration of a small Pennsylvanian amphibian (Diplovertebron). (*Chicago Natural History Museum.***)**

between the eye orbits. This marks the position of a third eye (so-called "pineal" eye). The aperture occurs also in primitive fishes, many fossil reptiles, and one living reptile. As a vestigial organ, this eye is present in all higher vertebrates, including man.

The stegocephalians probably originated in Devonian time. Skeletal remains are known in rocks of Mississippian age in Europe, but in America they have not yet been found in beds older than Pennsylvanian, which have yielded some 90 species of these animals. They continued as an important element in the land fauna of Early Permian time, but rapid increase in the number of reptiles pushed them into a subordinate place. Stegocephalians were rare in the later Permian, and they disappeared in the Triassic Period.

REPTILES

The most highly developed animals of later Paleozoic time are the reptiles, although it is possible that the beginning of mammals occurred before the close of the era. Reptiles, like amphibians and fishes, are cold-blooded, and in skeletal structure the more primitive reptiles can hardly be differentiated from certain stegocephalians. From an evolutional standpoint, however, the advancement of reptiles over amphibians is almost comparable to that of fishes over invertebrates. This improvement is seen mainly in the nature and mode of development of the egg. In amphibians and fishes, the eggs are necessarily laid in water. There is virtually no stored food material, and the almost embryonic newly hatched young are required to fend for themselves. Among reptiles, structures are introduced in the egg, which, for the first time, make the animal independent of water as a surrounding medium during at least the early stages of development. This is accomplished by the presence in the egg of an outer protective covering or shell, but mostly by the development of two membranes within the shell. One of these membranes (*amnion*) serves as a sort of water bag over the delicate embryo, preventing its drying up, and the other (*allantois*) is a sac, well supplied with blood vessels, which functions as a respiratory organ, the air passing readily through the porous outer shell. Food during embryonic growth is supplied by yolk substance within the egg. The significance of these structures is exceedingly great as regards conquest of the lands by vertebrate life, for the reptiles and their descendants, birds, and mammals, were

196. Skeleton of a Permian reptile from Texas. The animal shown here *(Ophiacodon)* is a near relative of the fin-backed pelycosaur reptiles, but it has normal dorsal processes on the vertebrae. Reptiles of this type attained a length of nearly 12 feet. *(American Museum of Natural History.)*

liberated from dependence on aquatic surroundings for growth in the egg and first life stages after birth. A few reptiles give birth to fully formed young.

The primitive, first-known reptiles, in rocks of Pennsylvanian age, were much like amphibians, for the limbs were short, hardly lifting the squat, plump body above ground. The head was armor-plated like that of the stegocephalians. The tail was generally long, the hand and foot five-fingered, and the body probably scale-covered but not armored. The teeth were mostly large, sharply pointed, and in some species distinctly curved backward, of use in catching and holding flesh. Most of the late Paleozoic reptiles were certainly carnivorous, but a few had rounded, blunt teeth that were not adapted for flesh-eating.

An interesting Permian fossil that so combines structural characters of amphibians and reptiles as to make classification very doubtful is *Seymouria* (Fig. 172). This animal is not actually a connecting link that is ancestral to true reptiles because undoubted reptiles of Pennsylvanian age are known.

The amphibian-like Pennsylvanian and Early Permian reptiles (cotylosaurs) are the stem from which, at about the beginning of Permian time, branched other reptilian types with higher, more lightly built skulls, longer legs, and variously different skeletal characters.

Many of the Early Permian reptiles were evidently sluggish creatures, but others were moderately active. Judging from general form and especially from characters of limbs and teeth, some waddled about in the shallow streams or swampy places, probably feeding on in-

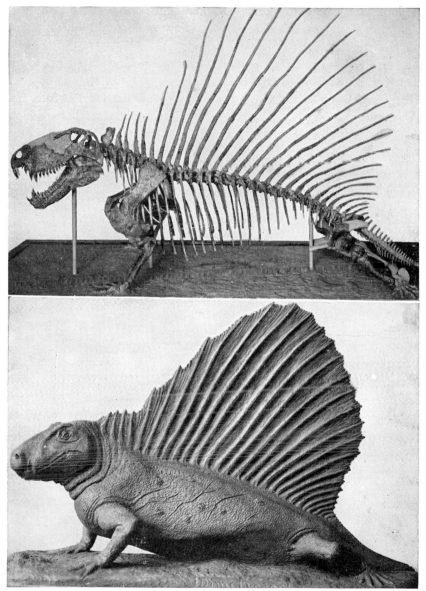

197. Skeleton and restoration of a characteristic fin-backed reptile *(Dimetrodon)* **from the Permian of northern Texas.** *(American Museum of Natural History.)*

vertebrates and grubbing succulent roots and stems. Others suggest the later insectivores. At least one type, with form much like the modern lizard, had well-formed slender limbs adapted for swift running, the leg bones being light and hollow as in birds. This creature may have been partly arboreal.

A few reptiles returned to the open waters to compete with and probably prey upon fishes, perhaps including types like those from which they themselves had descended a few million years before. Unlike the fishes and amphibians, however, the aquatic reptiles were exclusively air breathers, for no reversion from a higher type of respiratory structure, such as the lungs, to a lower, such as gills, is known in any animals that have once fully attained the air-breathing habit.

The most peculiarly specialized of the ancient Paleozoic reptiles were fin-backed forms (pelycosaurs), some of which attained a length of at least 8 feet. Along the back was a high fin, supported by bony spines of the vertebrae, the longer fin spines being as much as 3 feet high. Most of these animals were carnivorous, and they lived exclusively on land. It is not apparent that the dorsal fin was advantageous for either offensive or defensive purposes. These reptiles first appeared in Late Pennsylvanian time and became extinct before the end of the Permian Period.

Another interesting group (therapsids), which is important from an evolutionary standpoint, had teeth that are differentiated into types almost exactly corresponding to the incisors, canines, and molars of mammals. The skull has a distinctly mammalian appearance, which contrasts strongly with that of the ordinary reptile having jaws armed with teeth that are all of the same kind. The first mammals, of which the oldest known occur in Triassic rocks, are believed to have sprung from this stock.

13. The Triassic Period

Vividly colored Triassic badlands in the Painted Desert of northern Arizona.

Introduction

Beginning of Mesozoic time. The Mesozoic Era, which begins with the Triassic Period, is so named to indicate the intermediate nature of its organisms between ancient life of the Paleozoic and the modern types of the Cenozoic. Mesozoic time is well designated as the Age of Reptiles, because this group of animals dominated the land, sea, and air. Paleozoic reptiles were merely forerunners, and modern reptiles only a remnant of the Mesozoic hosts, which include the largest of all land animals, having lengths up to 87 feet and estimated weight of 50 tons. Such giant reptiles are exceeded only by whales, which are marine mammals that may exceed 100 feet in length and 70 tons in weight.

Type region. The name Triassic signifies threefold and was

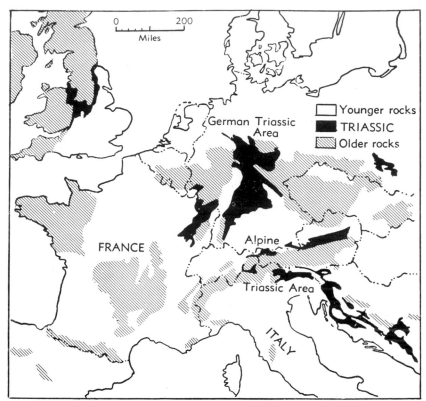

198. Distribution of Triassic outcrops in west-central Europe. The Triassic rocks were named from outcrops in Germany, but the region most important for correlation of Triassic deposits in other parts of the world is that of the Alps region, which contains abundant marine fossils.

adopted for the early Mesozoic deposits because they consist of three well-marked divisions in the part of Europe where first detailed studies of them were made. The type Triassic region is central Germany. The lower part of the section there is made up of continental red beds, the middle is composed of marine shale and limestone, and the upper division comprises red beds. Although this tripartite succession of strata is not at all characteristic of Triassic deposits in general, the name has been adopted throughout the world.

The standard for correlation of marine Triassic deposits is the section of the Mediterranean region in Europe, where Lower, Middle, and Upper Triassic are represented by highly fossiliferous limestone and other deposits.

Triassic Formations of North America

Recognition of Triassic in North America. Occurrence of Triassic deposits in North America is established partly from their position above known Permian and below Early Jurassic strata in some regions, but mainly on the basis of organic remains preserved in them as fossils. Among such fossils are both marine and nonmarine animals and a variety of land plants. Inasmuch as marine Triassic deposits are confined to the western part of the continent and deposits of this age in other areas are wholly nonmarine, age determinations depend on different groups of fossils.

Character and distribution of deposits. Marine Triassic deposits, consisting mostly of dark shale and limestone, are found lying unconformably on Permian or older rocks at many places in the western part of the continent from Mexico to Alaska (Fig. 199). The deposits are highly fossiliferous in some places, but in general the early Mesozoic strata and their fossils have not yet been studied in much detail. The thickest known section, amounting to more than 25,000 feet, occurs in central Nevada. Marine Triassic rocks are about 4,000 feet thick in California, and several hundred feet of beds of this age occur in Oregon, Washington, and Idaho. Much disturbed Triassic formations in British Columbia are distinguished by abundance of associated volcanic rocks and attain a thickness exceeding 15,000 feet.

Continental deposits of Triassic age are very widespread in the Rocky Mountain States and part of the adjoining country to the east. They consist mostly of rather evenly bedded, brilliantly colored sandstone and silty or clayey shale, representing deposits made by sluggish streams and laid down in shallow temporary lakes. The rock layers, which are mostly less than 1,000 feet in aggregate thickness, contain few fossils.

No known Triassic beds occur in the Mississippi Valley or Gulf region, but near the Atlantic, extending from North Carolina to Nova Scotia, are disconnected belts of very thick Late Triassic continental sediments associated with dark-colored igneous rocks. The sedimentary rocks consist mostly of red sandstone and shale that form fertile low-

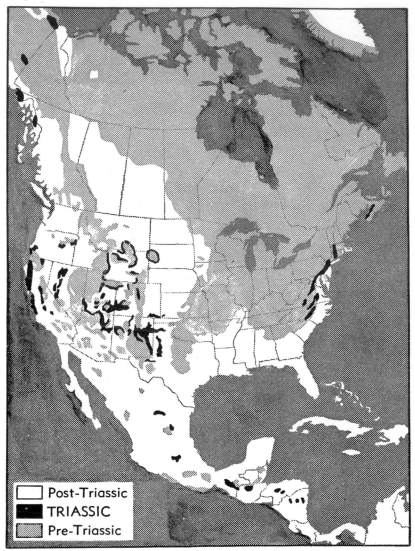

199. Distribution of Triassic outcrops in North America. The exposures occur in widely separated eastern and western portions of the continent; in the west, local outcrops are known from southern Mexico to Alaska.

land valleys, but locally there are conglomerates, dark-colored shales, and some coal beds. The igneous rocks are mostly resistant to erosion and form ridges. The average thickness of the Triassic rocks in this

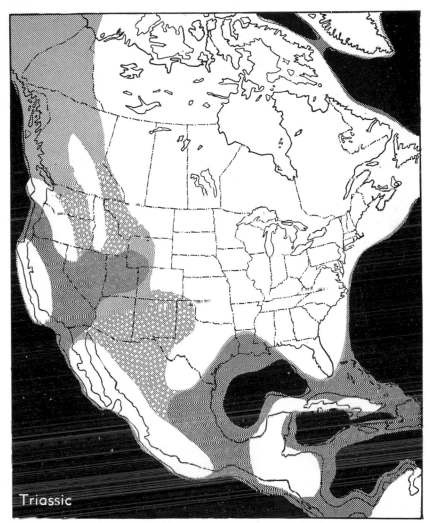

200. Distribution of Triassic seas. Oceanic areas are shown in black; the most persistent seaways on the continental platform are represented by dark gray; and areas submerged during only part of the period are indicated by light gray. Eastern North America seems to have been land throughout Triassic time. Areas of temporary marine flooding in the west are shown by dotted light-gray pattern. The western part of the continent is shown stretched out toward the Pacific to compensate for crustal shortening produced by post-Triassic mountain building.

region is at least 10,000 feet, and in some areas it is reported to exceed 20,000 feet.

201. Red sandstone beds of Triassic age in western Wyoming. These evenly layered rocks (Chugwater) were evidently deposited in shallow lakes or spread by sluggish streams over a flat plain. They lack marine fossils. *(N. H. Darton, U. S. Geol. Survey.)*

Divisions. Triassic rocks in North America are conveniently classed in three main parts, respectively designated as the Lower, Middle, and Upper Triassic Series. These do not correspond precisely to the threefold division of Triassic in Germany, correlation being based, instead, on the marine section of the Mediterranean area. The Early Triassic corresponds closely to the time represented in making

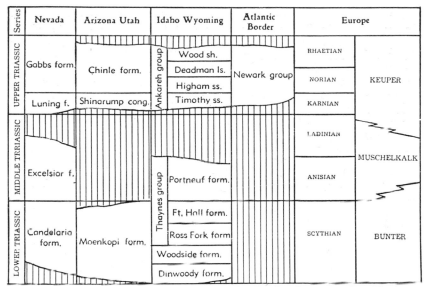

Series	Nevada	Arizona Utah	Idaho Wyoming	Atlantic Border	Europe	
UPPER TRIASSIC	Gabbs form.	Chinle form.	Ankareh group — Wood sh. / Deadman ls. / Higham ss.	Newark group	RHAETIAN	KEUPER
					NORIAN	
UPPER TRIASSIC	Luning f.	Shinarump cong.	Timothy ss.		KARNIAN	
MIDDLE TRIASSIC	Excelsior f.		Thaynes group — Portneuf form.		LADINIAN	MUSCHELKALK
					ANISIAN	
LOWER TRIASSIC	Candelaria form.	Moenkopi form.	Ft. Hall form. / Ross Fork form / Woodside form. / Dinwoody form.		SCYTHIAN	BUNTER

202. Time-rock divisions of the Triassic System and rock units of representative Triassic sections in North America. The vertical scale is not proportional to thickness or time duration, but the placement of names indicates correlation in age. The ruled areas denote absence of deposits.

the lower red beds deposits of the German Triassic section, but the line between Middle and Late Triassic belongs above the uppermost marine deposits of central Germany. Placement of continental Triassic formations in the geologic column requires correlation based on plant or animal remains of the land, and depends on knowledge of age equivalence of nonmarine and marine formations in reference sections of Europe.

Features of Triassic History in North America

Marine submergence of the Pacific border. The distribution and nature of formations exposed in the western United States, support inference that during Early Triassic time a shallow extension of the Pacific invaded California and Nevada, reaching eastward as far as Arizona and Idaho. This sea was confined to the old Cascadian geosyncline, which had been occupied repeatedly by Paleozoic marine waters, and as Triassic sedimentation progressed, the trough subsided slowly. The marine deposits diminish in thickness eastward and interfinger with continental formations that are widely distributed in the Rocky Mountain States. It is clear that the eastern margin of this Early Triassic sea shifted in position as time elapsed.

In the middle part of the period, the area submerged by the sea was mainly restricted to the Nevada-California region and western British Columbia. Abundant volcanic activity during this epoch, especially in the north, is shown by the common occurrence of extrusive igneous rocks interbedded with marine sediments, which also are largely composed of volcanic fragmental materials. Active volcanoes probably were numerous. The volcanic activity continued throughout Late Triassic time in British Columbia, but abated farther south where deposits belonging to this part of the Triassic consist mainly of shale and limestone.

Plains deposits of West Central States. Somewhat evenly bedded, bright-colored fine sandstone, siltstone, and shale, that are interpreted to represent alluvial deposits laid down in a plains environment, are widespread in West Central States. The country now comprising the Colorado Plateau in Arizona and Utah, the Rockies from New Mexico to Montana, and the western border of the Great Plains from Texas to the Dakotas, seems to have been a nearly featureless vast lowland plain throughout the Triassic Period. At least the western part, and perhaps all of it, sloped gently westward to the shores of the sea that occupied the Cascadian geosyncline. During the early part of the period, this plain was the site of very widespread but only moderately thick sedimentation. Sand and mud washed from the interior of the continent were spread out by the sluggish overloaded streams so as to form coalescent alluvial deposits, which, through alternate wetting and drying, were thoroughly oxidized. A prevailing red color is derived from the iron oxides distributed through the sediments. The even bedding and lateral uniformity of parts of the Early Triassic deposits suggest deposition in standing water, such as the temporary lakes now formed during times of rainfall in intermontane basins of the West.

Periodic and oft-repeated exposure of the sediments to the atmosphere is very unfavorable for preservation of plants or animals in a plains region, even though remains are buried here and there. Accordingly, the Triassic deposits of this region are mostly unfossiliferous. Exceptionally, the deposits yield identifiable impressions of land plants and bones of animals. Among the latter are fairly numerous skulls

203. Upper Triassic shaly deposits overlain by Lower Jurassic cliff-making sandstone. The Triassic beds (Chinle) of the outcrop in southern Utah shown here are less brilliantly colored than in the Painted Desert country, but they also contain petrified trees and rare bones of alligator-like aquatic reptiles. The unconformity at the top of the Triassic beds is a very even surface.

and some nearly complete skeletons of reptiles, especially crocodile-like forms that lived mostly in the water. On the whole, the western United States does not seem to have been a semidesert region, as inferred by some geologists on the basis of the red color and generally unfossiliferous nature of the beds. On the contrary, both physical and organic evidence points to a prevailingly moist condition.

Early and Middle Triassic erosion in eastern North America. Coincident with the crustal deformation that raised the Appalachian Mountain system, presumably near the end of Permian time, erosion began to attack the upraised folds, cutting downward through successively older Paleozoic rocks. The rock materials thus excavated must have been carried from the mountain area by both eastward and westward flowing streams, and they came to rest temporarily or permanently along the lower stream courses and in the sea. During Early Triassic time, the mountain belt was doubtless still rugged and erosion vigorous. No geologic record of these conditions is preserved, however,

204. Very evenly stratified Lower Triassic deposits along the Arizona-Utah boundary near Kanab. Shaly strata of the lower slopes and lower part of the cliff that weather in buttresses are unfossiliferous, dark red-brown beds that commonly bear ripple marks. They were evidently laid down in brackish water near the shore of a shallow inland sea; beds into which they grade westward contain marine invertebrates. The capping rock of the cliffs is a green-gray conglomeratic sandstone deposited by streams. It rests unconformably on the red-brown beds. (*J. K. Hillers, U. S. Geol. Survey.*)

and we can picture them only by inference. We do know that by late Middle Triassic time much of this country had been worn down to a smooth plain which cut evenly across complex rock structures, for this erosion surface is preserved in places beneath Late Triassic continental deposits.

The products of erosion in eastern North America during Early and Middle Triassic times were undoubtedly very extensive, but all those carried eastward now lie concealed beneath younger Mesozoic and Cenozoic deposits, mostly beyond the present Atlantic shore line, and those carried westward have been entirely removed by subsequent erosion except in distant areas beyond the Mississippi. Although the area of Early Triassic continental sedimentation in the Rocky Mountain region was far from the Appalachians, it is probable that some of these western deposits are products of mountain erosion in eastern North America.

Late Triassic valley deposits bordering the Atlantic. In the latter part of Triassic time, parts of the Appalachian region that had been eroded into a lowland plain, began to be covered by stream-borne deposits derived from adjacent land which was still elevated or which

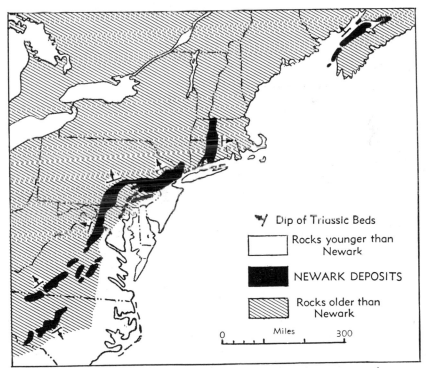

205. Distribution of Triassic outcrops in eastern North America. The Triassic rocks occupy structurally depressed belts distributed from North Carolina to Nova Scotia. The dip of the Triassic beds in each individual belt is uniform in direction.

206. Thin sandstone layers of Triassic age on Connecticut River at Turners Falls, Mass. The Triassic sandstone of this area has yielded numerous well-defined footprints of dinosaurs. The track-bearing sand and silt was presumably spread out on flat-floored valleys by streams. (*W. E. Corbin, Florence, Mass.*)

was pushed upward periodically by renewed crustal displacement. As sedimentation proceeded in the lowlands, these areas slowly subsided, until deposits in some of them became 20,000 feet or more in thickness. Remnants of these deposits, consisting of gray and reddish shale, silt, and sandstone, are distributed for 1,000 miles northward and northeastward from North Carolina. The basins of sedimentation, which may be compared to the great valley of central California and to partly enclosed basins between mountain ranges in Nevada, were downfaulted on one or both sides. Movement along the fault planes did not consist of a single displacement of great magnitude, but rather of many successive small movements. Thus, sedimentary filling of the valleys approximately kept pace with the subsidence of their floors. Proof that the movements occurred in this way is found in the presence of successively younger local deposits of coarse conglomerate, found at the borders of the valleys where streams built alluvial fans, one above another.

The chief areas of Triassic continental deposits adjacent to the

207. Conglomeratic Triassic rock consisting mainly of limestone fragments. This polished specimen of so-called "Potomac marble" from the vicinity of Reading, Pa., is largely made up of limestone fragments derived from Paleozoic formations. The source of the limestone is judged to have been not far distant, because limestone wears away rapidly during transportation. *(B. L. Miller, Pennsylvania Geol. Survey.)*

208. Hogback formed by dark-colored intrusive igneous rocks in the Connecticut River valley. This is Mount Tom ridge, which is crossed by the Connecticut River in the middle distance. The trap and associated sedimentary rocks are Triassic in age. *(W. E. Corbin, Florence, Mass.)*

209. A sill of Triassic trap in the Connecticut River valley. The irregularly jointed rock that makes a cliff is a trap. The projecting rock above the trap is fine-grained red-brown sandstone. (*W. E. Corbin, Florence, Mass.*)

Atlantic are shown in Fig. 205. One of the largest continuous areas of outcrop extends from northern Virginia across parts of Pennsylvania and New Jersey to southeastern New York, and another is found along the Connecticut Valley in Connecticut and western Massachusetts. These are fertile lowlands in which there are many fine farms, as, for example, in the country around Gettysburg, Pa.

The rocks of all the Triassic areas are similar in character, consisting mostly of reddish-brown sandy shale and sandstone. Some of the sandstones are thick and show cross-bedding, whereas others are very thin and grade laterally into shale. The common presence of feldspar grains in the sandy layers indicates dominance of mechanical over chemical weathering in the areas that supplied the sediments. These source areas

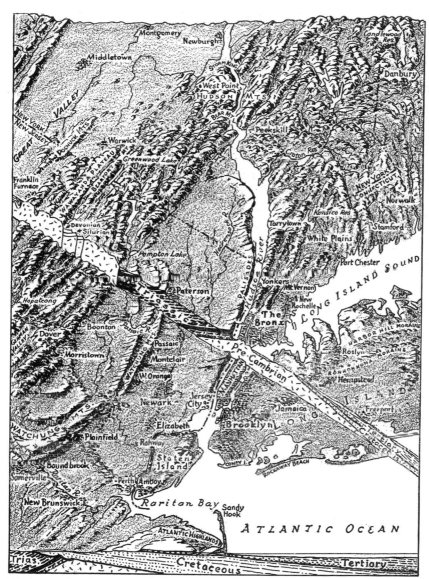

210. Map and geologic section showing features of the New York area. The broad lowland west of the Hudson, which is underlain by inclined Triassic strata, is interrupted by hogbacks of Triassic trap. (*Modified from drawing by E. Raisz.*)

undoubtedly consisted of adjacent uplands of the Appalachian Mountain belt, formed by the crustal disturbance of eastern North America near the close of Permian time.

Some of the Late Triassic beds in the Atlantic states are evenly stratified, suggesting deposition in shallow temporary lakes, such as occur in intermontane basins of Nevada and the Great Valley of California. Locally there are clearly marked footprints of land reptiles. The red color of the rocks and general absence of fossil remains are indicative of thorough oxidation of the sediments during or shortly after deposition. These features do not signify dry desert conditions, but rather they may be interpreted to denote temperate climate with alternate wetting and drying of the deposits.

The occurrence of black shale and coal beds in some of the Virginia and North Carolina areas indicates the existence of lakes and swamps, in or adjacent to which there was an abundance of plants. The nature of this vegetation is shown by many well-preserved plant fossils. It is recorded that the first coal mined for fuel in North America was obtained from some of the Triassic coal deposits of Virginia.

Igneous activity in the eastern Triassic basins. Recurrence of widespread volcanic activity during the time of Late Triassic sedimentation in eastern North America is shown by the presence of dark extrusive and intrusive igneous rock, associated with all the Triassic sedimentary basins. Most of this igneous rock, called "trap," is in the form of sheets lying parallel to the sedimentary strata. Most of the sheets represent lava flows, as proved by restriction of contact metamorphic effects to the lower side of the sheets, by the vesicular nature of the top of parts of the sheets, and by presence of lava fragments incor-

211. Typical Triassic ammonites. These two forms (*Arpadites*, left, *Clionites*, right) are alike in having external ribs and a furrow along the outer edge, but their shape in cross section is dissimilar. The sutures are not shown. Natural size.

porated in the base of overlying sedimentary layers. Some sheets, such as that which makes the Palisades along the Hudson opposite New York City, are sills. There are also dikes that intersect not only the Triassic sediments, but in places, run long distances through adjoining areas of pre-Triassic rock. That the lava was very liquid and that extrusion was of the non-explosive type is indicated by the evenness and enormous extent of some of the flows; originally these must have had an almost perfectly horizontal attitude. The igneous rocks are now tilted and broken by post-Triassic crustal movements, and because most of them are much harder than the adjoining sedimentary rocks, they form ridges.

Triassic Life

Conditions of preservation. Life of the lands in Triassic time is much less completely known than that of various other periods of past earth history. This is because well-preserved fossil remains are relatively scanty and local in distribution. There is no good reason, however, to think that land plants and animals were much less abundant or varied in the Triassic than later in the Mesozoic Era. Probably the real reason for relative paucity of Triassic organic remains in con-

212. Footprints of a two-legged dinosaur on a slab of Triassic sandstone. Just before burial by overlying sand, the smoothed part of the slab was under water, whereas the rough rain-pitted part was above water. (*W. E. Corbin, Florence, Mass.*)

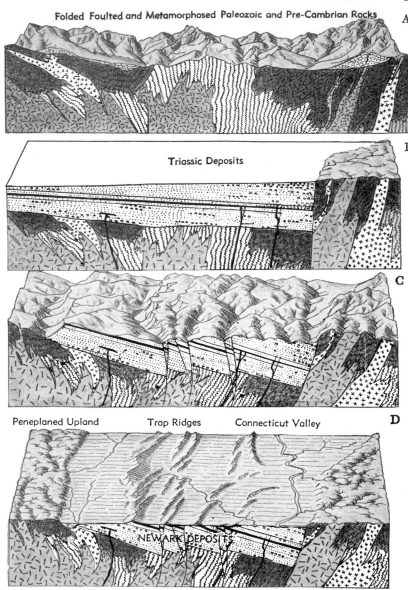

Folded Faulted and Metamorphosed Paleozoic and Pre-Cambrian Rocks   A

B

Triassic Deposits

C

D

Peneplaned Upland   Trap Ridges   Connecticut Valley

NEWARK DEPOSITS

215. Geologic evolution of the Triassic deposits in the Connecticut River valley. The diagrams represent *(A)* pre-Triassic rugged topography; *(B)* depression and covering by Triassic deposits of part of the peneplaned old-rock surface; *(C)* erosion of tilted and faulted Triassic strata surface in Early Jurassic time; and *(D)* the present landscape, which shows evidence of recent peneplanation followed by moderate uplift. *(Modified from Joseph Barrell.)*

Climate

The prevalence of red deposits in Triassic continental formations has been interpreted as meaning widespread arid or semiarid climate during much of the period. Opposed to this are the nature of plant and animal life of the time, insofar as known, and the indication in the rocks themselves of the existence of many sluggish streams and shallow-water bodies. The red color, derived from thorough oxidation of iron minerals, is most favored by alternate wetting and drying, rather than prolonged occurrence of desert conditions. Signs point neither to cold climate nor to widespread tropical conditions; probably both in eastern and western North America, temperate climates, characterized by alternating wet and dry seasons, prevailed.

Mountain Building

Palisades disturbance. After the epoch of Late Triassic valley deposition near the Atlantic, faulting and tilting of crustal blocks produced mountainous topography in a belt lying east of the present Appalachians. Probably this deformation, which was not accompanied by folding of strata, occurred near the close of Triassic time. Deposition in the valley basins was interrupted and the strata, including interbedded volcanics, were tilted so that they now dip mostly at angles of 15 to 30 degrees. The inclination is uniformly eastward in some outcrop areas, such as the Connecticut Valley, and westward in others, as in New Jersey and Pennsylvania. The structural pattern as a whole suggests that the observed belts of eastward- and westward-dipping Triassic, are remnants of a broad faulted anticlinal structure, the central part of which has been entirely eroded. This deformation is known as the Palisades disturbance, named from the Palisades of the Hudson opposite New York.

Close of the Period

The end of the Triassic Period is marked by the interruption of sedimentation and probably also by the Palisades disturbance. Marine waters that had occupied areas in the western United States during Late Triassic time retreated, and this country was not again submerged until the middle part of the Jurassic. An unconformity separates continental Late Triassic deposits from those belonging to the early part of the Jurassic, indicating uplift that changed conditions of deposition to those of erosion. In some areas, however, the boundary between the Triassic and Jurassic Systems is not well defined, and continental sedimentation may have been more or less continuous. There is no sign of crustal deformation at the close of the Triassic in western North America.

14. The Jurassic Period

Jurassic sandstone cliff in Zion National Park, Utah.

Jurassic Strata in Western Europe

Jurassic rocks, and the time they represent, are named from the Jura Mountains, along the borders of France and Switzerland. There, as in southern Germany and in England, deposits of this age consist mostly of shallow-water marine deposits that contain an extraordinary variety

Union Pacific Railway

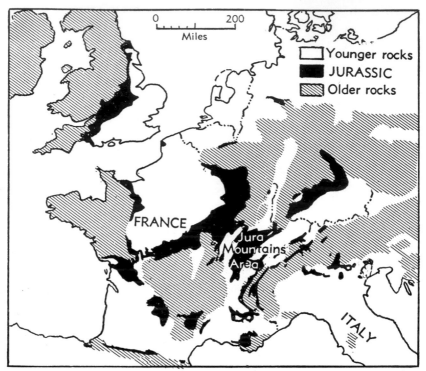

216. Distribution of Jurassic outcrops in west-central Europe. The Jura Mountains, from which the Jurassic System is named, extend along the border of France, Germany, and Switzerland. Other classic regions for study of Jurassic deposits are in northeastern France and England.

and abundance of well-preserved fossils. These are the fossiliferous beds that led William Smith, the Englishman who is called "father of stratigraphic geology," to the discovery, shortly before 1800, that various sorts of fossils were consistently restricted to certain beds, and accordingly, that successive rock layers could be distinguished on the basis of their contained fosil remains. It was Smith who first made this fundamental observation, which serves as prime basis for correlating fossil-bearing strata and which has guided correct classification of deposits according to geologic age. Study of European Jurassic formations has been particularly important in developing other essential principles of historical geology. Also, interest in its fossiliferous outcrops has led many able young men to become paleontologists.

The Jurassic deposits in Europe are clearly set apart as a natural geologic division of major rank, for they represent extensive marine transgression, after emergent condition of the continent at the close of Triassic time and before similar emergence at the end of Jurassic time. As a whole, also, the host of Jurassic organisms comprises an assemblage that differs notably from life of the adjoining periods, even though all Jurassic plants and animals are descendants of Triassic ancestors, and though Cretaceous forms of life developed out of Jurassic progenitors. The standard Jurassic section, which is based partly on outcrops in the Jura Mountains and adjacent country and partly on deposits in England, contains a dozen divisions that are classed as stages. These are divided in turn into zones that can be recognized very widely.

Occurrence of Jurassic Rocks in North America

Basis for recognition. Occurrence of marine deposits of Jurassic age in western North America and the Gulf of Mexico region is established by the presence of distinctive sorts of invertebrates, including especially various complex-sutured cephalopods; belemnites, which are primitive antecedents of the squids; various clams; and distinctive fragments of characteristic Jurassic crinoids. Continental deposits of Jurassic age in North America also have yielded a variety of vertebrate, invertebrate, and plant remains, which are identical or closely allied to corresponding organisms of the European Jurassic. Many of these fossils serve to identify a particular narrow zone within the succession of Jurassic deposits to which they belong. In general, however, the Jurassic formations of North America are much less fossiliferous than those of Europe and some other parts of the world.

Character and distribution of deposits. The most complete succession of Jurassic marine deposits in North America occurs along the Pacific border in California and Oregon. The section of these rocks, 10,000 to 15,000 feet thick, consists mainly of dark silty to sandy shale and sandstone, associated with much volcanic material. The rocks have been profoundly disturbed by subsequent deformation, which has partly metamorphosed them, broken them along large thrust faults, and brought them into such position that a large fraction of the original deposits has been eroded away. Outcrops occur in isolated patches. Fossils are not numerous nor very well preserved. Accordingly, details of geologic history in this region are not well known.

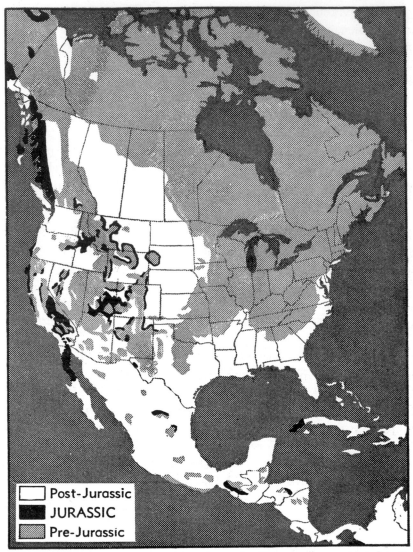

217. Distribution of Jurassic outcrops in North America. Exposures are restricted to the western part of the continent, but deep drilling in the Gulf region has shown the existence of buried Jurassic formations in Arkansas, Louisiana, and Texas.

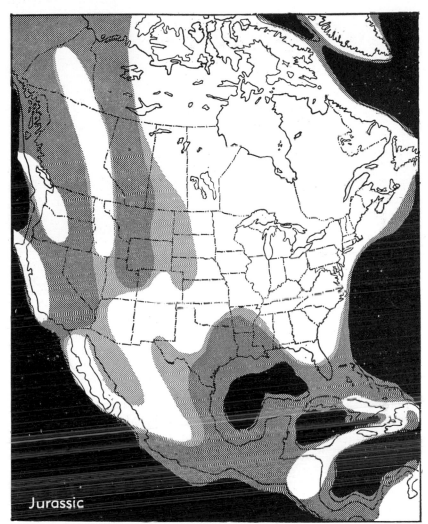

Jurassic

218. Distribution of Jurassic seas. Oceanic areas are shown in black; the most persistent seaways on the continental platform are represented by dark gray; and areas submerged during only part of the period are indicated by light gray. A sea extended northward from the Gulf of Mexico region into Arkansas, although deposits are now concealed by younger beds. Seaways from the Pacific and Northwest were relatively persistent. The western part of the continent is stretched out toward the Pacific in order to compensate for crustal shortening produced by post-Jurassic mountain building.

219. Hogback of Jurassic sandstone in southern Utah. This northward-looking air view, from a point on the San Juan River west of Blanding, shows at left a monoclinal valley carved in Triassic shale, and in the middle part of the view light-colored Jurassic sandstone that makes an escarpment known as "Comb Ridge." In the right background are Cretaceous strata, and along the sky line are intrusive igneous rocks that form the Abajo Mountains. *(Spence Air Photos.)*

Marine shale and sandstone, locally associated with calcareous deposits, are widely distributed in the Rocky Mountain region, and extend northeastward as far as the Black Hills in South Dakota. Contained fossils indicate the Late Jurassic age of these deposits, which are mostly less than 200 feet thick, although in Idaho they attain a thickness of about 5,000 feet.

Marine Jurassic strata, representing a seaway entirely distinct from those in western North America, are known in Mexico; western Texas near El Paso; beneath the surface of northern Louisiana, southwestern Arkansas, and northeastern and southern Texas; in Cuba; and in some other parts of the West Indies. The deposits include shale, sandstone, and limestone, and in the Louisiana-Arkansas area, anhydrite and salt.

Continental Jurassic deposits are widely distributed in parts of the west that contain also continental Triassic beds, but, unlike the Triassic, no strata of Jurassic age are known east of the Mississippi. Cross-

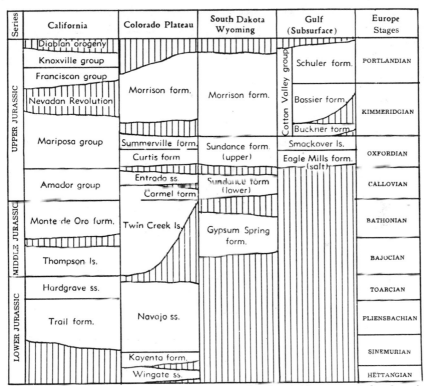

Series	California	Colorado Plateau	South Dakota Wyoming	Gulf (Subsurface)	Europe Stages
UPPER JURASSIC	Diablan orogeny				
	Knoxville group			Schuler form.	PORTLANDIAN
	Franciscan group	Morrison form.	Morrison form.		
	Nevadan Revolution			Bossier form.	KIMMERIDGIAN
				Buckner form.	
	Mariposa group	Summerville form.	Sundance form. (upper)	Smackover ls.	OXFORDIAN
		Curtis form		Eagle Mills form. (salt)	
	Amador group	Entrada ss.	Sundance form (lower)		CALLOVIAN
		Carmel form.			
MIDDLE JURASSIC	Monte de Oro form.	Twin Creek ls.	Gypsum Spring form.		BATHONIAN
	Thompson ls.				BAJOCIAN
LOWER JURASSIC	Hardgrave ss.				TOARCIAN
	Trail form.	Navajo ss.			PLIENSBACHIAN
					SINEMURIAN
		Kayenta form.			HETTANGIAN
		Wingate ss.			

220. **Time-rock divisions of the Jurassic System and rock units in representative Jurassic sections of North America.** The vertical scale is not proportional to thickness or time duration, but the placement of names indicates correlation in age. The ruled areas denote absence of deposits.

bedded sandstone, which in places attains a thickness of 2,000 or 3,000 feet, is the main type of continental Jurassic deposit found in the west. Outcrops are distributed from Arizona and southern Nevada to Idaho and Montana. Some of the most prominent cliffs and mesas of the Colorado Plateau country are made by these Jurassic sandstones; Zion National Park in southwestern Utah contains especially fine exposures of them.

Divisions. In western Europe, the Jurassic contains three main parts, which in upward order are frequently termed the Black, Brown, and White Jurassic, the first being predominantly composed of dark-colored shale, the second having prominent brown sandstone, and the third being composed mostly of light-colored limestone. Although these lithologic divisions have only regional significance, they are associated with differences of the faunas, and on the basis of faunal distinctions, we may recognize Lower, Middle, and Upper Jurassic in North America. Each of these is divided into time-rock units called "stages," having names derived from European localities, and these are employed in more detailed age classification of the Jurassic deposits wherever possible.

Features of Jurassic History

Submergence of the Pacific border. The chief feature of Jurassic history in the Pacific border region, extending from California to Alaska, is marine submergence that began early in the period and, with only minor interruption, persisted to near its close. We may note also that deposits laid down in this sea contain very little limestone; most of the sediments are fine to coarse products of erosion of near-by land, admixed in places with abundant volcanic materials.

During Early Jurassic time, lands adjoining this western sea were relatively low, for almost all the Lower Jurassic deposits are fine-textured.

The Middle Jurassic was an epoch of special explosive volcanic activity, as judged by prevalence of lava and tuff interbedded with the marine sediments, and by the volcanic origin of many constituents of the sediments.

Late Jurassic deposits were mostly dark muds, but in places these also are associated with much volcanic material.

Throughout the period, the Pacific border sea was separated by a land area from territory in the Rocky Mountain province, which temporarily was invaded by a shallow sea and which during other parts of Jurassic time was the site of extensive continental sedimentation. This intervening land area contains no Jurassic deposits but was undergoing erosion, and sediment from it was carried both westward and eastward.

Continental sedimentation in the Rocky Mountain region. During Jurassic time, there were no mountains where the Rockies now stand. This great area was then a featureless plains country, as shown by the extent and nature of widespread continental deposits, but the sea covered much of the plain in part of the Late Jurassic.

The continental deposits consist of red clay, fine silt, and fine- to

221. Jurassic sandstone resting on Triassic shale in southwestern Utah. This view of the Sentinel, a rocky pinnacle in Zion National Park, shows the base of the great sandstone mass that lies disconformably on weak Upper Triassic strata. *(Courtesy of Chicago and Northwestern Railway.)*

222. Cross-bedding in the Navajo sandstone, of Jurassic age, in southern Utah. The sandstone laminae, etched out by weathering, have varying inclination and one set of
cross beds is truncated by another. The outcrop is in Johnson Canyon near Kanab.
(R. C. Moore, U. S. Geol. Survey.)

medium-grained sandstone. The red beds are closely comparable to
those of Triassic age in the same region, and doubtless denote continuation of the same conditions of deposition. These were interpreted
in the preceding chapter, as the work of sluggish streams in a plains
country of very gentle slope, and deposition in shallow fresh-water
ponds of temporary existence. The effect of alternate wetting and drying in producing thorough oxidation of iron minerals, is seen in these
Jurassic deposits, as in similar sediments of Triassic and Permian age.

Scarcity of organic remains is a natural accompaniment of conditions of deposition that we have inferred. Nevertheless, there are local
deposits containing abundant teeth and bones belonging to animals
that roamed the plains. From such places many complete skeletons
have been collected. Some of the fossil-bearing spots seem to indicate
quicksands formed in backwater or eddy pools along Jurassic streams,
and some may represent water holes where the animals congregated.

Most of the Jurassic sandstone deposits, especially as seen in the
Colorado Plateau country, are very uniform in texture and strongly
cross-bedded. The grains are well rounded and sorted, like sand in the
dunes of the Sahara or other deserts, and some wind-faceted pebbles
have been found. These features show that the sand was carried into

the plateau country by winds, and that the sandstone was made by compaction and cementing of loose dune sand. The lithified sand-dune area marks an extensive Jurassic desert, which spread over territory in Nevada, Arizona, New Mexico, Colorado, Utah, Idaho, and possibly other states. Thin horizontal sheets of mud-cracked clay, a few yards in lateral extent, are found locally in the midst of the sandstone; such deposits call to mind the shallow evanescent ponds that may form between dunes after a rain—places where fine wind-blown sediment may be trapped until the water disappears.

Late Jurassic marine invasion of the western interior. Continental sedimentation in states of the Rocky Mountain area was interrupted late in Jurassic time by lowering of the plains surface, or elevation of sea level, to such extent that a shallow sea reached southward from the Arctic to the borders of Arizona and into Colorado and South Dakota. In Montana several hundred feet, and in Idaho at least 3,000 feet of limestone was laid down in this seaway, but in most of the submerged area the sediments consist of mud and sand. These deposits are recognized as marine in origin by the common occurrence of

223. Rainbow Natural Bridge in southern Utah. This great stone arch, south of Colorado River near Navajo Mountain, is carved in the Navajo sandstone of Early Jurassic age.

224. Varicolored shaly continental deposits of Late Jurassic age in central Wyoming. These deposits (Morrison) were laid by streams and in shallow lakes. They have yielded numerous fine skeletal remains of dinosaurs and fresh-water crustaceans (ostracodes) almost identical to fossils found in uppermost continental Jurassic beds of England.

marine fossils in them. Concentration of sea water in lagoons at the margin of the shallow sea, both when it was most extensive and during its retreat, is recorded by deposits of gypsum. No salt beds are known, however. This sea vanished before the close of Jurassic time.

Jurassic seas in the Gulf region.   Marine Jurassic deposits, which evidently represent invasion of shallow seas from the Gulf of Mexico, are found in extreme western Texas and adjacent parts of Mexico. There are no outcrops of Jurassic strata farther east in the Gulf region.

Deep drilling in southwestern Arkansas, northern Louisiana, northeastern and southern Texas, and northeastern Mexico, has demonstrated the existence in that area of a thick succession of marine Jurassic deposits lying unconformably below oldest Cretaceous strata. The Jurassic age of the buried formations is proved by many fossils obtained from well samples. Salt and anhydrite has been penetrated by some wells in this region. These minerals indicate the former existence of basins or lagoons containing concentrated brines, but there are also extensive limestone and marine shale deposits that denote normal marine conditions.

The total extent of Jurassic seas in the Gulf coastal region is not yet known, but it is probable that part of the coastal plain east of the Mississippi River is underlain by marine Jurassic sediments. If so, they are deeply buried, for a 10,000-foot well drilled in central Florida ended in the lower part of the Cretaceous.

Erosion in eastern North America. Absence of exposed Jurassic formations in any part of eastern North America, and the fact that no well borings along the Atlantic coastal plain have anywhere penetrated known Jurassic deposits, support the inference that during the Jurassic Period this entire region was undergoing erosion. We may conclude that the margin of the Jurassic sea lay somewhere east of the present coast line.

Even though erosion seems to have prevailed on land, alluvium must have been spread out along the lower courses of stream valleys, and it is likely that in some places sediment accumulated in lakes and was spread out by wind. Such deposits, however, have either been removed subsequently or, in areas occupied by Cretaceous strata, they have not been differentiated from the Cretaceous. There is no known evidence that the Appalachians or adjacent belts were sufficiently elevated to have mountainous relief, but the average elevation and slope of the land surface favored erosion rather than sedimentation.

Jurassic Life

Plants. Evergreens and the palmlike plants called "cycads" were dominant types of vegetation, as indicated by plant remains found in continental Jurassic deposits. Modern types of flowering plants, including trees like the oak, elm, maple, and poplar, had not yet made appearance, although they are known from the next following period. As in Pennsylvanian time, the land floras of the Jurassic seem to have

225. A Jurassic landscape. This restoration shows several flying reptiles (pterosaurs); the earliest known birds *(Archaeopteryx)*, which had teeth and a long lizard-like tail; tiny dinosaurs; and the characteristic palmlike Mesozoic plants called "cycado-phytes." *(C. R. Knight, Chicago Natural History Museum.)*

226. Restoration of the plated dinosaur, *Stegosaurus.* One of the most bizarre reptiles of all time is this small-brained, ponderous Jurassic dinosaur, some 20 feet long and 11 feet high at the hips. It was a herbivore that inhabited the western United States. (*U. S. National Museum.*)

been remarkably uniform throughout the world. It is even true that Jurassic plant assemblages from the Arctic and Antarctic regions differ little from those found in tropical areas.

Land animals. Land areas of Jurassic time, we may be sure, were abundantly populated by a varied assemblage of vertebrate and invertebrate animals. In the streams and other fresh-water bodies were many kinds of fishes, amphibians, reptiles, mussels, snails, crustaceans, worms, and water bugs; on dry land there were hordes of reptiles, diminutive archaic mammals, ants, and other crawling insects; in the air were flying reptiles, the earliest known birds, and a variety of winged insects, including moths and butterflies. This range is comparable to the animal life of modern time, even though only a small part of all the kinds of Jurassic creatures that actually lived are yet known.

The dominant kinds of Jurassic life were very different from those of the present day, for the earth was then ruled by reptiles. Among these reptiles, the dinosaurs were chief, and among Jurassic dinosaurs are the most ponderous land animals of all earth history. A majority of them were herbivorous, but some were flesh-eaters; some walked on four legs and others, holding the body semierect, used the front limbs as arms; some were aquatic or semiaquatic, whereas others were adapted for running swiftly on land. A few were armed with grotesque bony plates and spines. The main types of Jurassic dinosaurs and associated reptiles of other types are treated in Chap. 16, on evolution of life in the Mesozoic Era.

The oldest known birds, provided with teeth and having a lizard-like tail with many vertebrae, are reptilian creatures, which are classified as birds because they have feathers.

Marine life.   Marine deposits of the Jurassic Period contain fossil remains of plants and animals, which in many places are unsurpassed in variety, abundance, and perfection of preservation. The plants are represented especially by calcareous algae that built large reefs locally. Among animals, vertebrate types include fishes and reptiles; and shelled invertebrates represent all main phyla.

The Jurassic marine reptiles comprise four groups: the remarkably streamlined, fishlike ichthyosaurs; long-necked, squat-bodied types called "plesiosaurs"; sea lizards known as "mosasaurs"; and turtles. The limbs of all these reptiles are modified into flippers or paddles that are entirely unsuited for locomotion on land, but despite their adaptation for life in the sea, they were air-breathers.

The varied assemblage of marine invertebrates has chief value for correlation of Jurassic deposits laid down in shallow seas, and dominant among these are the complex-sutured coiled cephalopods called "ammonites." The ammonites were able to swim freely in the open ocean, as well as in shallow seas of continental areas. Also, after death of the cephalopod, the gas-filled chambered shell could float and thus be carried long distances by marine currents, just as the modern pearly nautilus is commonly transported after death of the animal. In these ways, identical kinds of Jurassic ammonites are found in widely separated regions of the world. They exhibit a remarkable variety of external ornamentation and pattern of the internal sutures. Their rate of evolutionary change was rapid, so that forms from different horizons are readily differentiated.

Another type of widespread Jurassic cephalopods is found in the ancestral relatives of the squids, called "belemnites," characterized by a dense cigar-shaped internal skeleton of calcite.

Jurassic echinoderms are especially represented by sea urchins and crinoids. The most common type of crinoids had a pentagonal or star-shaped stem that in some specimens had a length greater than 50 feet.

Foraminifers, sponges, corals, bryozoans, brachiopods, clams, snails, arthropods, and some types of worms include a host of species, which are distinguished from older and younger representatives of these groups.

Marine sedimentary deposits of various sorts that are distributed throughout northwestern Europe are exceptionally rich at many places in well preserved invertebrate fossils. These permit recognition of many faunal zones and are the basis for dividing the rock succession into widely recognized stages and lesser stratigraphic units.

One of the best known sedimentary rocks in Europe is the Solnhofen limestone of southern Germany. This Jurassic rock has an exceptionally fine grain and has long been the commercial standard for lithographic limestone. In addition, it contains a variety of exceptionally well-preserved fossils including many shelled invertebrates and some impressions of soft-bodied organisms such as jellyfish. Occurring in this limestone also are remarkably perfect skeletons of marine reptiles, such

227. Representative Jurassic ammonites. These most important invertebrate guide fossils are characterized by the external sculpture of the shells and extremely complex sutures marking the edges of internal chamber walls. The larger shell is *Idoceras,* and the smaller is *Cardioceras.* Natural size.

as the ichthyosaurs. The bones, which are in normal articulated position, are surrounded by an impression of dark carbonaceous matter representing the body outline of the animal.

Climate

The uniformity of land floras in widely separated parts of the world, including high and low latitudes, and associated cosmopolitan aspects of continental and marine faunas, all point to a prevailing mild equable climate during the Jurassic Period. In some areas, such as the southwestern United States, part of Jurassic time was evidently marked by such aridity as to produce truly desert conditions. In general, however, there seem to have been no strongly marked climatic belts, and no evidence of glacial climate is known anywhere.

Mountain Building and Close of the Period

Nevadan revolution. The closing part of the Jurassic Period was a time of very strong crustal deformation along the Pacific border of North America, from California northward to Alaska. Late Jurassic and older sedimentary deposits in this region were very closely folded, faulted, and metamorphosed by the mountain-making earth movements, which collectively are known as the Nevadan revolution. The highly disturbed rocks that furnish record of this deformation are extensively exposed in the Coast Ranges, Sierra Nevada, and Cascade Mountains, but the mountainous relief of these belts at the present day is a result of later earth movements.

The Nevadan revolution was accompanied by intrusion of granitic batholiths on a huge scale. Heat and pressure derived from these intrusions, together with gaseous and liquid emanations that forced their way into surrounding sedimentary formations, contributed importantly to metamorphism of the Jurassic and older strata. Valuable ore deposits of metals, such as the famous gold-bearing Comstock lode in western Nevada, are veins formed by solutions derived from the batholithic magma. Erosion during Cretaceous and subsequent geologic history

---

228. Great cliff of batholithic intrusive rock of Jurassic age in the Sierra Nevada of California. This view in Yosemite National Park affords a good exposure of part of the enormously extensive igneous masses *(granodiorite)* that were intruded into sedimentary rocks of the Cordilleran geosyncline at the time of the Nevadan mountain building.

has removed a large part of the original cover of the batholiths, and outcrops of the deep-seated igneous rocks now occur in belts 50 miles or more wide, extending nearly 400 miles in the Sierra Nevada and more than 1,000 miles northward into Canada.

The crustal movements and igneous activity belonging to the Nevadan revolution are associated with the close of the Jurassic Period, but they must have been distributed through a time totaling several ten-thousand years. Thus, the epoch of mountain building may have begun very late in the Jurassic and extended with diminishing intensity into Early Cretaceous time. In parts of this region, the Jurassic and older rocks were truncated by erosion before the oldest Cretaceous strata of the region were laid down.

15. The Cretaceous Period

The Grand Tetons in northwestern Wyoming, initially elevated in Late Cretaceous time.

Name and Type Region

The third and last division of the Mesozoic Era is known as the Cretaceous Period. The name, introduced in 1822, is derived from the Latin word *creta* (chalk), which is prominently exposed in the White Cliffs of Dover, southeastern England, and along the north coast of France, across the English Channel. This is the classic area where the Cretaceous deposits were first differentiated from the underlying Jurassic and overlying Tertiary. The character and fossil content of successive subdivisions, which comprise the standard section for com-

Chicago and Northwestern Railway

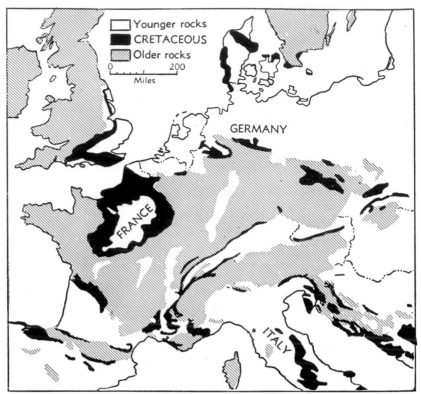

229. Distribution of Cretaceous outcrops in west-central Europe. The classic region in which rocks belonging to the Cretaceous System were first studied closely is in France and western Germany. Main divisions now recognized throughout most of the world were defined there. The outcrops in England and Denmark also are important.

parison and correlation with Cretaceous deposits in other parts of the world, have been defined from outcrops in France, England, western Germany, Belgium, Holland, and Denmark.

The Cretaceous System is well set apart as a major division of the geologic column, because important unconformities occur at both the base and the summit in most areas, and because the life of Cretaceous time has many distinguishing features that differentiate it from the preceding and succeeding periods.

Chalk or chalky limestone is by no means the only type of deposit occurring in the Cretaceous System; as a matter of fact, the chalk is far outranked quantitatively by shale and sandstone. There is much hard nonchalky limestone, and in places coal beds are prominent. Nevertheless, no other geologic system contains widespread chalk deposits, and the term *Cretaceous* is accepted as an appropriate designation for late Mesozoic rocks throughout the world.

Recognition of Cretaceous in North America

Guide fossils. Distinctive plants, invertebrates, and vertebrate remains that characterize Cretaceous deposits in northwestern Europe are found to be widely distributed in deposits of corresponding age in North America. These fossils serve not only to establish the Cretaceous age of the deposits containing them, but, despite differences due to regional variation, permit close correlation with subdivisions of the European standard section.

For purposes of such correlation, the ammonites are the chief guide fossils, because they show considerable evolutionary change from zone to zone and because, as swimmers, they could intermigrate freely between areas occupied by the sea. Echinoids are also useful guide fossils in some Cretaceous zones, and certain sorts of Cretaceous clams have nearly world-wide distribution. The microscopic shells of foraminifers of a type provided with calcareous globular chambers are characteristic of Cretaceous marine deposits throughout the world and form a large part of the substance of chalk beds. Although characteristic of the Cretaceous, these fossils are relatively long ranging within the system.

Character and Distribution of Deposits

Cretaceous formations of North America are conveniently treated in four parts according to their distribution: (1) along the Atlantic border, (2) the plains country adjacent to the Gulf of Mexico, (3) the Rocky Mountains and adjoining plains to the east, and (4) the Pacific border region. Although similar in some respects, the Cretaceous of each of these divisions shows differences from the others.

Atlantic border. A narrow belt of Cretaceous outcrops extends almost uninterruptedly along the inner border of the Atlantic coastal plain from Long Island, N. Y., to Georgia. The landward margin of the Cretaceous coincides with the physiographic feature known as the Fall Line, which marks the head of navigation on most rivers flowing into the Atlantic. Falls or rapids occur where streams pass from the

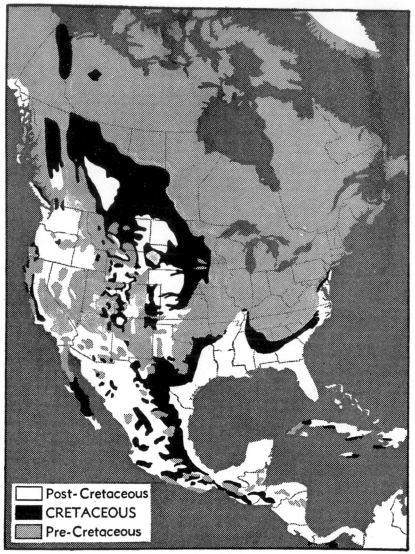

Post-Cretaceous
CRETACEOUS
Pre-Cretaceous

230. Distribution of Cretaceous outcrops in North America. Outcrops of Cretaceous formations are much more extensive than those of earlier Mesozoic systems. They form a
nearly continuous belt along the Atlantic and Gulf borders and cover an especially
large territory in the Great Plains and Rocky Mountains areas. Very thick deposits
are represented by narrow outcrops along the Pacific border.

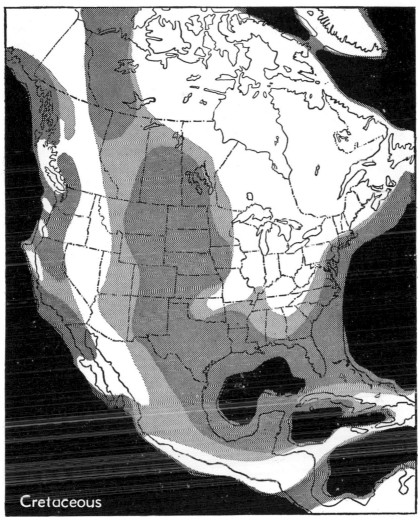

Cretaceous

231. Distribution of Cretaceous seas in North America. Oceanic areas are shown in black; the most persistent seaways on the continental platform are represented by dark gray; and areas submerged during only part of the period are indicated by light gray. The great submergence of the Western Interior during the middle and late part of Cretaceous history is the outstanding paleogeographic feature of the period. A narrow, persistent land mass separated this sea from the shallow seas that advanced from the Pacific.

hard rocks of the Appalachian piedmont plateau onto weak stratified rocks of the coastal plain, and the availability of water power at points accessible by marine shipping was the chief factor determining the location of many cities in the eighteenth and nineteenth centuries. Thus Trenton, Philadelphia, Wilmington, Baltimore, Washington, Richmond, Columbia, Augusta, and other large settlements are located along the inner margin of the Cretaceous outcrop.

At the base of the Cretaceous is a profound unconformity, inasmuch as the subjacent rocks in most places are resistant, strongly deformed, metamorphosed Pre-Cambrian rocks or late Paleozoic granite. Elsewhere, the Cretaceous rests on the beveled edges of tilted Triassic strata, or on truncated strongly folded Paleozoic rocks.

Cretaceous formations of the Atlantic border include both continental and marine deposits. The attitude of the beds is nearly horizontal, but there is a uniform gentle dip toward the sea, reflecting in part the original position in which the beds were deposited, and in part a gentle seaward tilting that is interpreted to represent slight crustal warping. Overlying Tertiary beds are nearly parallel to the Cretaceous and also dip seaward. The basal Cretaceous deposits consist of con-

232. Typical country formed by Cretaceous deposits in the Atlantic Coastal Plain. Most of the outcrop area is well covered by soil and vegetation, but the nature of the deposits may be studied along many gulleys and artificial exposures such as highway cuts.

233. Thin-bedded Cretaceous chalky limestone resting on dark Cretaceous shale. This outcrop in southwestern South Dakota shows Greenhorn and Graneros beds which are representative of marine deposits that are extremely widespread in the Great Plains and the Gulf and Atlantic coastal borders. *(N. H. Darton, U. S. Geol. Survey.)*

glomerate or sandstone, mostly of fluviatile origin, and these are variously followed by shale, sandstone, and calcareous beds, which in part contain marine fossils. Aggregate thickness in most places does not exceed 1,000 feet.

Gulf region. Cretaceous outcrops extend westward from Georgia in a belt that crosses central Alabama and swings northward east of the Mississippi to the southern tip of Illinois. West of the Mississippi, Cretaceous rocks appear in southwestern Arkansas, and in a widening belt are traced thence southwestward into Mexico. The Cretaceous of the Gulf region resembles that of the Atlantic border in its gentle seaward inclination, and in having a profound unconformity at its base. In most places, the rocks beneath the Cretaceous are Paleozoics, strongly folded in Georgia, Alabama, Arkansas, and Oklahoma, but

234. Coal beds and associated continental deposits of Cretaceous age in Alaska. This well-exposed succession of strata clearly records a several-times-repeated occurrence of coal-swamp conditions in this area. Periodic subsidences must have been the main factors in effecting this type of sedimentation. *(U. S. Geol. Survey.)*

nearly horizontal elsewhere. The folded Paleozoic rocks were smoothly truncated by erosion prior to deposition of earliest Cretaceous sediments. In part of the country west of the Mississippi River, buried Jurassic strata underlie the Cretaceous.

The lowermost Cretaceous deposits commonly consist of coarse sandstone or conglomerate, and this is followed by 1,000 to 3,000 feet of shale, sandstone, chalk, and chalky limestone. Most of the deposits yield marine fossils. The outcrops of successive formations are arranged in parallel belts, weak rocks forming lowlands and harder formations forming uplands or landward-facing escarpments, commonly tree-covered.

Rocky Mountain region.   From Mexico to far northwestern Canada and Alaska, sedimentary deposits of Cretaceous age are distributed through a broad belt that in places exceeds 700 miles from east to west. The Rocky Mountain chain approximately marks the axis of this belt, which extends eastward into the High Plains country, and westward across plateau and canyon country to borders of the Great Basin. The area marks the site of a geosyncline, in parts of which Cretaceous deposits attain a thickness of 15,000 feet.

235. Cretaceous shale and sandstone near Grand Junction, Colo. This air view of the Little Book Cliffs shows dark-colored Mancos shale of uniform texture, several hundred feet thick, capped by Mesaverde sandstone. The flat-topped plateau in the background is Grand Mesa, which is covered by lava. *(Spence Air Photos.)*

Both nonmarine and marine deposits are very extensive. Among the former is conglomerate, sandstone, shale, and thick coal beds, laid down by streams and formed in shallow lakes and swamps. Fossil land plants and remains of land animals are found in these continental formations. Strata of marine origin include chalk, chalky limestone, shale, and sandstone, which in places contain numerous shells of oysters and other invertebrates. Dark-colored shale deposits are especially prominent, and they are very uniform in character for huudreds of miles along the outcrop.

A noteworthy feature of Cretaceous deposits in this province is the lateral change of sedimentary facies, reflecting variations in conditions of contemporary sedimentation on land, in lagoonal areas along the coast, in shallow marine waters near shore, and in somewhat deeper offshore environments. Sedimentary deposits representing each of these habitats grade laterally into one another and interfinger, thus proving their equivalence in age.

Pacific border. Embayments of the Pacific spread inland across parts of California, Oregon, Washington, and British Columbia during Cretaceous time, occupying down-warped and down-faulted blocks throughout the belt that had suffered strong deformation in the Nevadan revolution. The deposits are rather local and somewhat variable, but some of them are exceptionally thick, in places exceeding 40,000 feet. The deposits comprise mostly shale and sandstone, which represent rock materials eroded from adjacent mountainous areas formed in the Nevadan orogeny.

Divisions

Cretaceous formations in North America are readily divisible into two main parts known as Lower Cretaceous and Upper Cretaceous. These parts are separated in most places by a prominent unconformity and by well-marked differences in the fossils representing both marine and nonmarine habitats. In the Gulf region, the Lower Cretaceous is commonly known as the Comanchean Series, and the Upper Cretaceous as the Gulfian Series. Several stages and substages are recognized, which in part are judged to correspond closely to similar time-rock divisions of the European section.

In Europe and other parts of the world outside of North America, deposits of Cretaceous age do not show a well-marked twofold division. Sedimentation during the period seems to have been fairly continuous, and on the basis of differences in fossils, the column is divided somewhat arbitrarily into Lower, Middle, and Upper Cretaceous. Each of these comprises a number of stages defined from localities in western Europe.

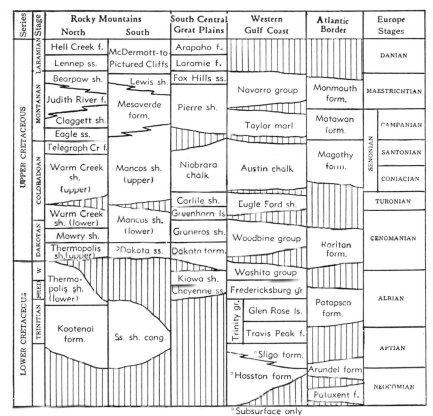

236. **Time-rock divisions of the Cretaceous System and rock units in representative Cretaceous sections of North America.** The vertical scale is not proportional to thickness or time duration, but the placement of names indicates correlation in age. The ruled areas denote absence of deposits.

Features of Cretaceous History in North America

Submergence of the Atlantic coastal border. The outstanding feature of Cretaceous history in eastern North America was gradual depression of the continental border. This down-warping brought to a close the erosion, which during Jurassic time had peneplaned a large part of the coastal region. The shore line shifted inland. Early in the Cretaceous, the shore line moved from a position well east of the present coast line to points approximating the modern sea border, and on the landward side of this Early Cretaceous shore, sluggish streams built a coastal plain of sand and mud. These fluviatile sediments com-

237. High bridge across the lower Pecos River in western Texas. The canyon valley of the Pecos near its confluence with the Rio Grande is carved in hard Lower Cretaceous limestone. These rocks cover a very large territory in central and western Texas.

prise the exposed Lower Cretaceous formations of the Atlantic region.

In the later part of Cretaceous time, the Atlantic sea moved farther inland. Marine sediments buried virtually all of the Early Cretaceous coastal plain and in many places came to rest on areas that had received no Lower Cretaceous sediments. Thus, marine Upper Cretaceous beds are seen resting directly on erosion-beveled Pre-Cambrian crystalline rocks. Nonmarine coastal plain sediments were doubtless spread over a considerable area in Late Cretaceous time, but subsequent erosion has removed most of this material.

Marine oscillations in the Gulf region. Cretaceous history in the region bordering the Gulf of Mexico is interpreted to have begun with landward shift of shallow seas, but the advance was not uniform along all parts of the coast nor was submergence steadily progressive. East of the Mississippi, no Lower Cretaceous rocks are exposed, and throughout a large area well borings show that Upper Cretaceous strata rest directly on Paleozoic or older rocks. Evidently, the sea did not occupy this region in Early Cretaceous time, and the attitude of the land surface was not changed so as to cause appreciable deposition of fluviatile coastal plains deposits.

West of the Mississippi, on the other hand, there was a considerable Early Cretaceous marine inundation. That the sea advanced gradually and steadily in the early part of the period is shown by the regularly greater landward extent of successive higher divisions of the Lower Cretaceous marine deposits. Higher beds overlap the lower and, along their landward margins, are found resting directly on pre-Cretaceous rocks. Most of the observed Lower Cretaceous rocks are marine, but marginal nonmarine deposits are also found preserved beneath sediments of the advancing sea. Eventually marine waters covered most of Texas, reached into Arkansas, and advanced to central Kansas.

Then came a great retreat of the Cretaceous sea. Large areas of recently formed marine deposits were uncovered and began to be eroded. In central Texas, beach sands at the margin of the restricted sea came to be deposited directly on limestone representing far offshore conditions in the immediately preceding epoch of transgressive seas. This major marine oscillation in the Gulf region serves to separate Early Cretaceous from Late Cretaceous time.

Renewed advance of the sea occurred in the latter part of the Cretaceous Period. This time, transgression was rapid, and the area of

238. A typical exposure of Cretaceous chalk in western Kansas. The chalk is light cream-colored to nearly white, evenly stratified and soft. The rock weathers readily and may be carved by running water into badlands, as shown in this view of outcrops in Logan County, Kans. *(Oren Bingham, Kansas Geol. Survey.)*

239. Cretaceous chalk in western Kansas. This erosion remnant, called "The Sphynx," is part of the pure calcareous Cretaceous deposits that have a total thickness of about 700 feet in Kansas. The beds yield numerous remains of marine invertebrates and some well-preserved skeletons of large fishes, swimming reptiles, toothed diving birds, and flying reptiles that fell into the water and were drowned many miles from nearest land. *(Oren Bingham, Kansas Geol. Survey.)*

submergence vastly exceeded the farthest reach of Early Cretaceous marine waters. The Gulf States east of the Mississippi were covered. The Mississippi Valley was flooded approximately to St. Louis, which, if it had existed in Cretaceous time, might have been a Gulf port; westward and northwestward, the sea gained access to the Rocky Mountain geosyncline, making a vast inland waterway that reached to the Arctic without interruption. During Late Cretaceous time, accordingly, no natural boundary separated the Gulf and Rocky Mountain provinces. Marine animals were able to intermigrate freely and, although chalk is more prominent in the south and in the Kansas region, the nature of deposits is much the same.

Sedimentation in the Rocky Mountain geosyncline. The sediment-filled trough known as the Rocky Mountain geosyncline, began to develop in early Mesozoic time, but it was not until the great marine inundation of Late Cretaceous time that the area became the site of very widespread thick deposits. During the early part of the period, stream and swamp deposits were formed in a large part of the geosyncline; in western Canada these beds attain a thickness exceeding 5,000 feet. The Lower Cretaceous contains coal beds and nonmarine organic remains.

About mid-Cretaceous time, the Rocky Mountain geosyncline was submerged by the sea. The initial Upper Cretaceous deposits in most places consist of sandstone, locally conglomeratic, representing materials worn from adjacent lands. The sandstone is not quite the same in age everywhere, as is shown by differences in its fossils from place to place and by the fossil content of conformably overlying strata. We conclude that the sea occupied some parts of the geosyncline earlier than others.

The thickest and most widespread deposit laid down in the trough, consists of dark silty shale of very uniform texture. Especially in the western half of the geosyncline, the shale is interbedded with sandstone, and there is a general increase in the thickness and prominence

240. Huge spheroidal concretions weathered from Cretaceous sandstone in west-central Kansas. The masses consist of tightly cemented sandstone that shows cross-bedding. The rock (Dakota) surrounding the concretions is less tightly cemented and consequently is weathered away readily. The sandstone represents part of deposits formed at the margin of the advancing Late Cretaceous sea that spread over the continental interior.

241. North face of the Mesa Verde plateau in southwestern Colorado. The plateau is formed of Cretaceous shale and sandstone that dip very gently southward. The shale (Mancos) is marine but the overlying sandstone (Mesaverde) is mainly nonmarine and in part of this region it is coal-bearing. *(Spence Air Photos.)*

of sandstone going westward. Increasing prominence of coarse sediments to the west, including the presence of nonmarine river-laid deposits, indicates that much detritus came from uplands that separated the Rocky Mountain geosyncline from the Pacific border region.

No such lateral transition in the Cretaceous sediments is found along the east margin of the geosyncline, and thus we may infer that lands near the sea in this direction were low. Inasmuch as the volume of Cretaceous clastic sediments in the geosyncline totals many hundred cubic miles, the amount of erosion demanded to supply these sediments is correspondingly great, and the chief area of erosion is inferred to have bordered the geosyncline on the west.

Infilling of the geosyncline resulted in gradual encroachment of land areas on the inland sea until, near the close of the period, marine waters almost disappeared. The last remnant of the interior sea is represented by marine deposits, classed as earliest Cenozoic, in western North Dakota.

Sea invasions along the Pacific border. Narrow seaways along the Pacific border were the site of very thick sedimentation in Cretaceous time. The deposits consist mostly of gravel, sand, and silt derived

242. Overhanging cliff of Cretaceous sandstone in Mesa Verde National Park. Cave shelters in the cliff walls of the sandstone (Mesaverde) were used by cliff dwellers for construction of their homes, built of stone masonry.

from the upland that separated the Pacific border from the Rocky Mountain geosyncline. As shown by features of bedding and by contained fossils, the sediments were laid down in shallow water, despite the fact that in places the total thickness of sedimentary materials is 8 miles. This signifies that the basins sank slowly as sediment was poured into them. Admixture of volcanic fragmental materials with the sediments, shows that there were active volcanoes, but the extent of volcanism was much less than in the Jurassic.

Cretaceous Life

Beginning of modern floras. The Cretaceous Period was a time of great advancement among land plants, for it was in this part of earth history that deciduous trees, like the elm, oak, maple, poplar, and a host of other flowering plants that dominate the modern world, made appearance. Evergreens, cycads, and ferns persisted, but it is the covered-seed plants, called "angiosperms," that are the most noteworthy Cretaceous plants. The new forms of vegetation include a large variety of flowering shrubs and herbs, as well as the trees growing along streams, scattered in groves on the plains, and crowded thickly in forests. Also came grasses and grains, and although many genera are the same as those living today, the species are different. They clearly reflect the influence of seasons in which alternation in conditions of warmth and moisture, or both, was the main control of plant growth and probably a main factor in origin of the angiosperms. Inasmuch as the plants are the primary source of food for animals, the advent of modern floras in Cretaceous time may reasonably be interpreted as an antecedent to the great expansion of mammals and birds during the Cenozoic Era.

Continued dominance of reptiles. Among vertebrates living on land, reptiles were the most numerous, largest, and most varied. Chief were the dinosaurs, which included both flesh-eating and herbivorous types. A group of dinosaurs especially characteristic of the Cretaceous are the large-skulled, horned ceratopsians, which persisted to the very close of the period and then abruptly disappeared. None of the known Cretaceous dinosaurs equal in bulk some of those from the Jurassic, but flying reptiles and some of those living in the seas, represent the peak of development of these creatures during the Mesozoic Era.

Remains of birds have been found in Cretaceous marine deposits, one type representing a tireless flier like the sea gull, and another a large wingless diving bird. These birds had teeth, but otherwise were more like the petrel and loon than their reptilian ancestors.

Lastly, among the Cretaceous land vertebrates are the mammals. These hairy, warm-blooded creatures were still small, relatively insignificant animals, that doubtless scurried to cover out of the pathway of the dinosaurs or other reptilian lords that they chanced to meet.

243. The Late Cretaceous three-horned dinosaur, *Triceratops*. This restoration authentically represents the appearance of these interesting last survivors of the dinosaur group, but we have no reason to suppose that dinosaurs gave particular thought to care of their young. As shown by nests of fossil dinosaur eggs, these were laid in the sand, to be hatched by the sun's heat. After emerging from their shells, the youngsters were doubtless left to fend for themselves. Flying reptiles *(Pteranodon)* may be seen in the background. *(J. P. Cowan, Courtesy of Hughes Tool Company.)*

Their multicrowned teeth suggest that they fed on insects, nuts, grains, and not improbably they learned to prey on the eggs of reptiles, which had been laid in the warm sand to hatch. In mental development and physical activity, they so excelled the sluggish reptiles that they became swiftly adapted to changed conditions of environment at the close of the Mesozoic Era, assuming dominance as the reptiles proved unable to cope with these changes.

244. Aquatic and flying reptiles of Cretaceous age. Skeletal remains of these reptiles are found in marine formations. The large swimming lizard (mosasaur) attained a length of 50 feet; near by is a large marine turtle. The hammer-headed flying reptiles (*Pteranodon*) are the largest known representatives of this group, attaining a wing-spread of 25 feet. (*C. R. Knight, Chicago Natural History Museum.*)

Invertebrate life. Shallow seas of Cretaceous time swarmed with foraminifers to such extent that their microscopic shells form a large part of the chalk deposits; they are also very abundant in many shale and some sand deposits. All main groups of larger marine inverte-brates, including those dwelling on the bottom of shallow seas and some that were able to swim freely in the open ocean, are well rep-resented in Cretaceous marine deposits. Dominant among these ani-mals are the mollusks, including especially a variety of clams and complexly sutured cephalopods. Characteristic Cretaceous pelecypods include thick-shelled oysters, large concentrically ribbed clams, and reef builders of peculiarly coral-like form, having steeply conical thick walls. Many types of tightly coiled cephalopods and some loosely coiled and straight forms occur in the Cretaceous rocks. These bear highly complex sutures, and many of them had external ribs, nodes, and spines. The largest coiled ammonites attained a diameter of more than 5 feet. Among echinoderms, there are free-swimming crinoids and extremely numerous sea urchins. Many of these fossils preserved in the chalk have extraordinary delicacy and beauty. As a whole, the Cretaceous marine invertebrates show approach to modern conditions in the rise of mollusks and prominence of echinoids, but they differ in prominence of ammonites which are entirely lacking in Cenozoic marine deposits.

Climate

Study of Cretaceous sedimentary deposits and fossils calls attention to many indications of climatic diversity. The prominence of angiosperms among vegetation of the land points to prevalent alternation of seasons, yet relative warmth and humidity are indicated by the widespread distribution of such plants as the fig and breadfruit, which now are restricted to subtropical or warm temperate climates; along with palms and cycads, these plants occur in Cretaceous deposits of Alaska and Greenland. On the other hand, evidence of Cretaceous glaciation is reported from eastern Australia, and among Cretaceous deposits are evaporites that indicate at least local aridity.

Variation in climate seems to be associated with the size, placement, and amount of relief of land areas of the globe. Times of lowlands and very extensive seas are marked by widespread warm, humid climate, whereas uplifted lands and prominent mountain ranges are associated with climatic diversity, which includes cold and dry climate in various places along with heat and humidity in others. Thus, we might expect that after the building of the prominent mountains formed by the Nevadan revolution in the Pacific border region, climatic diversity might especially characterize Early Cretaceous time in parts of North America. Subsequently, when seas spread very widely over North America and other continents, we may anticipate existence of equable climates, with warm temperatures extending to high latitudes. Persistence of uplands, and even mountains, is indicated, however, by the nature and quantity of sediments derived from these areas.

Mountain Building and Close of the Period

Laramian revolution. Toward the close of Cretaceous time, one of the major mountain-building epochs of world history affected North and South America and produced strong crustal deformation in Europe and Asia. This is known as the Laramian revolution, the name being derived from the Laramie Range in the Rockies of Wyoming. This was a time of folding, faulting, and considerable crustal elevation throughout the length of the Rockies, from Alaska to Mexico, and throughout some 5,000 miles of the Andean belt, from Colombia to Cape Horn. Compression seems to have been exerted chiefly from the west—that is, from the Pacific Ocean segment of the globe—against

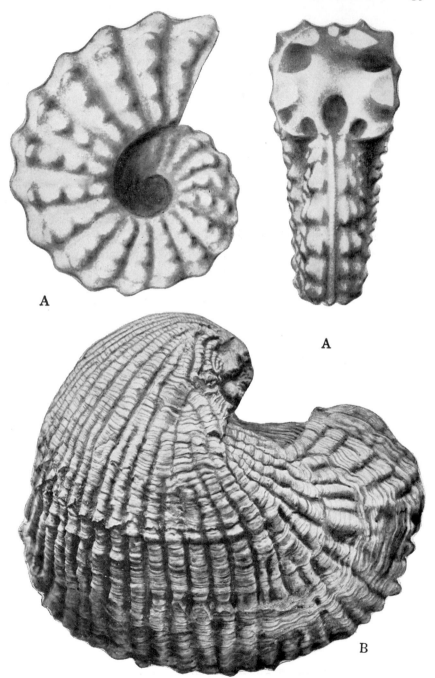

A

A

B

246. Folded Cretaceous strata in central northern Wyoming. This air view from a point north of Greybull, Wyo., shows Sheep Mountain and girdling hogback ridges and shallow valleys eroded in Upper Cretaceous strata. The beds, chiefly marine, were folded during the Laramian revolution near the close of Cretaceous time. *(Barnum Brown, American Museum of Natural History.)*

the American continent. Folding and metamorphism of rocks in the Andes, which are close to the Pacific, are very complex, but in the Rockies, which are many hundred miles from the Pacific border, rigidity of the compressed rocks was sufficient to prevent intricate deformation. Cretaceous and older rock strata are found turned up very steeply and locally overturned. Also, there are large thrust faults along which crustal blocks were pushed eastward several miles; but as a whole, the structure of the Rocky Mountains is much less complex than that of the Coast Ranges or Sierra Nevada country.

The geologic date of the Laramian revolution is indicated by study of the strata that respectively are affected or relatively undisturbed

---

245. A Cretaceous ammonite and thick-shelled clam. The ammonite *(A, Mortoniceras)* is only one of many Cretaceous types of these complexly sutured cephalopods. The clam *(B, Exogyra costata)* is a close relative of the oysters, distinguished by unusual thickness of its shell. Like many other Cretaceous invertebrates, these are important guide fossils. Natural size.

247. Steeply upturned Paleozoic beds along the east front of the Rocky Mountains in southeastern Wyoming. The prominent hogback ridge, in which the beds stand nearly vertically, is formed by Pennsylvanian strata, and the valley at right is carved in red shale of Permian age. Adjoining outcrops farther east show deformed Mesozoic strata, including Cretaceous, whereas near-by Tertiary deposits are not folded. These structural features are part of the record of the Laramian mountain building near the close of Cretaceous time. *(N. H. Darton, U. S. Geol. Survey.)*

by the deformation. Thus, along the Front Range of the Rockies in Colorado, very late Cretaceous rocks are found steeply upturned and overthrust in places by faults, which proves that in this area the disturbance was initiated some time later than the time of making these beds. Near by, there are unfolded Early Tertiary (Eocene) deposits in which reworked sediments derived from the uplifted Rockies can be identified. The deformation is dated as belonging between a time late in the Cretaceous and early in the Tertiary. Similar observations in other areas prove that the movements involved in the Laramian revolution were not all at precisely the same date—some are a little earlier, others a little later, and precise dating in several places is not determinable. As a whole, the mountain building is definitely associated with the close of Cretaceous time and the beginning of the Tertiary Period. Associated with geographic and organic changes, particularly as marked by the abrupt disappearance of the dinosaurs and rapid rise of mammals, we recognize the end of the Mesozoic Era and beginning of the Cenozoic.

16. Nature and Evolution of Mesozoic Life

Tyrannosaurus, of Late Cretaceous age, greatest of the flesh-eating dinosaurs.

Age of Reptiles, Ammonites and Cycadophytes

No part of earth history offers record of such strange and varied life as that of the so-called "medieval era" of life development. The culmination of reptiles in size, numbers, and differentiation of kinds was accompanied by a very remarkable adaptation of members of this class to almost every type of environment and mode of life. Dinosaurs, the "terrible lizards," were the rulers of the land, attaining a ponderous bulk unequaled in history of land animals. Few, if any, predaceous creatures can rival the carnivorous dinosaurs in ferocious dagger-like teeth and claws, and no armored, vertebrate animals of other type or time are more bizarre than some of the armored dinosaurs. Land reptiles of this time included true lizards, and in the waters of the land

C. R. Knight, Chicago Natural History Museum

there were turtles and crocodiles. One group of reptiles developed a batlike form, becoming suited for flight in the air. From reptiles, also, the birds were derived. Several reptilian stocks became specially modified for life in the sea, some acquiring a fishlike form that made them entirely unable to travel on land. The Mesozoic is well named the Age of Reptiles.

Among invertebrates, there are many interesting organisms. The complexly sutured, tight-coiled, and externally ornamented cephalopods, known as ammonites, are undoubtedly the most distinctive and important. An almost incredible variety of these shells is represented by Mesozoic fossils, but none are known from younger rocks. As regards evolution of invertebrate stocks, therefore, the era may be designated appropriately as the Age of Ammonites. The appearance of very abundant cephalopods of the squid type is evidenced by innumerable cigar-shaped "guards," which form part of the internal shell structure. Pelecypods and gastropods increased greatly in importance and in similarity of form to modern types. Sea urchins were much more common and varied than at any earlier time.

In terms of plant life, the Mesozoic Era may be called the Age of Cycadophytes, because these palmlike plants, which are comparatively unimportant in modern floras, dominated the plant assemblage of the earth's medieval time.

Contrasting features of Mesozoic and Paleozoic life. A general characteristic of Mesozoic organisms, which may be emphasized, is the contrast with Paleozoic life. So great is the change that early geologists were convinced that a world-wide catastrophe must have wiped out existing forms of life at the close of the Paleozoic Era, and that a new creation at the beginning of Mesozoic time repopulated the earth with different kinds of plants and animals. Difference in the complexion of Mesozoic life is shown by (1) disappearance of such animals as the trilobites, blastoids, and archaic types of crinoids, bryozoans, and corals; (2) the great decline of such an abundant and characteristic Paleozoic group as the brachiopods; (3) the rapid development and differentiation of such groups as the ammonites among invertebrates, and the reptiles among vertebrates, and (4) the introduction of new types of plants and animals. Most of the Mesozoic classes of organisms flourished for a time and then died, without seeing the beginning of Cenozoic time.

248. Skeletons and eggs of an early ceratopsian dinosaur which was hornless. The fossils (*Protoceratops*) shown here were collected from Late Cretaceous deposits in Mongolia. (*American Museum of Natural History.*)

The changes in life at the close of the Paleozoic Era, great as they are, should not lead us to overlook the fact that all phyla, many orders, and not a few families and genera, survive from Permian into Triassic or later times. The Triassic invertebrate faunas include several forms that differ only in minor ways from Permian predecessors. Among vertebrates, also, there are Triassic reptiles in both Europe and South Africa that are almost identical with Permian species. The later faunas are descendants of the earlier ones, and present knowledge indicates plainly that the two are not so sharply differentiated at the boundary of the eras as was once supposed.

Dominance of reptiles is the outstanding character of life on the earth during the Mesozoic Era. The progress of these animals, as of any kind of life, may be measured (1) by their numbers, variety, size, and similar physical characters, (2) by their success in getting food, in avoiding or conquering enemies, and in adapting themselves effectively to environment, and (3) by the extent to which they became fitted to all possible modes of life. In the Triassic, Jurassic, and Cretaceous Periods, reptiles achieved extraordinary abundance and variety of form and stature. They learned to feed on many kinds of plants, fresh-water and marine invertebrates, fishes, amphibians, other reptiles, and doubtless some of the primitive mammals. Their only real competitors were members of their own class. They became re-

250. Skeleton and carbonized impression showing body outline of an ichthyosaur. This fossil, from Jurassic marine shale in western Germany, clearly shows the adaptation of ichthyosaurs for aquatic life. They attained a length of 8 feet or more. (*American Museum of Natural History.*)

entirely by the tail, which bore a good-sized fin, and there was also a dorsal fin.

The *flying reptiles* (and likewise the birds, which developed out of an entirely different reptile line) probably learned first to glide and only later to fly. Adaptation to flight through the air is seen in a general lightening of the bones of the skeleton, but especially in a very remarkable modification of the structure of the forelimbs, among true flying reptiles for support of a membranous wing, and among birds for a wing clothed with feathers.

This progressive modification of the reptile group into divergent branches, with different modes of life and the consequent effects on body form and structure, are outstanding features in the Mesozoic history of life.

Plants

General character of Mesozoic floras. Notwithstanding the fact that the plants of Mesozoic time are the direct descendants of late Paleozoic species, and that several of the latter lived essentially unchanged into the Triassic Period, the floras of Mesozoic age are distinctively new and different. The dominant plant group was that of the palmlike cycadophytes, but ferns and conifers were nearly equal in number of species. Most of these were short or only moderately tall, so that one of the main contrasts with the Pennsylvanian floras consists in the absence of gigantic scale trees and cordaites. The horsetail family had several generic representatives, among which some of the very early Mesozoic forms were colossal. The ferns were relatively small, quite unlike the Paleozoic vine- and treelike seed ferns. A general exception to the small average size of Mesozoic plants is seen in some of the conifers, which grew to a height of more than 100 feet. In late Mesozoic time, the highest type of seed-bearing plants (angiosperms), which are dominant today, made appearance and became the most important element in the vegetation of all lands.

Cycadophytes. This interesting plant group, which is characteristic of the Mesozoic Era, is closely related to the modern cycads, which are represented by many living species in tropical and subtropical regions. Cycads have a woody trunk with a large central pith cavity; the outer part is cloaked by a mat of hanging dead leaves or bears closely spaced scars that mark the former attachments of leaves. The trunk is very short and bulbous in some species, about as wide as high, but in others it attains a height of more than 50 feet. At the top is a

251. A type of living cycad. The palmlike leaves and nature of the trunk of this modern plant *(Dion edule)* correspond closely to those of common Mesozoic cycadophytes. *(G. R. Wieland.)*

252. Leaves of a Jurassic cycadophyte *(Ctenophyllum).* Natural size.

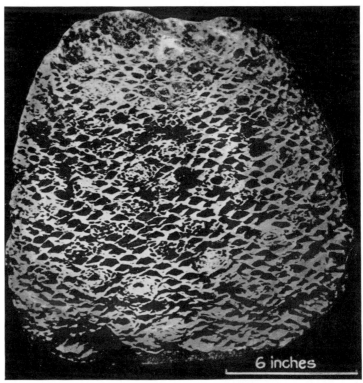

253. Trunk of a Cretaceous cycadophyte *(Cycadoidea)* from Maryland. *(E. W. Berry.)*

Nature

the onl
the log
greates
standir
tered a
subseq
origina
ture a
replac
that i
purpl

Jura
kinds
and b

Fer
know
of the
Trias
ginia
swam
kind
teris
The
but l

H
lanti
ants
5 in
in sr

Fi
plar
mos
whi
Japa
ginl
trui
bea
bas

254. Restoration of a Cretaceous fossil cycadophyte flower (Cycadoidea). *(G. R. Wieland.)*

graceful crown of long, palmlike leaves which have a strong stem axis and very numerous narrow elongate leaflets at the two sides. A large cone at the crest of the cycad in most living species contains the reproductive elements.

Fossil cycadophytes had very interesting true flowers, in which a circle of male spore-bearing stamens surrounded a pear-shaped female organ provided with numerous seed ovules. Some fossils show separate male and female flowers, though both may have been borne by the same plant. At least 40 different cycadophyte species have been recognized in Triassic coal-bearing deposits near Richmond, Va. One of the most abundant kinds (*Sphenozamites*) had leaves up to 4 feet in length, with lateral leaflets 8 to 10 inches long and as much as 4 inches wide. During the Jurassic Period, the cycadophytes were dominant in the land vegetation, for approximately two fifths of all the known plant fossils are of this type. If cycad species were relatively as numerous today, we should have some 40,000 different kinds. The Jurassic forms were very widely distributed and fairly uniform in character, for practically the same kinds of leaves occur in rocks of this age in England, northern Greenland, Alaska, Oregon, Australia, and Antarctica.

Cretaceous cycadophytes are also abundant, but mostly quite different from earlier types. Trunks, flowers, fruits, and seeds are common. The trunks were mostly less than 4 feet tall and about the same in diameter, their sides being covered by pits that mark the attachment of leaf fronds and fruits. Following Early Cretaceous time, the chief cycadophyte types declined and disappeared.

tails of structure, the ginkgo stands apart from all other plants. It en-
joys the distinction of being probably the oldest living kind of tree.
It has come down so little changed that it is difficult or impossible to
discover differences between fossils and present leaves. In Oregon
there are beds containing beautifully preserved ginkgo leaves by the
hundred. Jurassic deposits in Alaska, Greenland, northern Europe, and
Siberia also contain them. Naturally this plant occurs in later Mesozoic
and in Tertiary floras, but it does not stand out so prominently as in
the Jurassic, when the host of modern-type leafy trees had not appeared. It became extinct in North America during the Tertiary Period
but, when reintroduced by man from its native habitat in China, it
was found to grow luxuriantly.

Flowering plants.   The highest type of plants, dominant in modern
floras, are the flowering plants (angiospermophytes), in which the
seeds are inclosed in a protecting case or fruit. Two classes are recognized: (1) monocotyledons, which start with a single leaflet, lack a
differentiation of the stem into pith, wood, and bark, and have parallel-
veined leaves, and (2) dicotyledons, which start with two leaflets,
show division into pith, wood, and bark, and have leaves with a network of veins. The first group includes the grasses, cereals, palms,
lilies, and the like, while the second contains most of the forest trees,
such as maples, oaks, elms, and a great variety of shrubs and herbs.

No certainly identifiable angiosperms are yet known below the
Lower Cretaceous, where leaves referred to 16 modern families of
flowering plants suddenly make their appearance. These include the
willows, poplars, beeches, oaks, elms, laurels, sassafras, figs, grapes,
and other familiar living groups. The species are all different from
those of today. The Upper Cretaceous floras, represented by very
abundant well-preserved leaves, show a strongly dominant angiosperm
content with many modern-looking elements. In Greenland and Alaska,
there are Upper Cretaceous plant-bearing beds, containing conifers
and hardwoods that include many of the same species found in the
central and southern part of the United States. Among them are extinct representatives of the dogwood, persimmon, fig, tulip tree,
eucalyptus, sycamore, breadfruit tree, and many others that today
mainly inhabit moderately warm climates. The breadfruit tree is
limited at present to within 20 degrees of the equator.

Invertebrates

PROTOZOANS

The important fact about fossil protozoans during Mesozoic time is their abundance and great variety in the Cretaceous rocks. The chalk and chalky limestone of this age, which are practically world-wide in occurrence, contain multitudes of the minute shells of foraminifers. The geologic formations penetrated by drilling in the oil-field regions of Louisiana, Texas, and northeastern Mexico, are successfully identified by study of shells of this type washed from the well cuttings. In this connection may be noted the discovery, at shallow depth in certain Gulf Coast oil wells, of abundant Cretaceous species of foraminifers mingled with Tertiary species, the age of the rocks being evidently Tertiary. The fact that the Cretaceous types are all slightly worn, whereas the others are fresh and unmutilated, supports the conclusion that the older shells were weathered and transported from some Cretaceous outcrops, and redeposited with shells of much younger species that were living at the time.

Although foraminifers were extremely abundant in late Paleozoic time, when some of them were important rock builders, little is known of protozoans during the Triassic Period. They were fairly abundant in Jurassic time, the majority of species resembling Cretaceous forms.

SPONGES

Both siliceous and calcareous sponges are abundant in some Mesozoic rocks. The former occur in limestones, but the latter only in sandy or muddy sediments deposited in shallow near-shore waters. This accords with conditions in living species, for the siliceous sponges inhabit moderately deep water, while the calcareous types predominate in shallow water. The chief development of siliceous sponges is seen in thick beds of these fossils, highly varied in kinds, in Jurassic limestones of central Europe, and again in Upper Cretaceous rocks of western, central, and southeastern Europe. The common occurrence of flint in many of the Mesozoic formations, especially in Cretaceous chalk, indicates that siliceous sponges of the more primitive sorts were also abundant, for the separated skeletal elements (spicules) of these largely supply the silica. Many kinds of calcareous sponges appear in the Triassic rocks of the Alps region, in parts of the European Jurassic, and in the Cretaceous.

COELENTERATES

Corals. The corals of Mesozoic time are similar to those living in the warm shallow seas of the present day, and both of these differ from the ancient Paleozoic corals in having a basic sixfold symmetry. The structural plan is very clearly seen in many genera, which show six main radial walls (septa) and more or less numerous subordinate ones. Both single-horn corals and compound, colonial types occur, but the latter greatly predominate. Most types are long-lived, persisting through two or more of the Mesozoic periods, and some have lived from the Triassic to the present.

In North America, most Mesozoic rocks contain few corals, partly because marine deposits are restricted, except in the Cretaceous. In Europe, however, there are large numbers of reef-building corals in some of the Triassic formations of the Alps region. The Jurassic is especially rich in corals at very many places, and they occur in high latitudes as well as in the equatorial belts, indicating widespread warm waters. The Cretaceous beds locally contain many corals.

Hydrozoans. Two types of hydrozoans are represented among Mesozoic fossils. One consists of colonial polyps that secrete dense calcareous layers at the base, forming a deposit very much like that of the Paleozoic stromatoporoids. Some of these lime-secreting hydrozoan colonies were especially abundant in the Mediterranean region in Jurassic time. The other consists of jellyfishes, which, though they contain no hard parts, are known from remarkably perfect impressions in the very fine-grained lithographic limestone of Jurassic age at Solnhofen, Germany, and in some flinty concretions of Late Cretaceous age. The Solnhofen beds are famous for the variety and perfection of their fossils, which include, in addition to common marine invertebrates, several kinds of insects, marine reptiles, and the two only known specimens of the earliest birds.

ECHINODERMS

Crinoids. The Mesozoic crinoids are more like those of the present than any that lived in Paleozoic time. Virtually all the Paleozoic kinds of crinoids had disappeared before the close of the Permian, and a

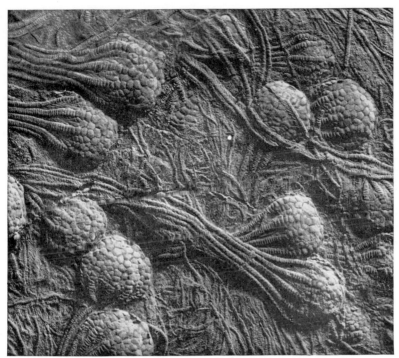

256. Portion of a slab covered with specimens of a free-swimming crinoid. These crinoids (*Uintacrinus*) were found on a thin limestone interbedded with chalk of Cretaceous age in western Kansas. About one-third natural size. (*University of Kansas, Natural History Museum*)

new order, which includes the Mesozoic and modern crinoids, appeared in the Triassic.

The most interesting fossils of this class in the Jurassic rocks are specimens (*Pentacrinus*), which show the complete calyx with attached arms, measuring as much as 3 feet in height and width. The entire length of stem in some individuals may have been more than 50 feet, exceeding any other known crinoid. The separated stem segments, like small five-pointed stars, are common in some American Jurassic marine strata, but well-preserved crowns that are exhibited in many of our museums come from Europe.

An equally striking but very different form (*Uintacrinus*) of Cretaceous age was a free-swimming stemless crinoid, having slender arms as much as 4 feet long, outstretched from its globular calyx. This

257. Fossil starfishes of Cretaceous age. This slab of Austin chalk from Austin, Tex., contains an unusual number of beautifully preserved starfishes *(Austinaster mccarteri). (Courtesy Texas Memorial Museum.)*

crinoid is known in England, Germany, France, Australia, and western America, especially in Kansas, from which the most remarkable specimens come. They are found on thin sheets of limestone, the surface of which is crowded as closely as possible with beautifully preserved individuals with arms attached.

Echinoids. During Mesozoic time, the sea urchins or echinoids began the climb toward their present position of prominence. Fossil remains of the group are very abundant and widespread, especially in the Jurassic and Cretaceous rocks. Chief features of their history in the era are (1) rapid increase in numbers and variety and (2) progressive specialization of (*a*) the regular echinoids toward increased spinose ornamentation and (*b*) the irregular echinoids toward increased eccentricity of position of mouth and anus, and a marked bilateral instead of radial symmetry. Many echinoid species are important index fossils.

BRYOZOANS

The abundant Paleozoic bryozoans belong chiefly to two orders, which are restricted to that era. Those of the Mesozoic, and also of later time, belong almost wholly to two other orders (cyclostomes, cheilostomes), of which the first has very simple cylindrical tubes and rounded apertures, but the second has a complex organization. In many of them is a mechanism that serves to extend the animal from its little cell and to close the aperture by a movable lid when it withdraws into its tube. The bryozoans expanded astonishingly during Cretaceous time and have been important ever since.

BRACHIOPODS

This class of shelled animals, which had been so abundant and varied in the seas of Paleozoic times, is tremendously reduced in the Mesozoic Era, although locally there were very numerous individuals belonging to a few species. The most important persisting types were smooth-shelled and more or less simple in outline. They are characterized especially by the internal calcareous support for the brachia, which is in the form of a loop. Angularly plicated shells with pointed beaks and no calcified brachial supports occur locally. The spire-bearing brachiopods were represented by a few forms that lasted until Early Jurassic time. Lastly, there were the very simple, thin-shelled calcium phosphate types (like *Lingula*), which have persisted practically unchanged from very early Paleozoic time down to the present day. The brachiopods of the Mesozoic are a declining race, but it is interesting to observe that the kinds that survived the changes of closing Paleozoic time are, in the main, the simple and conservative in structure, neither highly specialized nor degenerate, and some of these have been able to survive to modern time.

PELECYPODS

The bivalved, bottom-dwelling mollusks, called "pelecypods," assumed greater prominence in Mesozoic faunas than in those of Paleozoic time. Before the Triassic, they had been common locally and varied in form, but altogether a conservative, relatively simple class of animals, which was distinctly secondary in importance to others. A gradual but marked change is seen among clams of the Mesozoic Era. Many of the ancient types lived on, but the majority of species acquired a higher type of structure, as indicated in the more complexly specialized hinge teeth and other features, and their actual and relative numbers gave them a much more prominent place in the life assemblage. Some were beautifully ornamented; some developed a more peculiar and strangely specialized form than any other known pelecypods; and some attained a huge size that probably exceeds all others of this class.

One of the most important groups was that of the oyster (*Ostrea*) and its allies. The first oysters had appeared in Pennsylvanian time, but during the Mesozoic they expanded remarkably and were much more important than today. Distinguishing features of the oyster family are the distorted form and unequal size of the two valves, which result from the cementation of the shell to foreign objects during part or all of the life of the animal, the presence of only one instead of two muscles to hold the valves together, and the absence of distinct hinge teeth. The larger, deeper valve is beneath, and the smaller, flatter opposite valve is above, fitting over the other like a lid. Some of the Mesozoic oysters were not unlike modern kinds, but several had radiating ribs or plications. Two members of the oyster family that were especially abundant and important horizon markers in the Jurassic and Cretaceous rocks, are *Gryphaea* and *Exogyra*. Some specimens of these had a shell nearly 2 inches thick. In places, fossils of these types are so numerous that rock layers several feet thick are mainly composed of them, and when the strata disintegrate, the ground may be literally blanketed with shells. One of the most common and widely distributed pelecypods in some of the Cretaceous formations is called *Inoceramus*. The shell is rounded in outline and marked by prominent concentric grooves and ridges. A few species attained gigantic size, measuring 4 feet across.

The subtriangular shells of *Trigonia*, distinguished commonly by ornamentation of nodes or ribs that differ in the anterior and posterior portions of the shell, are characteristic of Mesozoic formations. They are relatively more prominent in the Jurassic System than in other rocks of the era.

In the middle and especially the late part of Mesozoic time,

258. Representative Mesozoic invertebrate fossils. All the figured forms except *E* (Jurassic) are from Cretaceous rocks. Pelecypods include *A (Trigonia), B (Gryphaea), C (Crassatellites),* and *D (Pecten); F* is one of the irregular sea urchins *(Hemiaster);* a gastropod of modern aspect is shown in *G (Lirosoma);* cephalopods include the internal shell of a squidlike form, *E (Belemnitella),* and complexly sutured coiled shells, *H (Pseudoschloenbachia)* and *I (Pervinquieria).* Natural size.

peculiarly specialized pelecypods known as "rudistids," developed a shell having the form of a horn coral, covered at the top by a nearly flat lid. The shell walls may be excessively thick, and the height of the coral-like lower valve more than 2 feet. The abnormal features of these pelecypods are evidently the result of a sedentary, fixed mode of growth on the sea bottom, where they generally lived in closely crowded colonies, the remains of which may form thick beds of limestone. These pelecypods abound in the warmer water deposits of Cretaceous time.

Fresh-water mussels are common in some of the Mesozoic continental formations.

GASTROPODS

Gastropods are a common but not a dominant element in the invertebrate life of the Mesozoic. Many of the species belong to well-established families that date back to early Paleozoic times, but a very large number of new ones, representing more advanced biological orders, were introduced during the era. The latter are characterized externally by various ornamental features, but especially by the presence of a tubelike elongation of the shell in front of the aperture, that is, at the end of the shell opposite the spire, for accommodation of a siphon. Species of gastropods belonging to the air-breathing group are known in some Mesozoic continental deposits.

CEPHALOPODS

The most interesting of the marine invertebrates of Mesozoic time are the cephalopods. They are also one of the most abundant, widespread, and stratigraphically important classes. The four-gilled, external-shelled types are dominant, and include both nautiloids, characterized by simple sutures, and ammonites, which have complex sutures. The two-gilled cephalopods (belemnoids, sepioids), with internal shell, also occur and in some strata are abundant.

Nautiloids. The nautiloids, although common in Mesozoic seas, were greatly overshadowed by the host of ammonites. Most of them were tightly coiled and highly involute, like the modern nautilus, and some attained a diameter of more than 12 inches. There is a tendency toward complication of the sutures, such as marked the ammonoid (ammonite-like) branch, but this did not proceed farther than development of a few rounded inflections.

Ammonites. The beginning of specialization of external-shelled cephalopods, which culminated in the exceedingly complex Mesozoic ammonites, dates back to the Silurian Period. Their development is chiefly manifested (1) in increasing complication of the sutures, (2) in external ornamentation, but also (3) in the form of the shell, (4) in modifications of the aperture, and (5) in increase in size.

The sutures (junction of the shell partitions with the inner wall of the shell) are only moderately curved or angulated in the simplest ammonoids. This type was characteristic of the later Paleozoic rocks, but some of the ammonites of the Triassic are little, if any, more advanced. An increased number of bends and angles in the suture line, accompanied by a progressive complication in pattern, marks the development of most Mesozoic ammonites. The diversity is amazing, but each type of suture is constant, according to genus and species. Because even slight changes in the sutures are readily determinable, and with other characters permit definite recognition of specific differences, these shells are well fitted to serve as markers of stratigraphic zones and of geologic time. They lived in enormous numbers, were distributed all over the world, and underwent comparatively rapid change.

External ornamentation of the ammonite shells consists of lines, ridges, nodes, or spines, and the variety of form and arrangement of these is very great. Some shells are smooth, but the vast majority carry some sort of surface decoration. Around the outer margin of many coiled shells is a ridge or keel; in others there is a groovelike depression; in still others this part of the shell is not differentiated.

The form of ammonite shells shows much variation. All but a few are coiled in a plane, but among these are evolute types in which all the whorls are completely visible from the sides, whereas others are involute, the outer whorls partly or entirely concealing the inner ones. The cross section of the shell ranges from very narrow and laterally compressed, to very broad and vertically flattened. Several genera have an elevated spiral shell, which is typical of most gastropods but is abnormal among the cephalopods. A few specialized, degenerate types have shells with very erratic twists and bends. Others show reversion toward an ancestral primitive state in the tendency to uncoil and be-

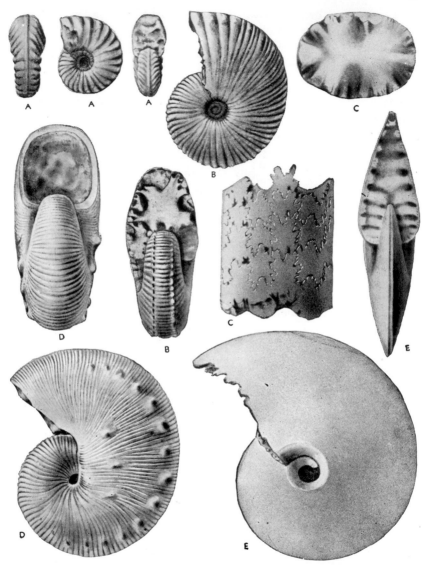

259. Typical Mesozoic cephalopods belonging to the group of ammonites. *A (Ceratites)* is a Triassic shell; the others *(B, Discoscaphites; C, Baculites; D, Acanthoscaphites; E, Placenticeras)* come from Cretaceous rocks. Natural size.

come straight. These peculiar forms are a mark of approaching extinction, for they appear toward the close of the career of various branches of the ammonites.

The aperture of most ammonites, where known, is unconstricted, and the edges of the shell mouth are smooth or gently curved. In some, however, the lateral margins are extended very prominently forward, or the ventral portion of the shell projects like a beak. A few exhibit very narrow, abnormal apertures, which is an overspecialized character presaging disappearance of these evolutional branches.

Average Mesozoic ammonites have shells that measure a few inches in diameter. Some genera are characterized by robust size, having shells more than a foot in diameter, and a few attained gigantic proportions, measuring 5 feet or more across. If one of these mammoth forms could be uncoiled, the shell would measure not less than 20 feet in length.

Study of the distribution of ammonite species in the Mesozoic rocks shows not only that a large proportion are restricted to a narrow vertical range, making them valuable as index fossils, but that in a broad way the genera and families of the Triassic are almost wholly distinct from those of the Jurassic. In turn Jurassic forms differ from those of the Cretaceous.

The abundance, variety, and complexity of evolutional modifications among ammonites during their heyday in Mesozoic time, followed by their rapid decline and utter extinction, constitute a remarkable chapter in the record of life on the earth. It is paralleled, however, by the history of various other classes of animals and plants, which more or less slowly advanced to a certain point, then expanded rapidly to a peak, only to decline to a small remnant of their former greatness, or to vanish entirely. This seems to be a lesson of life—adolescence, adult virility, senility, death.

Belemnoids. The two-gilled cephalopods, to which the modern squids, cuttlefishes, and octopuses belong, are interesting creatures that boast a respectably ancient lineage, but the importance of their geological record is much less than that of their cousins, the ammonoids and nautiloids.

The body of the extinct cephalopods called belemnoids was elongated, cylindrical, and pointed at the posterior end. The head bore a circlet of powerful muscular tentacles, armed with rows of little hooks on the inner sides. The abdomen contained a rather large ink bag, filled by an extremely opaque brownish-black fluid, which could be ejected by the animal so as to form a dense cloud in the water and conceal retreat. This ink bag may be represented in fossils by a dark-colored carbonaceous residue.

The shell of the belemnoids was internal and consisted of three parts: (1) a chambered cone, somewhat resembling a simple, straight-shelled nautiloid, (2) a delicate shoehorn-like projection extending forward from the mouth of the cone, and (3) a solid cigar-shaped piece, that fits around the pointed end of the cone and extends some distance beyond it. It is this last, called the "guard" or "sheath," that is most commonly found as a fossil. It shows a fine prismatic, radiating structure around the long axis.

More than 350 species of belemnoids are known from Jurassic and Cretaceous rocks. In some strata, shells of this type occur by the millions and are found all over the world. Their name, first used nearly 400 years ago, means thunderbolt and refers to the fancied resemblance of these fossils to the weapons of the gods.

CRUSTACEANS

Trilobites disappeared at the close of the Paleozoic Era, but a great number and variety of other crustaceans, some of them surprisingly like modern species, occur as fossils in Mesozoic rocks.

Ostracodes are very numerous in many of the Mesozoic strata, but they belong almost wholly to types unknown in Paleozoic rocks. On the other hand, a majority of the Mesozoic ostracode genera have persisted to the present day. These fossils are a valuable aid in identifying formations and zones encountered in wells that penetrate the Cretaceous rocks.

Cirripeds, the barnacles, are fairly well known in Cretaceous beds, although not common. Some are much like living species.

Higher crustaceans of many sorts, including the lobsters, crayfish, crabs, and other kinds, made their appearance during the Mesozoic. Remarkably preserved specimens, in which all the appendages are complete, occur in some deposits, especially the famous Solnhofen limestone, of Jurassic age, in Germany. An interesting group that is well represented in Jurassic and Cretaceous rocks is that of the decapods.

INSECTS

As now known from a series of wonderful fossil insect collections of Pennsylvanian and Permian age, many important insect orders had

260. Skeleton of a large Cretaceous marine fish from the chalk of western Kansas. Some specimens of this fish *(Portheus)* attain a length of 15 feet. Many other kinds of marine and fresh-water fishes of Mesozoic age are represented by fossils. *(University of Kansas, Natural History Museum.)*

been established before the beginning of Mesozoic time. The best record of insects in the Mesozoic comes from Jurassic rocks in Europe. Besides cockroaches, dragonflies, and other "first families" among the insects, the Mesozoic rocks contain representatives of the true bugs (Hemiptera), both terrestrial and aquatic; the flies (Diptera), with some 30 Jurassic species; butterflies and moths; the ants, wasps, and bees; beetles; locusts and crickets; plant lice; caddis flies; scorpion flies; lacewing flies; and May flies.

Vertebrates

FISHES

Practically all groups of known fishes are represented by fossils found in Mesozoic rocks. The appearance of the majority is distinctly more like that of modern types, and the structural character of the skeleton, scales, and fins trends strongly toward those dominant today. Especially important is the introduction of the teleosts, or true bony fishes, which include approximately 90 per cent of living kinds.

The Triassic strata of the Atlantic Coast region have yielded an interesting assortment of well-preserved fish fossils, which show the regularly arranged rhombic scales of the body, the fins, and the plates of the head, but reveal little of the partly ossified skeleton. They lie on their side and are flattened to paper thinness on bedding planes of the rock. Jurassic fishes are rare in North America but are common in Europe.

The Cretaceous marine deposits of the United States contain fairly abundant fish remains. Shark teeth of various sorts, some sharply pointed like those of modern sharks, and others broadly flattened for crunching and grinding, have been collected from many outcrops of shale and chalk. Fish scales occur abundantly in many Cretaceous beds and are especially characteristic of some. A few types are as much as 1 inch in diameter. The long bony fish spines, vertebrae, and fossils showing the complete bony skeleton with associated scales and fins are found. Some of these fishes attained a length of 15 feet, and as indicated by numerous large pointed teeth, were fiercely predaceous in habit.

Main features in the Mesozoic history of the fishes are (1) the dominance in fresh waters of the "ray-finned" bony fish (actinopterygians), which are types leading to the teleosts, (2) the invasion of the sea by this group, which in Paleozoic time was mainly restricted to fresh water, and (3) a revival of sharks, skates, and rays, which had nearly disappeared at the close of the Paleozoic Era.

AMPHIBIANS

The beginning and rise of amphibians, the lowest type of land vertebrate, are part of the Paleozoic record. Mesozoic types of these animals are most common in Triassic rocks. The early Mesozoic amphibians belong chiefly to the broad- and heavy-skulled stegocephalians called "labyrinthodonts," some of which were 15 feet long. Their bodies were bulky, the tails short and stumpy, and the legs so short that it seems they could hardly have carried the body without dragging it on the ground. It is probable that the weight of the body was buoyed up in the water most of the time. These large amphibians did not persist beyond the Triassic. The first of the batrachians (frogs, toads) appeared in the Jurassic Period, and the first urodeles ("salamanders") in the Early Cretaceous.

REPTILES

Dinosaurs

Age of Dinosaurs.   The Mesozoic Era frequently is called the Age of Dinosaurs, because these creatures were the most striking animals of the time and were world-wide in distribution. They dominated the lands for some 140 million years, from Early Triassic until the close of the Cretaceous Period.

Some dinosaurs were small, little larger than a hen, but others attained the greatest size of any land-living vertebrates, reaching a weight of perhaps 50 tons, a length of at least 85 feet, and a height of 20 feet or more. Most dinosaurs were plant-eaters, but some were fierce beasts of prey that fed on the flesh of other dinosaurs, and doubtless any other sort of animal they could capture. Some were slow-moving ponderous beasts of the plains and forests; a few were evidently lithe swift-running forms; and others were aquatic or semi-aquatic types that lived in lakes, rivers, and swamps. All had a body covering of horny scales, somewhat like those of modern lizards, but this was supplemented in some by development of thick bony plates that made a strong defensive armor. As a whole, therefore, the dinosaurs were a highly varied assemblage that became adapted to a wide variety of habitats. Although they were cold-blooded creatures and were characterized by amazingly small brain size in comparison to bulk of the body, they were certainly successful forms of organic growth. They held place at the head of the procession of life for a very long time.

The name "dinosaur," meaning terrible lizard, is familiar to almost everyone, whether he knows about other fossils or not. Skeletal remains and restorations are well displayed in several of our great museums. Also, dinosaurs have been publicized by cartoonists and in commercial art. Yet it is very difficult to visualize these reptiles as living, breathing animals that roamed the lands in numbers where we now live. It is an interesting task in our study to become acquainted with at least the main types of dinosaurs and to construct as accurate a picture as we can of life on the earth during the age of dinosaurs.

Skeletal study of the dinosaurs, especially of the skull, shows that, among modern reptiles, they are most closely related to the lizards, snakes, and crocodiles. Among fossil forms, they show kinship with the flying reptiles (pterosaurs) and an important group of Triassic reptiles known as "thecodonts," which are judged to be the ancestral stock that gave rise to the dinosaurs. Diagnostic similarities of thecodonts and dinosaurs include structure of the skull, and a special type of hip girdle, in which bones of the pelvis were strengthened and modified, in order to support the body when carried mainly or wholly by the hind legs. The thecodonts were an early group of reptiles that show adaptation for two-footed locomotion. The front limbs were reduced in size and became handlike, useful for grasping. The strong

261. Skull of a tyrannosaur showing dagger-like teeth. This skull is 43 inches long, 40 inches high, and 35 inches wide; the teeth are 3 to 6 inches long. *(American Museum of Natural History.)*

hip bones, stoutly joined to the backbone, became a sort of fulcrum on which movements of the body were pivoted, a long tail acting as counterbalance to the fore part of the body. Similar features broadly distinguish the dinosaurs, even though a majority of them reverted to a four-footed mode of locomotion.

Dinosaurs are divisible into two main groups, one of which—the lizard-hip (saurischian) dinosaurs—has a thecodont type of pelvic girdle, whereas the second—the bird-hip (ornithischian) dinosaurs—shows modification of pelvic structure toward that of the birds.

Saurischian dinosaurs. The lizard-hip dinosaurs are first recognized in Triassic rocks, but they are most abundant and widely known from Jurassic deposits; some persisted to the very close of the Cretaceous Period. They include divergent stocks having different form, food habits, and general mode of life. One group, mostly flesh-eaters, maintained a bipedal mode of walking and gradually lost the functional use of the fore limbs, which became greatly diminished in size.

A good example of these dinosaurs is the Jurassic *Allosaurus,* which attained a length of about 35 feet and stood some 15 feet in height. Its hind limbs were long, strong, and powerful, and the great claws at the tips of its outspread toes indicate that the feet were used not only for walking but for holding prey. The much smaller front limbs were also armed with large sharp talons and were doubtless used for grasping and tearing flesh. The skull of *Allosaurus* is large, relatively narrow, and deep, and edges of the wide gaping mouth were armed with long, dagger-like teeth. Heavy jaws, sharp teeth, and claw-armed limbs are equipment of a beast of prey. The large size of this dinosaur indicates that no contemporary animal of Jurassic time was safe from his attack. Indeed, fossil bones of the largest known dinosaurs, which belong to the plant-eating group, have been found that show the marks of the allosaur's teeth.

Greatest of the carnivorous dinosaurs is *Tyrannosaurus,* which lived in the latter part of Cretaceous time. Complete skeletons, found in the western United States, indicate that this animal had an over-all length of 50 feet, a height of 20 feet, and a weight of some 10 tons. The tyrannosaur is not merely a larger, more ferocious edition of the allosaur, but he shows greater specialization in skull and teeth, and in the further reduction of the forelimbs and hands.

Other saurischian dinosaurs walked on four legs, had relatively small heads, and show by the nature of their teeth that they fed exclusively on various sorts of plants. They were herbivores. A typical example of them is *Brontosaurus,* which inhabited western United States in Jurassic time. It was one of the most ponderous of all known dinosaurs. The hind limbs were notably larger and more massive than the forelimbs, but all four feet were short and broad, somewhat like those of an elephant; the neck and tail were long. It is judged that the brontosaurs lived mostly in shallow ponds, lakes, and streams, where the water would help support their enormous bulk. One reason for thinking that these animals lived at least partly in the water is the location of the nostrils at the very top of the skull, as is common in some other aquatic air-breathers. Several dinosaurs are known to have had webbed feet, and to have been able not only to wade but to swim. Presumably, these animals fed on the lush vegetation of marshy areas, as well as plants on land. The brontosaur's head was no bigger around than the neck, and even if this dinosaur spent most of its time

262. Restoration of the ponderous plant-eating dinosaurs called "brontosaurs." These animals, which attained a length of about 85 feet and an estimated weight of 50 tons, are judged to have been semiaquatic in habit. (*C. R. Knight, Chicago Natural History Museum.*)

eating, one can hardly understand how the needs of body metabolism could be supplied, unless all movements were very sluggish, and food demands of such a cold-blooded reptile were very much lower than in a mammal of like bulk.

Ornithischian dinosaurs. In general, the bird-hip dinosaurs, which were plant-eaters, show more variation and specialization than are seen among the saurischians. Four main types are readily differentiated among the ornithischians: duck-billed, plated, armored, and horned dinosaurs.

1. Among several genera of the duck-billed dinosaurs known from Jurassic and Cretaceous rocks of Europe and North America, we may select *Trachodon* as representative. The duckbills, like their thecodont ancestors, walked on the hind legs and carried the body in a relatively upright position, using the long ponderous tail as counterbalance. *Trachodon*, which attained a height of 15 feet, was a relatively large duckbill that lived in Late Cretaceous time. The skull and jaws were broadened and flattened. Unlike the saurischians and other dinosaurs, which had teeth only along the margins of the jaws, the floor and roof

of the trachodon's mouth were wholly covered with peglike teeth, closely packed to form paved surfaces, admirably suited for crushing and grinding. As many as 2,000 such teeth have been counted in a single skull.

2. The plated dinosaur, called *Stegosaurus,* is one of the most bizarre animals of the Mesozoic Era. It lived in western North America during Jurassic time. When full grown, it was about 20 feet long and 11 feet high over the hips. This dinosaur had stout pillar-like legs, and although it walked on all four feet, the front limbs were barely half as large as those behind. The skull was small, narrow, and pointed in front. Chief characteristic of the stegosaurs is the presence along the back of a great bony frill, formed by pointed plates standing in a double row. The largest of these plates, located over the hips, measures more than 2 feet across. On the tail were four long, curved, horny spikes. What use or benefit this decidedly unwieldy dorsal crest may have had for the stegosaur is not at all clear. The bony plates along

263. Model of a duck-billed dinosaur. Although this dinosaur walked on its hind legs, like the carnivorous dinosaurs, the toes are not armed with claws, and the duck-billed mouth is paved with grinding teeth. *(U. S. National Museum.)*

264. A Jurassic landscape in the western United States showing two stegosaurs. Characterized by their huge bony plates along the back and spines on the tail, these small-headed, four-footed dinosaurs are one of the strangest known reptiles. *(C. R. Knight, Chicago Natural History Museum.)*

the back and the spines on the tail could hardly have served very effectively as a defense mechanism. We may suppose that, unless the allosaurs or other contemporaneous hunters did not have sense enough to make a flank attack, the plated dinosaurs must have furnished their share of meals to the carnivores.

3. Cretaceous rocks have yielded the skeletons of truly armored dinosaurs, and one of these, which resembles a giant armadillo, is known as *Ankylosaurus.* The skull and the whole area of the arched back was strongly protected by bony masses that fitted closely together, but permitted movement between them. At the sides and along the club-shaped tail were laterally directed large spines. Squatted low on its short legs, the ankylosaur should have been well able to protect itself from carnivorous enemies such as the tyrannosaurs.

265. Restoration of a Cretaceous armored dinosaur. Skeletons of these animals (*Paleoscincus*), collected in western Canada, show that the back and sides were covered by thick bones. (*E. M. Fulda, American Museum of Natural History.*)

4. Among the last and most highly specialized of the dinosaurs, are the horned dinosaurs, or ceratopsians. They appeared on the scene in Late Cretaceous time and persisted until the close of the period. Although they walked on all four feet, the hind limbs were notably larger than those in front. The body and tail were relatively short. Their outstanding character was the very large bony head that bore a prominent horn or horns and carried a backward-projecting shield over the short neck. The jaws were toothless, but at the front was a strong parrot-like beak. The earliest known horned dinosaurs, found in Cretaceous rocks of Mongolia, resembled later ones, except in having only the rudiments of a horn and in attaining maximum size of only 5 or 6 feet. Nests of fossilized eggs belonging to this dinosaur have been discovered, and in some of the eggs, bones of unhatched embryo horned dinosaurs have been found.

Greatest of the horned dinosaurs is *Triceratops*, which lived near the close of Cretaceous time. This animal attained a length of 20 or 30 feet and had a skull some 8 feet long from the tip of its beak to

266. Nest of six dinosaur eggs, from Cretaceous sandstone in Mongolia. Some of these eggs, as large as that of an ostrich but more slender, contain bones of unhatched dinosaurs *(Protoceratops). (American Museum of Natural History.)*

the back of the neck shield. Above each eye was a strong horn and between these, farther front, was a shorter one. *Triceratops* was seemingly an inoffensive plant-eater. When attacked, it should have been fairly safe so long as it faced the enemy. That some of them had arguments among themselves, and settled matters by combat, is indicated by discovery of fossil skulls that show healed grooves and fractures, representing injuries seemingly made by another horned dinosaur.

Disappearance of the dinosaurs. A major question concerning the dinosaurs, which is very unsatisfactorily answered, is the reason for their abrupt and utter extinction at the close of Mesozoic time. These animals had been rulers of the land on all continents of the globe during more than 100 million years. They were still numerous and varied in the closing part of Cretaceous time. Yet not one of the dinosaurs, so far as known, persisted in the Cenozoic Era. Suggested explanations of this disappearance include: (1) climatic and other great physical changes associated with post-Cretaceous mountain building, which altered environment in such manner as to prevent adaptation of the dinosaurs to the new conditions; (2) the rise of much more intelligent animals belonging to the mammals, which may have furnished too keen competition, especially if some of the small mammals preyed on the eggs of dinosaurs; and (3) spreading disease of some unknown sort, which may have wiped the dinosaurs out.

Natu
attaine
was lo
for ca
and tl
strong
pulsio
and tl
lived
like tl

Mo:
living
knowi
slende
larges
table
jointe
largei
only 1

MARINE REPTILES

All reptiles are air-breathers, and this suits them for life on land. During the age of reptile dominance in the Mesozoic Era, however, different groups of these animals found it advantageous to seek their food supply in the sea. As time elapsed, they became increasingly at home in this wholly different sort of environment. The body outline was streamlined to permit easier and faster swimming, and limbs, which had been adapted to walking or running on land, slowly changed in the direction of appendages for swimming, serving either as oarlike paddles or as fins that aided in orientation of the body. This modification of limbs resulted in notable shortening of the bones of the upper leg and arm, and in elongation and flattening of the fingers and toes, which were joined together laterally by flesh and skin. Ultimately, these adaptations made the aquatic reptiles entirely unsuited for getting around on shore. Fossil remains of unborn young within the body of the mother have been observed, proving that some of these animals did not return to the beach even for laying eggs. Four main groups of Mesozoic marine reptiles are recognized: ichthyosaurs, mosasaurs, plesiosaurs, and turtles.

Ichthyosaurs. Fishlike reptiles, called "ichthyosaurs" (fish lizards),

267. Model of *Triceratops*, largest of the horned dinosaurs. These dinosaurs, which lived in the latest part of Cretaceous time, had no teeth at the front of the jaws, but a turtle-like beak instead. The skull of some specimens is 8 feet long. (*U. S. National Museum.*)

269. R
their s
Histor

lizards lived in the Cretaceous seas; some of the best skeletons have been found in the chalk of western Kansas.

Plesiosaurs.   Another group of aquatic reptiles that appeared in Triassic time and persisted into the Late Crataceous, comprises the plesiosaurs. Their chief characteristics were a small head, long neck, short broad body, and large powerful flippers that furnished locomotion. A plesiosaur has been described as "a snake strung through the body of a turtle." The largest known plesiosaurs had a length of 50 feet. These reptiles were probably much slower, more cumbersome swimmers than the ichthyosaurs or most fishes, for paddles are poorer propelling organs than a tail, but the long supple neck probably aided the plesiosaurs in catching fish. The occurrence of a number of rounded and polished gizzard stones, in association with plesiosaur skeletons, indicates that these reptiles did not depend on teeth to grind up food.

Turtles.   During Mesozoic time, as at the present day, there were turtles that lived in the sea. Their rounded body is flattened above and below, and encased in a bony or horny sheath. Flippers furnished the means of swimming. One of the marine turtles from the Cretaceous had a length of 11 feet and a width across the front flippers of 12 feet.

FLYING REPTILES

Some of the Mesozoic reptiles, collectively known as "pterosaurs" (wing lizards), learned to fly and eventually became highly modified for life in the air. The specialization of their skeleton is seen particularly in the modification of the arms to form supports for wide membranous wings, and in the general lightening of the bones of the skeleton. The limb bones are hollow and air-filled, as in birds. The wing structure of the pterosaurs, however, differs from that of birds, in which finger bones are fused together as support for strong feathers that grow from the skin. It differs also from the wing of the bat, which uses several elongated fingers to support the wing membrane. The pterosaur wing was supported by a very elongated fourth finger; the other fingers were short and could be used by the animal to hang from rocks or trees. Probably these reptiles could glide and soar better than they could fly by fluttering their poorly designed wings.

Pterosaurs range in size from creatures smaller than a sparrow to the great *Pteranodon,* found in the chalk beds of western Kansas, which attained a wingspread of more than 26 feet. The head of this huge flying reptile bore a long, sharp-pointed beak, and also a nearly equally long bony crest, which gives a most peculiar pickax-like appearance. The entire skeleton of *Pteranodon,* even in its mineralized state as a fossil, weighs hardly 5 pounds. Some pterosaurs had long tails, whereas others seem to have been tailless. The flying reptiles first appeared in Late Triassic time and persisted until near the close of the Cretaceous.

It is a curious fact that nearly all discovered remains of flying reptiles are preserved in marine deposits. The pterosaurs could soar through the air above land undoubtedly, and probably they did so. If they died on land, their bones happened not to be buried in stream or lake deposits where they might be preserved. The characteristic association of fossil flying reptiles with salt-water deposits, commonly also in places that must have been many scores of miles from nearest land, has been interpreted to mean that these animals lived on fishes, like several sorts of modern sea birds. They may have been able to glide almost tirelessly above the waters, but, as already noted, there is no reason to think that they were skillful, swift flyers. Presumably they could alight on the sea surface and rise again, else the supposition that their diet consisted largely of fishes must be discarded. That the flying reptiles were themselves captured and eaten by marine animals, such as the mosasaurs, perhaps, is suggested by observations of fossil hunters working in Cretaceous marine shale deposits of the Dakotas. Barnum Brown, of the American Museum of Natural History, recently spent part of a field season searching for pterosaur remains in the strata just mentioned and he was successful in finding some skeletons. Mostly, however, he discovered here and there only wing bones—nothing else. He concluded that the meaty part of the animals had been devoured by some marine beast of prey which had cast aside the leathery wings because they were entirely lacking in food value.

How pterosaurs could have gotten about when they were not flying is hard to understand. Surely they could not walk on their hind legs in bipedal manner, like a bird, nor does it seem that they could have waddled awkwardly on all fours, with wings folded back and using their three small front toes on the ground. These front toes obviously were useful for clutching a tree limb or rock ledge, and it is possible that the flying reptiles may have hung upside down like a bat.

270. Restoration of toothed diving bird from the Cretaceous of western Kansas. Skeletons of this bird *(Hesperornis)*, 6 feet long, show specialization in the lack of wings and the peculiar sideway articulation of the swimming legs. *(American Museum of Natural History.)*

BIRDS

Among fossil remains of Mesozoic backboned animals, are skeletons of birds. They comprise the most ancient known representation of the feathered clan, but if it were not for preservation of feathers associated with their skeletons, these extinct animals surely would be classified as reptiles. They would be judged to represent a divergent stock of reptiles, because they resemble the pterosaurs in having light hollow bones and very strong hip and breast girdles, yet differ greatly from pterosaurs in arm structure. They are clearly allied to the same group of reptiles that gave rise to the dinosaurs.

Unlike all modern birds, those of Mesozoic age had jaws lined with short, sharp teeth. Wing structure, on the other hand, corresponds to that of modern birds in that stiff, hard feathers, which are highly modified scales, are attached to the skin covering the fingers and lower arms, so as to make a flying surface that is very unlike that of the pterosaurs. Moreover, the development of feathers furnished a means of insulation that permitted evolution of a warm-blooded body, as in the mammals. Warm-blooded animals are adapted to a more active life than sluggish cold-blooded creatures.

The oldest known fossil birds (*Archaeopteryx, Archaeornis*) are represented by practically complete skeletons from Upper Jurassic rocks in Germany. They were pigeon-sized flying creatures that had a long lizard-like tail, extended laterally on each side by a row of feathers. The bones of the forelimb that form a wing are like those of a lizard in having the same number of joints and in having four separate fingers terminating in claws.

Marine Cretaceous rocks, representing former sea bottom that was many miles distant from the nearest land, have yielded the remains of a strong-winged archaic sea gull (*Ichthyornis*) that also had teeth. This bird must have been able to fly long distances over the Mesozoic seaways, now and then diving downward for fish.

Largest and most specialized of the known birds of Mesozoic age, is a large swimming and diving bird (*Hesperornis*) that somewhat resembles the modern loon. It attained an over-all length of 6 feet, as shown by well-preserved skeletons found in the Cretaceous chalk of western Kansas. The long strong legs indicate a powerful swimmer, but the joints at the pelvis show that the limbs could be moved only sideward and outward, not forward or backward, like those of modern birds in walking and swimming. *Hesperornis* would have had much trouble trying to get about on land. Although primitive in having many sharp teeth at edges of the jaws, this bird was specialized in having lost all functional use of its wings, which indeed were so rudimentary that they could not be used for paddles like those of a penguin.

MAMMALS

Remains doubtfully classed as mammalian, the stock to which man and the higher animals of the present belong, are found in the Triassic, but definitely recognizable primitive mammals occur in the Jurassic and Cretaceous rocks. The fossils consist of teeth, lower jaws, and fragmentary parts of the skeleton, all of which show that these animals were diminutive, rather insignificant creatures. Two groups are distinguished: (1) herbivorous forms, having teeth provided with several tubercles (multituberculates) and (2) probably insectivorous mammals, smaller than the first group and having sharp-cusped teeth.

The multituberculates appeared in the Late Triassic and persisted to Eocene time. They are the most abundant and successful type of

Mesozoic mammals. Probably they were egg-layers, but of this there is no proof.

The sharp-cusp-toothed mammals of probable insectivorous habits were small shrewlike creatures, which are judged to include the ancestors of the mammals of Cenozoic time. Most important are the trituberculates, which are known from Late Jurassic rocks of England and Wyoming, and from Late Cretaceous beds. Several primitive tiny opossums occur in Cretaceous deposits of North America.

The brain cavity in the skulls of Mesozoic mammals indicates that the intelligence of these animals was low as compared with later mammals, but it was higher than that of any of the reptiles. The mammals did not offer serious competition to the reptilian rulers of the Mesozoic world, but their line persisted, and with the decline of the dinosaurs, they began to expand sharply and to branch out in many directions. The rise of the mammals to rulership of the lands is the main theme of the Cenozoic history of life.

17. The Tertiary Period

Early Tertiary lake deposits at Bryce Canyon, Utah.

Chicago and Northwestern Railway

Definition

The Tertiary Period comprises all but a very small fraction of elapsed time belonging to the Cenozoic Era, which, according to computation based on study of radioactive minerals, began about 60 million years ago. The Quaternary Period, in which we now live, follows the Tertiary and is estimated to represent approximately 1 million years. Thus,

Tertiary is almost, but not quite, synonymous in span with Cenozoic. We recognize Tertiary as a period because it has become fixed in geologic literature of the world. The name was introduced in the middle of the eighteenth century to include geologically young deposits of mainly unconsolidated nature that overlie divisions then called "Primary" and "Secondary." Except in some European countries, use of these terms has long been abandoned.

First detailed study of Tertiary formations was made in the broad structural basin that encloses Paris in northern France, and accordingly this has been taken as the classic region for differentiation of standard divisions of the Tertiary section. A better standard of reference could hardly have been found, because it offers a nearly unbroken succession of highly fossiliferous deposits, in which marine formations alternate with continental beds. The Tertiary marine fossils of the Paris Basin are mostly preserved very beautifully, and they may be collected in abundance at many outcrops. The nonmarine deposits in places yield numerous vertebrates and other organic remains of the land. The study of some of these fossil vertebrates led the famous anatomist Cuvier to the conclusion—new and important at the time of its publication in 1812—that bones found in the Tertiary strata near Paris belonged to extinct species of animals having characters quite unlike any known living creatures.

Occurrence of Tertiary Deposits in North America

Recognition of Tertiary.   Cretaceous rocks of the Atlantic and Gulf coastal plains, and along the Pacific border in North America, are overlain by marine and nonmarine deposits, largely unconsolidated, that are obviously of geologically late origin. This is shown by their position above Cretaceous as uppermost part of stratified sedimentary materials in many localities, and it is strongly suggested, although not proved, by their widespread lack of induration. Many beds are abundantly fossiliferous. Comparison of assemblages of marine fossils, especially those of the eastern United States, with successive Tertiary faunas of the Paris Basin, abundantly demonstrates their close correspondence. Most genera are the same, and many species are almost identical. Thus, reasonably precise correlation of Tertiary deposits on opposite sides of the Atlantic is not difficult.

Marine deposits of Tertiary age along the Pacific more closely resemble the geologically recent marine deposits of eastern Asia than those of Europe, but there are enough cosmopolitan organisms to permit fairly satisfactory detailed correlation of this section also. An interesting and puzzling problem that is not yet solved, however, is partial lack of agreement between correlations based on foraminifers and correlations based on other marine invertebrates.

Land-plant remains also are generally similar, but are less readily and exactly correlated than the marine fossils.

The interior of North America, west of the Mississippi, contains very widespread continental deposits that are younger than Cretaceous. The great bulk of these belong to the Tertiary, and can be rather precisely dated by comparison of their plant and vertebrate remains with those of continental deposits interbedded with marine formations of the coastal plains. Thus, we have well-established grounds for recognizing and correlating most of the Tertiary formations of the continent. Study of the nature and fossil content of these deposits permits us to interpret the historical geology of Tertiary time in some detail, and to learn fascinating features of the evolution of mammals and other animals of recent earth history.

Character and distribution of formations. The Tertiary deposits of North America are naturally treated in three sections according to geographic distribution: (1) Atlantic and Gulf coastal plains, (2) Western Interior region, and (3) Pacific border region (Fig. 271). Marine strata form a large part of the section in the first and third areas, but the second is composed almost exclusively of continental deposits. Description of chief lithologic and structural characters and thickness of the Tertiary formations in these regions is given in connection with the outline of geologic history of the period.

Divisions. Both in Europe and in North America, the Tertiary System is recognized as containing main divisions that in upward order are named Paleocene, Eocene, Oligocene, Miocene, and Pliocene. These names are derived from a classification introduced about 100 years ago, based on the proportion of still-living species presumed to be represented among fossils collected from the marine Tertiary rocks.

The names of the Tertiary main divisions are formed from combination of the Greek word *kainos,* meaning recent, with other roots, as follows: Paleocene (*palaios,* ancient), Eocene (*eos,* dawn), Oligocene

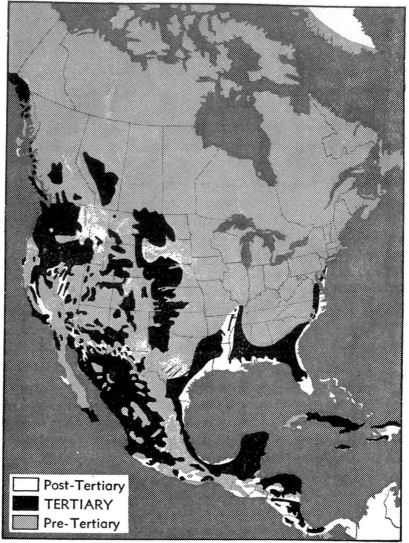

271. Distribution of Tertiary outcrops in North America. The large extent of Tertiary deposits, both in coastal areas and the interior of the continent, is shown by this map. Almost everywhere, the Tertiary formations are bordered on all sides by older rocks.

(*oligos,* little), Miocene (*meion,* less) and Pliocene (*pleion,* more). Actually this nomenclature based on comparison with modern marine faunas means comparatively little, because of variation from one region

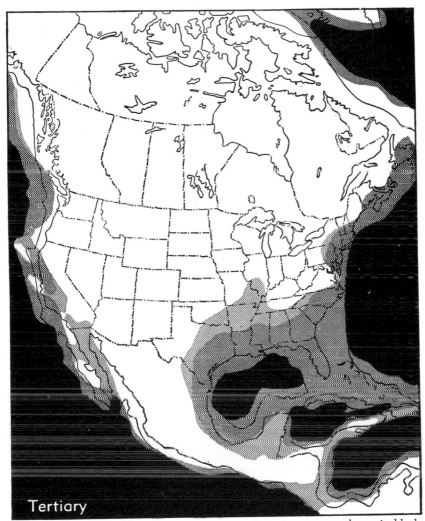

Tertiary

272. Distribution of Tertiary seas in North America. Oceanic areas are shown in black; the most persistent seaways on the continental platform are represented by dark gray; and areas submerged during only part of the period are indicated by light gray. The chief feature of Tertiary paleogeography is approximation to outline of the continent as it exists today. Extensive continental sedimentation, not represented on the map, occurred in the Western Interior.

to another and because close study indicates that hardly any living forms are precisely the same as those found in Early Tertiary marine formations. Also, comparison of marine organisms yields data entirely different from those provided by study of land vertebrates or plants. The divisions, however, are valid, because they record major oscillations of sea and land during the period and because they are defined by easily recognized distinctions of the faunas. Continental deposits of differing age also contain assemblages of mammals that are quite distinct one from the other.

Features of Tertiary Deposits and History

ATLANTIC AND GULF COASTAL PLANTS

Atlantic border. The coastal plain along the Atlantic, from Long Island to Florida, contains outcrops of Tertiary formations lying on

Series	Pacific Border	Western Interior	Gulf Coast	Atlantic Border	Europe Stages
PLIOCENE	Pico form.	Ogallala group	Citronelle form.	Caloosahatchee f.	ASTIAN
	Repetto form.				PLAISANCIAN
					PONTIAN
			Pascagoula clay	Yorktown form.	SARMATIAN
MIOCENE	Modelo form.	Hemingford group			TORTONIAN
			Hattiesburg clay	St. Marys form.	HELVETIAN
	Rincon sh.			Choptank form.	BURDIGALIAN
	Vaqueros ss.	Arikaree group	Tampa ls.	Calvert form.	AQUITANIAN
			Chickasawhay marl	Suwannee ls.	CHATTIAN
OLIGOCENE	Sespe form.	White River group	Vicksburg ls.		RUPELIAN
			Red Bluff clay		TONGRIAN
		Duchesne River f.			LUDIAN
		Uinta form.	Jackson form.	Ocala ls.	BARTONIAN
EOCENE	Tejon form.	Bridger form. / Green River form.	Claiborne group	McBean form.	AUVERSIAN
	Domengine f.				LUTETIAN
	Meganos form.	Wasatch form.	Wilcox form.	Wilcox form.	CUISIAN
					YPRESIAN
PALEOCENE	Martinez form.	Fort Union form.	Midway group	Clayton form.	THANETIAN
					MONTIAN

273. **Time-rock divisions of the Tertiary System and rock units in representative Tertiary sections of North America.** The vertical scale is not proportional to thickness or time duration, but the placement of names indicates correlation in age. The ruled areas denote absence of deposits.

274. Portion of the Atlantic Coastal Plain in Florida. Much of the area underlain by Tertiary formations in the coastal plains belt has a nearly flat surface; it is timber-covered or cleared for raising crops. Harder strata, especially sandstone, make hilly topography or low inland-facing cuestas.

the seaward side of the Cretaceous outcrop belt. In many places, the Tertiary extends to the present coast line, but elsewhere the Tertiary is separated from the sea by a narrow fringe of post-Tertiary deposits. The beds slope seaward at the rate of 20 or 30 feet to the mile, oldest beds having their outcrops farthest inland, and youngest occurring nearest to the sea. The formations consist mostly of soft clays and silts, interbedded with sand and some calcareous layers. Tertiary limestone deposits in Florida are associated with some of the largest springs in the United States.

Most of the strata yield readily to erosion. The topography of the outcrop areas is featureless, except for low hills or landward-facing escarpments made by some harder strata, and except for local stream dissection.

Gulf coastal plain. The coastal plain in the states bordering the Gulf of Mexico is much wider than that along the Atlantic, and the outcrop belt of Tertiary strata is correspondingly wider. South of the Rio Grande in Mexico, the plain is much narrowed, but it occupies virtually all of the peninsula of Yucatan.

At the outcrop, an alternating succession of continental and marine deposits is found, harder strata forming hilly uplands that commonly are well timbered, and weak rocks forming flat farm land. The outcrops form bands running approximately parallel to the coast, except in the neighborhood of the Mississippi River, where they curve north-

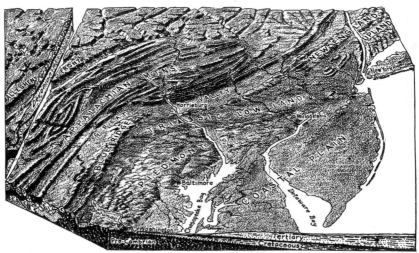

275. The Atlantic Coastal Plain and adjacent provinces in the Chesapeake Bay and New Jersey region. The relation of coastal plain sediments to underlying crystalline rocks is shown in section. The stratified sediments dip gently seaward, the Tertiary at lower rate than the Cretaceous. (*Redrawn from E. Raisz.*)

ward; here continuity of the belts is interrupted by post-Tertiary alluvial deposits of the Mississippi flood plain. As along the Atlantic, the oldest Tertiary formations are exposed farthest inland, and the youngest occur nearest the coast.

The beds dip seaward at angles of 30 or 40 feet to the mile and, as shown by numerous well borings, thicken rapidly in this direction. In southern Louisiana and southeastern Texas, the total thickness of Tertiary deposits is computed to be approximately 20,000 feet. Inasmuch as the nature of the deposits and their contained fossils indicates that they were laid down in shallow water (and some of them above sea level), this means that the crust must have subsided approximately at the rate of accumulation of the sediments. This is a geosynclinal belt at the margin of the continent.

Extent of marine invasion. Retreat of the sea in the Atlantic and Gulf regions at the close of Cretaceous time is indicated by the unconformity that separates the Cretaceous from the oldest Tertiary deposits. Throughout much of the present coastal plain area, there was evidently a time during which weathering and erosion of the exposed Mesozoic and older rocks were dominant. Then the sea invaded the land, extending beyond the innermost borders of the present Tertiary outcrop. In places, shallow marine waters extended beyond the Cretaceous onto older rocks. Although the maximum extent of the invasion probably did not reach many miles beyond the line of present Tertiary outcrops, it is obvious that erosion in later Cenozoic time has stripped away the original edge of the Early Tertiary marine deposits. At this time, near the beginning of the Tertiary Period, the sea reached northward into southern Illinois and southeastern Missouri.

Oscillations of the sea margin. Subsequent retreat of the sea is shown by occurrence of Middle and Late Tertiary continental beds at many places on the seaward side of outcrops of Early Tertiary marine deposits. The continental beds contain abundant plant remains and include beds of lignite. In a down-dip direction, as shown by samples from deep well borings, the nonmarine strata are found to pass at certain points into marine deposits, and from observations of this sort we can tell how far the sea retreated at different epochs. Deposition of marine beds covering nonmarine deposits proves local readvance of the Tertiary sea, and still higher nonmarine strata indicate retreat of the marine waters. The sea margin oscillated in this manner throughout Tertiary time, but in general, each flooding of the margins of the continent was less extensive than the one before. Thus the coast line gradually approached its present outline. The land area was progressively enlarged by outward building of sediments that more than compensated the downwarping at the continental borders.

Salt domes. A distinctive feature of the Tertiary coastal plains country in the Gulf region is the large number of salt plugs that penetrate the Tertiary beds from below. The plugs are cylindrical masses of rock salt, vertical-sided, circular, or elliptical in cross section, and 1 or 2 miles in diameter. On their flanks, the Tertiary strata are bent steeply upward against them, and an arched cover of Tertiary strata of varying thickness extends over the summit of the salt plugs. Accordingly, these structures are known as "salt domes." In the upbowed cap rock and upturned porous strata surrounding the salt masses, great accumulations of oil and gas have been formed in many places. The salt is not of Tertiary age, but is derived from pre-Tertiary sedimentary layers, probably formed during the Mesozoic Era. Thick layers of salt interbedded with Jurassic strata have been penetrated by deep wells in northern Louisiana (Chap. 14). Because the salt is light and relatively mobile, the weight of overlying sediments has forced it upward, like grease in a grease gun, wherever it can find escape. As shown by wells and observations in mines, the salt of the plugs is highly contorted as a result of its upward thrusting through the Tertiary deposits.

Erosion of the Appalachian and Mississippi Valley Regions

It is certain that the eastern and northern interior parts of North America, inside the coastal plain belt, were undergoing erosion throughout Tertiary time. Evidence supporting this conclusion includes the fact that (1) no deposits of consequence belonging to this period occur anywhere in the region mentioned; if such deposits had been formed, they could hardly have been stripped away entirely in the short time since the close of the Tertiary. (2) Study of the post-Cretaceous coastal plain sediments indicates their derivations from the interior of the continent, in part from areas closely adjacent to the plains and in part from distant sources, just as the present Mississippi River drainage carries sediment from headwaters of the Ohio

276. Geologic section of the Spindletop salt dome in eastern Texas. This typical salt dome, located at the south edge of Beaumont, Tex., has a cylindrical core of salt about a mile in diameter. Its nearly flat top is covered by hard caprock, mainly composed of dolomite and anhydrite that is encountered in wells at a depth of slightly more than 1,000 feet. The Tertiary formations surrounding the salt plug have been turned upward around it by vertical thrust of the rising salt mass. More than 130 million barrels of petroleum have been produced from the flanks and caprock of this dome. *(Humble Oil and Refining Company. Courtesy of Texas Memorial Museum.)*

and Missouri to the Gulf. (3) Effects of geologically recent erosion are found in features of the present land surface in the continent interior.

Peneplanation. The marks of prolonged erosion are most clearly evident in the Appalachian Mountains, where upturned edges of folded rocks are found smoothly beveled. Such even truncation of inclined rocks can be accomplished by wave work along a coast line, but in a

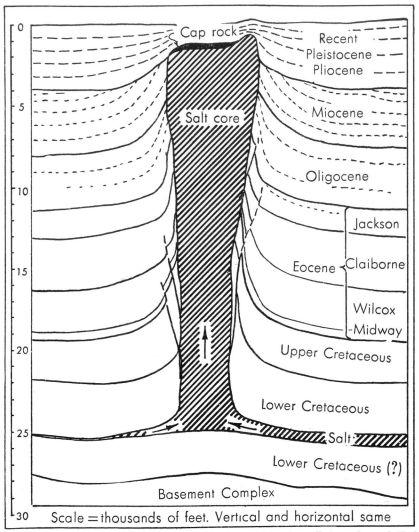

277. Diagrammatic section of a salt dome in the Gulf region. No wells have been drilled deeply enough to penetrate all of the rock divisions represented in the section with thicknesses as shown. Data from several areas are combined here with hypothetical drawing of the base of the salt plug.

broad inland area, such as the Appalachian region, it can mean only thorough peneplanation by the work of streams. The even sky line of Appalachian Mountain ridges, as typically shown in eastern Pennsylvania, marks the trace of an erosion surface that is known as the

Schooley peneplain. Undoubtedly much erosion occurred during the Mesozoic Era, but several lines of evidence indicate that the Schooley peneplain is not much, if any, older than mid-Tertiary.

When this peneplain was formed, the land surface was near base level, a few scores of feet at most above the sea. Except for monadnocks and unreduced uplands, such as the White Mountains area in New England and country of the Great Smokies in western North Carolina, the Appalachians were reduced to a featureless lowland that merged with the coastal plain. Rivers on this lowland crossed hard and soft rocks, uninfluenced by structure of rocks composing the plain. This was the nature of the land surface throughout much of Tertiary time. Then, in the latter part of the period there was a change. The whole region was moved vertically upward several hundred feet, and parts were upwarped more than 2,000 feet. This caused rejuvenation of the streams and relatively rapid erosion of weak rock belts, but hard rocks were worn down little. Main streams, like the Susquehanna and Delaware Rivers, were able to maintain their courses across hard rocks, and the places where they cut through the mountain ridges are known as water gaps; lesser streams became adjusted to the outcrop belts of weak strata. Eventually, extensive lowlands were etched out at the new base level, the relatively even surface of these lowlands being cut across the edges of weak formations. This is known as the Harrisburg erosion surface. A second rejuvenation has caused streams

278. Even-crested Appalachian Mountain ridges at the Susquehanna water gap near Harrisburg, Pa. The even summits of the mountains define the level of the Schooley peneplain. The nearest ridge is formed by Silurian sandstones (Tuscarora and Clinton). Those in the middle and far distance are composed of Mississippian sandstone (Pocono). *(Pennsylvania Geol. Survey.)*

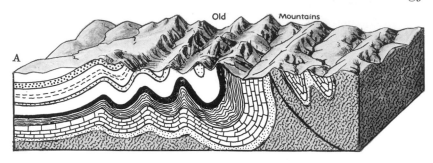

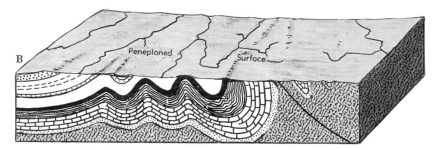

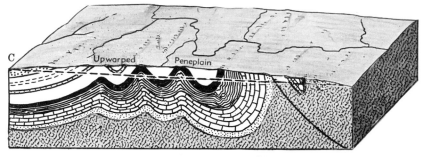

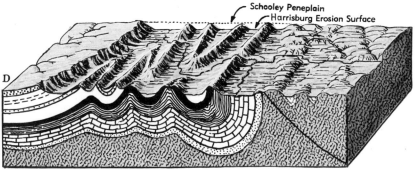

to incise their valleys to depths of several hundred feet below the Harrisburg surface and, accordingly, remnants of the Schooley peneplain are very high above the present valley bottoms. The greatest height of the warped Schooley peneplain above present sea level is about 4,000 feet.

Tertiary erosion in the Appalachian Mountain region thus comprises the completion of base leveling recorded by the Schooley peneplain, carving of valleys beneath the level of the Schooley peneplain down to the Harrisburg surface, and probably part of the erosion represented by valleys lying below the level of the Harrisburg surface. It is important to observe that, whereas the structure of the Appalachian Mountains was determined by earth movements near the close of Paleozoic times, the mountainous relief of this region is due entirely to erosion in late Cenozoic time, after upwarping of the Schooley peneplain.

The nearly flat-lying rocks of the Mississippi Valley and Great Lakes regions were also subject to erosion in Tertiary time. Some upland surfaces in this region may correspond to the Schooley peneplain in the Appalachians, but remnants of peneplaned surfaces are much less easily and definitely recognized in flat-rock country than where beveling of folded rocks is found. Also, the Mississippi Basin seems not to have been much uplifted during recent geologic history.

Erosion and Deposition in the Western Interior

Rocky Mountain region. The crustal deformation in the Rocky Mountain region, which brought the Mesozoic Era to a close, provided conditions that favored rapid erosion of some areas and accelerated deposition of erosion products in others. These conditions prevailed

---

279. Development of physiographic features in the Appalachian Mountain region. A. Irregular mountainous topography developed on folded rocks after the Appalachian revolution near the close of Permian time. B. Peneplaned surface produced by very prolonged erosion (Schooley peneplain before uplift.) C. Upwarped peneplain, amount of uplift being measured by the dotted line on the near face of the diagram. D. Present state of topographic development in the Appalachian Mountains after successive uplifts; weak strata have been carved into valleys, whereas the summit levels of hard rocks furnish trace of the Schooley peneplain.

throughout a large part of the western interior of the continent. The wearing away of the mountains supplied large quantities of gravel, sand, silt, and clay, which were carried by streams to adjoining plains and intermontane basins. In places, there were extensive lakes that became gradually filled by even-layered, fine sediments, mostly shale but including some fresh-water limestone.

The Tertiary deposits of the western interior region differ from those of the continental borders in that they are almost exclusively non-marine. Also most of them are highly variable in thickness and litho-logic character, inasmuch as they strongly reflect local conditions of topography and the nature of rocks undergoing erosion in near-by source areas of the sediment.

West of the Rocky Mountain front, Tertiary deposits are chiefly associated with structural basins within the mountain area. These depressions between uplifted parts of the range began to receive the products of erosion from the mountain areas early in Tertiary time; some of them are now found filled with stream-borne gravel, sand, silt, and clay to depths of 20,000 feet or more. Lake deposits occur in some of them; the most noteworthy are those of the Green River Basin in southwestern Wyoming and northwestern Colorado. Here, finely

280. Evenly bedded deposits of a great Eocene lake in northeastern Utah. This formation (Green River), more than 2,000 feet thick, covers an area of 50,000 square miles in Utah, Colorado, and Wyoming. It is rich in oil, which may be obtained from the shaly beds by distillation. *(D. E. Winchester, U. S. Geol. Survey.)*

281. Oligocene continental deposits in the Badlands of South Dakota. These river-laid silty deposits have been intricately carved by rain wash and stream erosion into gulleys, buttes, and ridges. In places, many well-preserved bones of mammals of the plains have been collected from these strata. *(N. H. Darton, U. S. Geol. Survey.)*

laminated oil shale, 2,000 feet thick, contains fresh-water organic remains from which more than 100 billion barrels of oil could be distilled. Beautifully preserved skeletons of fishes come from these lake deposits in Wyoming.

Plains region east of the Rockies. The plains country east of the Rocky Mountains, from New Mexico and Texas northward far into Canada, is blanketed by Tertiary continental formations ranging from oldest to youngest. The deposits were laid down by streams, which, by lateral shifting of their courses, built coalescent sheets and lenses of alluvial detritus, so as to form very gently sloping aggradational plains of vast extent. This depositional process was not a continuous or uniform one throughout all of the plains region, however. The earliest Tertiary deposits, for example, are confined to territory near the mountains in eastern New Mexico, Colorado, and Montana. In western Kansas and northwestern Texas, on the other hand, there are

282. Upper Oligocene (Brule) clay deposits near Chadron, in western Nebraska. (*N. H. Darton, U. S. Geol. Survey.*)

no Early Tertiary strata, and here uppermost Tertiary alluvial deposits rest directly on eroded Mesozoic and Paleozoic beds.

Divisions of the Tertiary, representing successively younger parts of the system, are identified by their fossil remains, chiefly many kinds of mammal bones, but including also the leaves of trees and shrubs and fossil seeds of grasses. Thus the changing nature and areas of sedimentation in the plains can be determined, and times of temporary interruption, accompanied by erosion, may be identified. Coal swamps existed early in Tertiary time in much of the Wyoming, Dakota, Montana, and Alberta portions of the plains country.

Marine deposits in North Dakota. A single area of marine strata, which are classed as belonging to earliest Tertiary, occurs in western North Dakota, where 200 to 300 feet of dark shaly beds containing oysters, foraminifers, and other marine organisms overlie uppermost Cretaceous dinosaur-bearing beds, and interfinger laterally with basal Tertiary plant-bearing continental deposits. This interesting, isolated occurrence of marine strata gives record of the last remnant of the great interior sea, which in Cretaceous time had stretched from the

Gulf of Mexico to the Arctic. Some of the fossils are most like forms occurring in marine deposits at the base of the Tertiary in the Gulf region, but there is no evidence at all of any salt-water connection between North Dakota and the Gulf at this time.

Colorado Plateau region. The high plateau country of Utah is capped by Tertiary sedimentary formations and extrusive igneous rocks, mostly basaltic lavas. The brilliant color and fantastic sculpture of some of these rocks, as seen in such places as Bryce Canyon, attract interest of the tourist, but such attraction is superficial compared to that offered by this region to students of Tertiary geologic history. In Middle Tertiary time the plateau country was broken along several long north-south faults. The ruggedness of this region at the present day is partly an expression of these structural movements, but mainly the work of tremendous erosion accomplished during Cenozoic time. This erosion has stripped away Tertiary and older rocks from many thousand square miles of the plateau country, causing retreat of the cliff margins of the plateaus and mesas and carving an intricate network of impassable canyons. Although the main drainage pattern and much of the denudation of the plateau region, as now seen, had been accomplished at the close of Tertiary time, the carving of the Grand Canyon and the deepening of innumerable tributary canyons of the Colorado River are mainly the work of post-Tertiary erosion.

Great Basin and Columbia Plateau region. To the west and north of the Colorado Plateau are the Great Basin and Columbia Plateau, which comprise semidesert country extending westward to the front of the Sierra Nevada and Cascade Range. Tertiary continental deposits and igneous rocks are very widespread in this region, but almost all the Tertiary rocks belong to the later half of the system. Nevada contains many north-trending mountain ranges formed by complexly folded and thrust-faulted Paleozoic and Mesozoic rocks. Between the mountains are wide, flat-floored desert valleys, which are underlain by fills of Late Tertiary and Recent sediment. The borders of the valleys, on one or both sides, approximately coincide with normal faults having displacements of several hundred to some thousands of feet. The country is thus broken into crustal blocks, and materials eroded from the uptilted edges of the blocks have been carried into depressions formed by down-dropped portions of the blocks. The fact that older Tertiary beds are mostly lacking and that the bottom portion of fills begins with Late Tertiary (Miocene) indicates that the block faulting occurred chiefly before the mid-part of the period. The presence of post-Tertiary faulting and of earthquakes originating in this region shows that the Great Basin has not yet reached crustal stability.

The Columbia Plateau lies north of the Great Basin. It comprises an area of about 200,000 square miles, in which innumerable sheets of basaltic lava are found interbedded with clay, sand, and reworked volcanic material. As shown by sections exposed along the Snake, Columbia, and other major streams, the lavas were poured out on country of considerable topographic relief, composed mainly of Paleozoic and Pre-Cambrian rocks. The lavas and associated sedimentary materials, that filled in irregularities of the old land surface, accumulated ultimately to a thickness of 5,000 feet in places. Fossils, including both plant and vertebrate remains, contained in the sedimentary strata, are mid-Tertiary and younger, which shows that the enormous volcanic activity belongs in the later part of the Tertiary Period. Con-

283. Mount Hood in northern Oregon, near Portland. The sides of this Tertiary volcanic cone have been made angular by water and ice erosion. The mountain, which has a summit elevation of 11,225 feet, rises steeply above the erosion surface marked by accordant tops of the Cascade Mountains. (*Courtesy of Chicago and Northwestern Railway.*)

284. Crater Lake, in southwestern Oregon. This lake, which is 2,000 feet deep and about 6 miles in diameter, is more than 6,000 feet above sea level. The precipitous walls surrounding the lake rise 500 to 2,200 feet above the water. From this jagged rim the country slopes away in all directions, as from a volcanic cone. In fact, the mountain is an old Tertiary volcano. Wizard Island is a volcanic cone within the crater. *(Courtesy of Chicago and Northwestern Railway.)*

tinuation of igneous extrusion in post-Tertiary time is plainly indicated by the freshness of lava flows and cinder cones in many places, such as the Craters of the Moon area in southern Idaho. Volcanic mountains in the adjacent Cascade Range, such as Mt. Rainier, Mt. Hood, Mt. Adams, and others, have not been active in historic time, but eruptions have occurred in recent years at Mt. Lassen in northern

California. Crater Lake, in southern Oregon, was formed by the explosive destruction of the top portion of one of the Tertiary volcanoes, Mt. Mazama.

PACIFIC BORDER

Tertiary history of the Pacific border of North America is distinguished by the considerable erosion of uplifted crustal blocks in the Sierra Nevada and Coast Ranges, accompanied by thick sedimentation in depressed adjacent blocks, the largest of which comprises the Great Valley of California. The blocks are bounded by faults along which movements have occurred repeatedly, and associated compressive stresses have folded the Tertiary strata with varying intensity at different times during the period. Angular unconformities are found

285. Sea cliff near La Jolla, Calif., showing Tertiary rocks. The deposits consist of unevenly stratified sandstone that contains numerous concretions. Tertiary formations of the California region are characterized by variation from one area to another and by great aggregate thickness.

286. Signal Hill oil field, near Los Angeles, Calif. This is one of the highly productive California oil fields, developed in Tertiary rocks. The anticlinal structure that controls accumulation of the oil is topographically expressed by the broad hill. *(Spence Air Photos.)*

between various divisions of the Tertiary, and there is great inequality in thickness of the deposits from place to place. Marine formations predominate, but there are also continental sediments. Aggregate maximum thickness of all these deposits exceeds 50,000 feet, but such thickness is not found in any one area.

The Sierra Nevada, which border the California Valley on the east, are composed mainly of Late Jurassic granitic rocks that were exposed and peneplaned by pre-Tertiary erosion. The peneplaned surface is tilted toward the west and disappears beneath Tertiary and younger sediments of the Great Valley. Along the east front of the mountains is a major fault, along which rocks of the range have been moved upward, and those of the Great Basin dropped greatly, at some points (as in Death Valley) below sea level. The upward movements that have produced the modern Sierra Nevada, began about mid-Tertiary

287. Tertiary formations in the southern part of the Great Valley of California. The depression lying between the Sierra Nevada and Coast Ranges of California was repeatedly invaded by water from the Pacific during Tertiary time, and this basin contains continental deposits belonging to this period also. Parts of the area are rich in petroleum. The view shows part of the Buena Vista oil field and the city of Taft. *(Spence Air Photos.)*

time, and erosion of the many deep valleys, such as Yosemite and Feather River Canyon, have been carved during Late Tertiary and subsequent time.

In western Oregon and Washington, the Cascade Mountains are essentially a northward continuation of the Sierra Nevada, and they also were pushed upward by essentially vertical movements in Late Tertiary time. Parts of this range contain thick accumulations of Early Tertiary sedimentary and igneous rocks, now tilted and faulted, and above these occur Late Tertiary and Quaternary volcanics. Folded Tertiary deposits are confined to the Willamette and Puget Valleys, west of the Cascades. The Coast Range, which forms mountainous uplands between these valleys and the sea, is composed of strongly folded and faulted Tertiary marine and nonmarine deposits, the latter containing many coal beds.

288. The San Andreas fault, intersecting Tertiary rocks in California. This fault line, traced from the coast north of San Francisco for a distance of more than 500 miles southeastward, is one of the major boundaries between crustal blocks that in Tertiary time were buried by varying sorts and thicknesses of deposits. Displacements along the fault have occurred as recently as 1906 when movement caused the San Francisco earthquake. Strongly deformed Tertiary rocks of the Indio Hills and alluvial deposits are seen in this view to terminate at the fault line. *(Spence Air Photos.)*

Tertiary Life

Both on land and in the sea, noteworthy differences are recorded by fossils known from earliest Tertiary strata and those of late Mesozoic age. Among vertebrates of the land, the oustanding changes are disappearance of dinosaurs, flying reptiles, and toothed birds, and with the vanishing of these forms, there is a rise to dominant position of early types of mammals and advent of modern types of toothless birds. From the sea, the specialized aquatic reptiles, such as plesiosaurs, ichthyosaurs, and mosasaurs, were gone, and there were no

289. Restoration of Late Tertiary horses and elephants. Skeletal remains of these and many other mammals are abundant in Tertiary formations of western North America. The fossil forms shown in this restoration are of Pliocene age. Both horses and elephants became extinct in North America in Quaternary time. (*American Museum of Natural History.*)

longer any ammonites among marine invertebrates. These are remarkable changes, and they are seemingly greater in view of their abruptness.

Tertiary mammals were no longer exclusively diminutive creatures, like ancestors of these animals in Mesozoic strata. Small mammals persisted, but along with them were some that exceeded the elephant in size and weight. One of the evolutionary trends was the average increase in size, and another the specialization of teeth and limbs. The mammals multiplied greatly in variety and numbers and became adapted to all sorts of habitats on land, in the air, and in fresh and salt water. The main types of Tertiary mammals, together with other organisms, are described in Chap. 19. We may note here only the facts that mammalian fossils are chief in importance among organic remains of continental Tertiary deposits, and that the bones found at many horizons have great value for correlating the strata laid down in different basins.

Marine invertebrate faunas of Early Tertiary time are especially characterized by abundance of relatively large disk-shaped foraminifers having very numerous internal chambers. These fossils, collectively called "nummulites" (little coin), are so abundant in Eocene strata of the Mediterranean and Himalayan regions, that they are important rock builders. They occur also in equivalent deposits of the Gulf and Caribbean region of the Western Hemisphere. Other types of foraminifers are abundant in younger Tertiary deposits and are much used for correlating beds penetrated in deep wells.

On the whole, marine invertebrates of Tertiary age show great similarity to faunas living on the shallow sea bottom today and, as already noted, this resemblance increases upward from Paleocene to Pliocene. Gastropods and pelecypods are dominant types of shelled animals, but most of the phyla are well represented. Inasmuch as Tertiary time is almost coextensive with the Cenozoic Era, it is appropriate to reserve most of our survey of Tertiary life for Chap. 19.

Many well-preserved leaves of land plants occur in some continental Tertiary beds. They represent living genera of trees, shrubs, and grasses, for the most part. They furnish valuable evidence concerning climatic environments, and many of these fossils are very useful for correlation of zones.

Climate

Throughout most of Tertiary time, the United States, most of Europe, and various other lands now belonging in cool, temperate zones, had a warmer, wetter, and more equable climate than now. This is indicated by occurrence of subtropical types of trees, including palms, as far north as Saskatchewan and Alberta, and by common occurrence of large alligators, such as now roam the bayous of Louisiana and swamps of Florida. In far northerly latitudes of Alaska, Greenland, and Siberia, were forests of large redwood, elm, oak, walnut, and other trees that denote a moderately warm, moist, temperate climate. Fossil leaves of the magnolia and fig trees have been found in Tertiary deposits of Alaska.

In contrast to this widespread evidence of warm, moist climate,

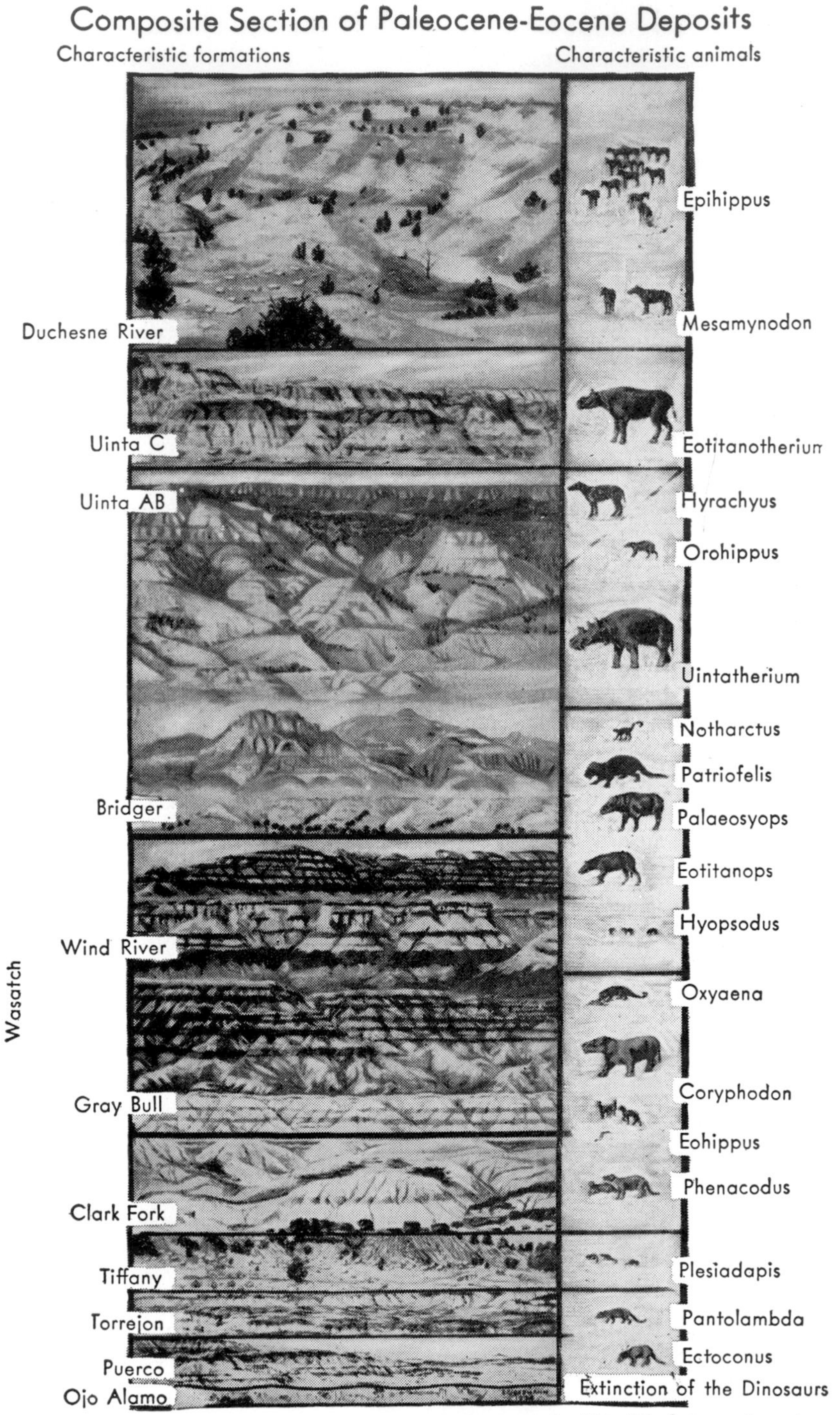

Composite Section of Paleocene-Eocene Deposits

Characteristic formations

Characteristic animals

- Epihippus
- Mesamynodon

Duchesne River

Uinta C
- Eotitanotherium

Uinta AB
- Hyrachyus
- Orohippus
- Uintatherium

- Notharctus
- Patriofelis

Bridger
- Palaeosyops
- Eotitanops
- Hyopsodus

Wind River
- Oxyaena

Wasatch
- Coryphodon

Gray Bull
- Eohippus
- Phenacodus

Clark Fork

Tiffany
- Plesiadapis

Torrejon
- Pantolambda

Puerco
- Ectoconus

Ojo Alamo
- Extinction of the Dinosaurs

290. Early Tertiary continental deposits and typical mammals. (*Modified from American Museum of Natural History.*)

Composite Section of Oligocene Deposits of North America

Characteristic formations · Characteristic animals

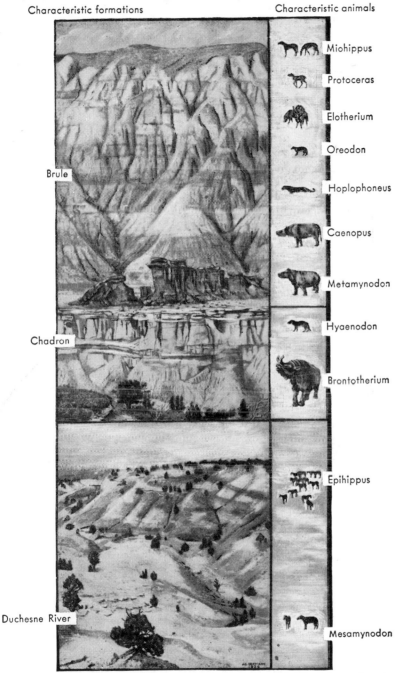

Miohippus

Protoceras

Elotherium

Oreodon

Brule

Hoplophoneus

Caenopus

Metamynodon

Hyaenodon

Chadron

Brontotherium

Epihippus

Duchesne River

Mesamynodon

291. Oligocene continental deposits and typical mammals. (*Modified from American Museum of Natural History.*)

292. Late Tertiary continental deposits and typical mammals. (*Modified from American Museum of Natural History.*)

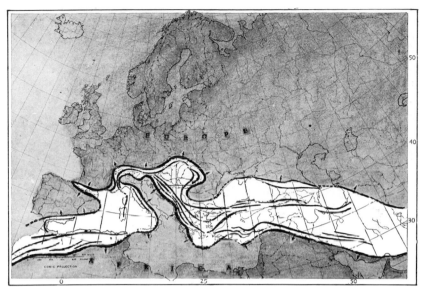

293. The Alpine mountain fold belt in southern Europe. The axes of main mountain chains are shown in black, with arrows indicating the direction of folding and thrusting of the rocks. The fold system, produced mainly by deformation in Tertiary time, represents great squeezing and uplifting of the thick sedimentary strata laid down in the geosynclinal belt, which in Mesozoic and Tertiary time separated the relatively rigid crustal masses of Europe in the north and Africa in the south.

glacial deposits of Eocene age have been found in southwestern Colorado. Cold climate seems to be associated with formation of mountains, which modify atmospheric circulation, induce precipitation, and make for local climatic variation. The Tertiary glacial deposits in Colorado are related in origin to mountains of the Laramian revolution. As these mountains were worn down and as sediments derived from them were poured into adjacent basins, a lowland type of warm uniform climate prevailed in this region during later parts of the Tertiary Period.

Mountain Building

The Tertiary Period embraces part of earth history when mountain building, unusual in magnitude and world-wide extent, deformed the earth crust. The folding and faulting associated with this mountain building were not concentrated in time near the close of the period, nor do they seem to have been going on steadily during the period.

There were epochs, as during the Eocene, when seas were comparatively expanded over parts of the continents, and both the type of sedimentation in various basins and the regularity of sequence of deposits bear witness to the absence of noteworthy mountains near the areas of deposition. Such evidence points to at least temporary crustal stability.

Strong mountain-making movements can be dated as belonging within the Tertiary Period, however, and insofar as the geologic date of deformation can be determined precisely, the times of crustal unrest in different places seem mainly to coincide with changes that define boundaries of the Tertiary epochs: Paleocene, Eocene, Oligocene, Miocene, and Pliocene. Thus, the chief folding and faulting of rocks witnessed in the structurally complex Pyrenees Mountains, between France and Spain, can be shown to belong at or near the close of Eocene time, because Eocene and older rocks are greatly disturbed, whereas Oligocene and younger strata on the flanks of the uplift are not affected.

The Alps Mountains are the result of several distinct deformations. Parts of this region were involved in late Paleozoic folding, but uplifted rocks of such ancient date were worn down long before the modern Alps were made. Evidence of considerable displacement of Alpine formations, indicating uplift of mountains in the Mediterranean area, is identified as approximately coincident with the Laramian revolution at the close of the Mesozoic Era. Other crustal movements occurred in different parts of the Alps, Carpathians, Apennines, and related ranges of the great Alpine chain, near the close of the Eocene, at the end of the Oligocene, during and near the close of the Miocene, and near the close of Pliocene time. The most general and profound deformation is judged to belong in late Miocene. The topographic elevation and ruggedness of the modern Alps are attributed mainly to post-Tertiary vertical upwarping of the highly disturbed strata that had been folded and faulted during the several orogenies mentioned.

The Himalayas, Andes, and Coast Ranges of the Pacific border of North America, also were made chiefly during Tertiary time, although all had undergone earlier deformation. In the Himalayas, there are Early Tertiary marine strata at elevations of 20,000 feet above sea level.

18. The Quaternary Period

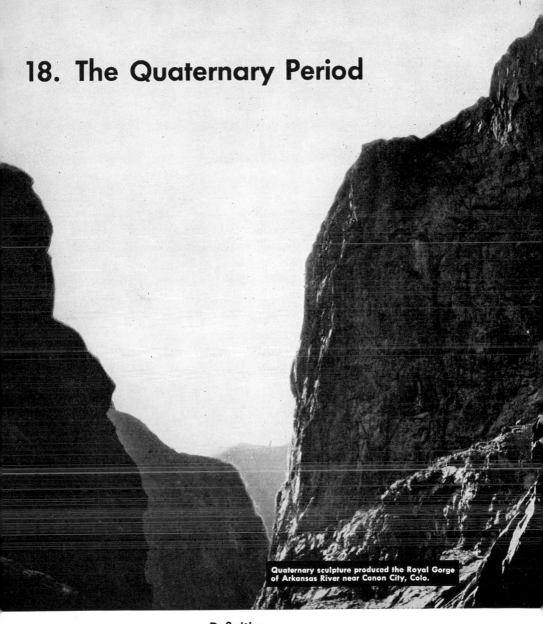

Quaternary sculpture produced the Royal Gorge of Arkansas River near Canon City, Colo.

Definition

Quaternary time is very short compared with other geologic periods, but, because it includes the present and most recent geologic past, its history is especially interesting and important to man. The beginning of the Quaternary Period dates back a mere million years or so, and therefore the record is so recently inscribed, that multitudinous details can be read clearly. Not only are there many sorts of sedimentary deposits and large quantities of igneous rocks, but the work of erosion during the period is marked by innumerable features of the present land surface. Historical geology merges here with physiography.

The outstanding feature in the history of Quaternary time is extensive continental glaciation in the Northern Hemisphere. Although ice covered only a fraction of the total land surface of the globe, effects of the glaciation were world-wide, for important changes in climate and conditions of erosion and deposition affected nonglaciated as well as glaciated territory. Changed environments influenced life on land and to some extent in the sea. World-wide changes of oceanic levels were caused by the removal of water to make the continental glaciers, and by the return of water when the glaciers melted. In addition, there were crustal disturbances, which include broad warping of continents and local mountain-making movements.

After the rocks called Tertiary were defined, the name Quaternary came to be applied many years ago by French and German geologists to the unconsolidated surficial materials, such as the alluvium of stream valleys, recent deposits in lakes and swamps, dune sand, and glacial deposits.

It was not at first understood that the widespread glacial materials of northern Europe and North America were deposits made by great continental ice sheets. These deposits were called "drift," because it was thought that they were carried by icebergs that drifted in waters of Noah's flood. When the boulder-laden bergs chanced to graze bedrock beneath the water, scratches (striae) were made on the bedrock and boulders.

When Agassiz, in 1837, pointed to evidence that glaciers of the Alps had formerly spread far out on the plains at the foot of the mountains, and suggested that all of northern Europe had been buried by a huge glacier in comparatively recent geologic time, the scientific world was incredulous. The correctness of Agassiz's deductions, however, has been established completely and irrefutably. The deposits of continental glaciers have foremost importance among Quaternary formations and, as commonly defined, Quaternary time is considered to have begun with initiation of the continental glaciation that followed the making of Tertiary deposits.

294. Exposure of typical glacial till forming part of a moraine that runs the length of Long Island, N. Y. Deposits formed by melting of glacial ice are a characteristic type of sedimentary record of Quaternary time in glaciated parts of North America. These regions also contain much stratified drift. (*W. C. Alden, U. S. Geol. Survey.*)

Occurrence of Quaternary Deposits in North America

Recognition of deposits. Throughout the glaciated portions of North America, deposits formed by ice and by melt water from ice can be recognized as belonging to the Pleistocene Series, or at least to the Quaternary System. We must remember that glaciers of Recent age exist in the far north and in western mountain ranges of the continent. Also assignable to the Quaternary are stream-laid sediments, old soil layers, peat deposits, loess, and lake beds that overlie or are interbedded with glacial till, or otherwise are linked definitely with glacial materials. These relations prove contemporaneity with some part of Pleistocene deposits or age younger than glacial materials. Clay, sand, and other sediment laid in existing or extinct lakes of glacial origin, are partly or wholly Pleistocene, but they may include Recent materials. These and many other sorts of surficial formations may be distinguished as Quaternary in age by taking account of their physiographic and structural relations, lack of consolidation, and fossil content. There are no simple means or uniformly applicable rules for

295. Bare-rock glaciated upland surface on Mount Desert Island, Maine. This view clearly shows how erosion by an ice sheet tends to smooth topography by grinding away rock obstructions in its path. Materials eroded from this area were deposited farther south. *(W. C. Alden, U. S. Geol. Survey.)*

differentiating all types of Quaternary deposits, even in the glaciated regions.

In land areas of the continent that never were covered by Quaternary glaciers, the problem of recognizing sedimentary and igneous formations that should be assigned to post-Tertiary time is often very difficult. Geologically very recent units may be classed confidently as Quaternary, but if evidence points to geologic age appreciably greater than very recent, there may be question as to placement of the units in Quaternary or Tertiary. Organic remains, if present, may furnish important help, both directly, by permitting correlation with fossil-bearing deposits associated with glacial formations, and indirectly, by giving information as to probable climatic environment.

Marine deposits are being formed today on most parts of the continental shelf, and at varying rate, similar deposits undoubtedly were formed in the same places during earlier Quaternary time. In addition, the sea is known to have invaded, in comparatively recent time, parts of the continent that now are above sea level, for evenly stratified sediments containing marine organic remains of near-modern types are found. Some of these deposits overlie glacial materials. In general, the marine Quaternary formations lie conformably on latest Tertiary deposits of similar origin, and the boundary marking the base of strata classed as Quaternary is commonly placed just below the lowest beds containing fossils that indicate a cold-water assemblage. Such definition, however, is somewhat arbitrary and is not well correlated with methods of separating Tertiary and post-Tertiary nonmarine deposits.

Distribution and character of Quaternary formations. Glacial deposits are found in an area of about 4,000,000 square miles in northern North America, or nearly one half of the continent, which was cov-

296. A glacial erratic, 8 inches in longer diameter, scratched and smoothly abraded on one face by ice action. This boulder, from glacial drift in Iowa, shows nearly uniform direction of fine striations, which signifies that it was held rigidly in the ice during abrasion. Naturally, such striae on a boulder are valueless in throwing light on the direction of ice movement in the area where the boulder was deposited. (*W. C. Alden, U. S. Geol. Survey.*)

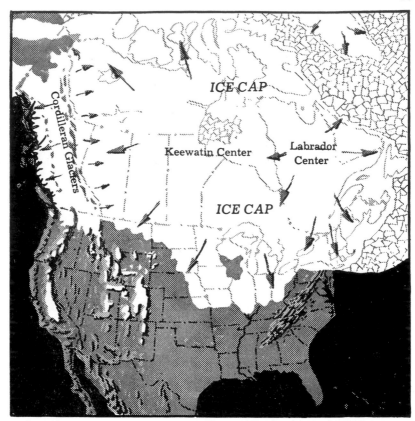

297. Maximum area covered by ice in Quaternary time and centers of glacial movement.
Glacial ice did not cover all of the area here represented at any one time. The ice
reached southward varying distances at different times and places, and the map is a
composite of all these advances. Although glaciated territory surrounds unglaciated
country in southwestern Wisconsin, the latter is judged never to have been entirely
surrounded by glacial ice. The shaded land areas of North America contain various
types of nonglacial Quaternary deposits.

ered by glacial ice during part of the Pleistocene Epoch. The glaciated
region includes almost all of Canada, Newfoundland, and Greenland,
and reaches southward in the United States almost to the mouth of
the Ohio. The southern border of the drift-covered area is roughly
defined by the courses of the Ohio and Missouri Rivers.

Quaternary formations and surface features, outside of the glaciated area, are the result of work by wind, running water, ground water, lakes and swamps, the sea, and organisms living on land or in the sea.

The Atlantic coastal plain, from New Jersey to Florida, is covered by a veneer of Quaternary deposits consisting of clay, loam, sand, gravel, and peat or swamp muck; in parts of the north, there are scattered ice-floated boulders. These materials, which are partly marine and partly nonmarine, largely conceal older formations on the interstream areas, and are chiefly confined to parts of the plain below an elevation of about 250 feet. They rest unconformably on older formations, from Tertiary to Pre-Cambrian. Well-defined terraces, carved and built by the sea at different levels, show that at different times in Quaternary Period the level of the sea was higher than now. A considerable part of Florida is mantled by Quaternary marine limestone of shelly, oolitic, or marly character. Similar deposits are now being formed offshore and coral reefs are being built.

The plains region bordering the Gulf of Mexico contains marine Pleistocene sand and clay, exposed in a belt 15 to 20 miles wide along the shore in western Florida and Alabama. Flat lowland, 50 to 100 miles wide along the Louisiana and Texas coast, is composed of Quaternary clay, sand, and calcareous material. As shown by well records, the thickness of these deposits locally exceeds 2,000 feet, showing that the coastal region has progressively sunk as sediment was laid down.

Stream deposits form a very important part of the Quaternary formations of the Gulf region, for they comprise not only the great delta and flood plain of the lower Mississippi but alluvial deposits of many other streams. During Quaternary time, the Mississippi delta was built seaward not less than 125 miles.

Stream deposits of valleys, terraces, and uplands, and wind deposits, including loess and dune sand, are the chief Quaternary materials of the great interior plains region south of the glaciated territory. Part of the calcium-carbonate-cemented sand and gravel that mantle the high plains east of the Rockies is undoubtedly of Pleistocene age, as is indicated by animal remains contained in these deposits. The calcium carbonate is carried by percolating ground water and deposited from it by evaporation, forming caliche. In this way it makes a cap rock, which retards stream erosion and serves to preserve great areas of featureless plains, as especially well shown in western Kansas and northwestern Texas.

In the Rocky Mountain region and mountainous area farther west, Quaternary deposits include huge quantities of boulders, gravel, sand, alluvium, clay, and calcareous material in valley bottoms, lake beds, talus piles, alluvial fans, landslides, and spring deposits. Formation of all of these is taking place at the present time. The deposits of streams and sheet wash vastly predominate over those of lakes, wind, and other agents of sedimentation. The large depressions between the many mountain ranges of the Great Basin are deeply filled with Quaternary water-borne waste, the thickness of which is measured locally in thousands of feet. Boulders, cobbles, and finer detritus are carried downward from the mountains by torrents and deposited in rudely stratified fans sloping toward depressions, which may be occupied temporarily by shallow lakes (playas).

The Pacific border region contains very thick accumulations of Pleistocene and Recent fluviatile gravels, sands, and clays, as well as marine deposits near the coast, which in places are nearly 1,000 feet

298. Nonglacial Quaternary deposits in the valley of Snake River, southern Idaho. The evenly layered thin strata shown in this view consist of fine volcanic materials and water-worn pebbles laid down in a shallow lake. They are one of the many sorts of nonglacial deposits made during Quaternary time. (*W. C. Alden, U. S. Geol. Survey.*)

299 The summit of Mauna Loa, a great volcanic mountain in Hawaii. Volcanism was active during Quaternary time in many places and continues to the present day. This view shows steep-walled craters and lava streams. The slope of the mountain is unusually low because of the highly fluid nature of the lava. (*U. S. Army Air Force.*)

above present sea level. Diastrophic movements, involving folding and faulting of the rocks, accompanied by earthquake, have been so numerous in late geologic time that the region is undergoing change from this cause almost continuously. Steeply tilted and faulted Pleistocene beds are found. Some narrow coastal plains are recently elevated portions of the sea floor.

Igneous rocks of Quaternary age are generally not clearly differentiated from those belonging to the late part of the Tertiary, but the western part of North America contains many extensive lava flows and cinder cones that clearly are geologically very young. Some of the lava covers comparatively recent alluvium of stream valleys, and in many places the surface of the flows shows ropy and cindery structure identical with recently congealed lava of the Hawaiian volcanoes. Because there is little or no soil, vegetation has as yet not been able to gain a foothold upon the lava. Cinder cones appear as though they were formed but yesterday, and might at any time resume their growth.

Divisions. The Quaternary Period is divided into two very unequal

300. Mount Edgecombe, a volcanic mountain in southeastern Alaska. This is a recently active volcano of the explosive type that erupts large quantities of ash and pumice. (*U. S. Navy.*)

parts: the Pleistocene Epoch, comprising about 98 per cent of the period, and the Recent Epoch, including the remainder.

The Pleistocene Series includes deposits of glacial, fluviatile, lacustrine, eolian, volcanic, and marine origin. The Recent Series, likewise, comprises all these types of deposits, and it is obvious that the boundary separating the main divisions of the Quaternary is rather artificial. If glacial climate, which prevails today in high latitudes, recurs a few thousand years hence in the latitude of St. Louis or Boston, new invasions of continental ice sheets will obliterate cities and farms. Then it will be clear that present time should be classed as a subdivision of the Pleistocene, and not as a separate epoch.

The Pleistocene glacial deposits are divisible into four main parts, which are separated by unconformities. These parts are the deposits of as many distinct glaciations of the continent. Just as in other periods, advances of the sea on the land are marked by marine deposits and the retreats by unconformities, so invasions of the Pleistocene continental glaciers are recorded over thousands of square miles by till and fluvioglacial debris, and times of deglaciation are marked by weathering and erosion of the glacial deposits that constitute unconformities.

Proof that the glacial history of the Pleistocene Epoch is really complex and that there were a number of advances and retreats of the glaciers, separated by long interglacial ages, is second in importance only to the establishment of the fact of continental glaciation itself. Demonstration of multiple glaciation in the Pleistocene has come mainly through work during the past 50 years in the Mississippi Valley region, but it is well shown also in Europe. Divisions of the Pleistocene deposits are time-rock units classed as stages, of which some are glacial and some interglacial. The names of these units are applied also to corresponding time divisions, called "ages." The classification is shown in the accompanying table (Fig. 301).

Series	North America STAGES		Great Lakes and Mississippi Valley	Lower Mississippi Valley	Europe STAGES
RECENT	(Unnamed)		Alluvium, lake and swamp deposits, peat, dune sand	Alluvium, lake and swamp deposits, and marine deposits	River, lake, glacial, wind, and marine deposits
PLEISTOCENE	Wisconsinan (glacial)	Mankatoan	Mankato till	(Valley cutting)	Würmian (glacial)
PLEISTOCENE	Wisconsinan (glacial)	Caryan	Cary till	(Valley cutting)	Würmian (glacial)
PLEISTOCENE	Wisconsinan (glacial)	Tazewellian	Tazewell till	(Valley cutting)	Würmian (glacial)
PLEISTOCENE	Wisconsinan (glacial)	Iowan	Peoria loess / Iowa till	Prairie formation	Würmian (glacial)
PLEISTOCENE	Sangamonian (interglacial)		Sangamon gumbotil	Montgomery f.	Riss-Würmian (interglacial)
PLEISTOCENE	Illinoian (glacial)		Illinois till	(Valley cutting)	Rissian (glacial)
PLEISTOCENE	Yarmouthian (interglacial)		Yarmouth gumbotil	Bentley formation	Mindel-Rissian (interglacial)
PLEISTOCENE	Kansan (glacial)		Kansas till	(Valley cutting)	Mindelian (glacial)
PLEISTOCENE	Aftonian (interglacial)		Afton gumbotil and gravel	Williana formation	Günz-Mindelian (interglacial)
PLEISTOCENE	Nebraskan (glacial)		Nebraska till	(Valley cutting)	Günzian (glacial)

301. **Time-rock divisions of the Quaternary System and rock units in representative Quaternary sections of North America.** The vertical scale is not proportional to thickness or time duration, but the placement of names indicates correlation in age. The ruled areas denote absence of deposits.

Features of Quaternary History of North America

GLACIATION

Centers of ice growth.   Two chief centers of ice growth from which glacial movement radiated have been identified in North America. One of these, in the northeast, is known as the Labrador center; the other, located somewhat west of Hudson Bay, is called the Keewatin center. Subordinate centers are identified in high land south of Hudson Bay, Newfoundland, Nova Scotia, and New Brunswick. Each of these centers is indicated by configuration of the glacial moraines, striae on bedrock, and lack of depositional or erosional ice action in an area that is surrounded by marks of diverging ice movement. Mountainous parts of western Canada and northwestern United States were largely buried beneath the Cordilleran ice sheet. There was extensive mountain glaciation in various ranges of the western United States.

Much of Alaska escaped glaciation, as also did southwestern Wisconsin and small parts of adjoining states, known as the "driftless area." This unglaciated territory, over 10,000 square miles in extent,

302. Glacially carved bedrock near Clinton, Mass. The parallel grooves on this bedrock surface clearly define the direction of glacial movement in the area. (*W. C. Alden, U. S. Geol. Survey.*)

is surrounded on all sides by country that at one time or another was occupied by the ice, but it was never an island in a "sea" of ice.

Multiple glaciation. The upper Mississippi Valley and adjacent Great Lakes region of the United States contain a remarkable record of at least four entirely distinct glaciations, of long interglacial ages that separated the successive glaciations, and of post-Pleistocene history.

Wisconsin, Minnesota, and neighboring country are a land of lakes and irregular hummocky topography, characterized by variously shaped, unevenly disposed hills and poorly drained depressions. Bedrock is mostly concealed by a mantle of glacial till, boulders, gravel, and sand. There are drumlins, kames, eskers, outwash plains, terminal moraines, recessional moraines, and large areas of ground moraine. The insignificant alteration of this glacial topography by stream work or other erosive agencies, since the time of glaciation, and the lack of appreciable weathering in the materials composing the drift attest the comparative recency of glaciation.

It was naturally supposed at first that the glaciation evidenced by these topographic features and by the little-weathered till constituted the entire glacial record of Quaternary time. Increasing cold at the beginning of Pleistocene time led to the formation of an ice sheet that spread widely, and increasing warmth toward the close of the Pleistocene caused melting and disappearance of the ice sheet.

This simple picture does not accord, however, with observations that in Illinois, Iowa, and elsewhere there are widespread deposits of deeply weathered glacial till and, further, that characteristic features of glacial topography are almost lacking in these regions. Seemingly, this much-weathered drift represents glaciation altogether different from, and very much older than, that marked by practically unaltered till and unmodified glacial topography. If this is the case, the older glaciation evidently extended considerably farther south than the later. Most exposures of glacial till in the north show only one drift sheet, the most recent, resting on ice-eroded bedrock. In the south, however, there are many places where one drift sheet overlies another, the contact being marked by change from the much-weathered and decayed upper portion of the older drift, to the fresh unweathered drift at the base of the overlying sheet. In places, there are beds of peat and old soils, some with remains of land animals and roots of

303. Glacial moraines and direction of ice movement in parts of Michigan, Indiana, and Ohio. The morainal pattern of late Wisconsin drift is more clearly defined than that of earlier Pleistocene drift. The moraines mark successive edges of ice tongues called "lobes." *(After Taylor and Leverett, U. S. Geol. Survey.)*

forest trees, above the older drift and buried by the younger. The later ice advance formed a veneer of deposits overlying the older, but in many areas it removed little or none of the underlying material.

Study of the weathering of glacial drift shows that, under the influence of dissolved oxygen and carbon dioxide in water that soaks into the ground, there are progressive chemical changes, which extend downward at unequal rates. Oxidation of iron compounds takes place, making yellowish, brownish, and reddish colors, and more slowly there are solution and removal of calcareous material. Still slower than leaching of calcium carbonate is the removal of the soluble parts of silicate minerals. The zones defined by these unequally progressive changes form the so-called "soil profile," whose nature and thickness are a measure of the extent (and, other things being equal, the time) to which weathering has proceeded. Under topographic conditions of poor drainage, which are common in glaciated areas, the characteristic final alteration product of till is a dark, sticky gumbo-like clay, called *gumbotil*, the dark color of which is due to the reduction of iron by organic compounds derived from overlying vegetation. A gumbotil thus marks very prolonged weathering of a till.

Drift sheets and interglacial materials. The oldest known glacial deposits of the Mississippi Valley region comprise the Nebraska drift sheet, which is seen in Nebraska, Kansas, Missouri, Iowa, and possibly farther east. The deposits left by the Nebraskan glacier consist of boulder clay or till and associated sands and gravels, the thickness in some places being 100 feet or more. The southern limit of the Nebraskan invasion is marked approximately by the lower course of the Missouri River. The ice that occupied the western Mississippi Valley region came from Keewatin center. The extent of the Nebraskan glaciation in the east and in the northwest is unknown, because the deposits have been subsequently obliterated or concealed, or they are unrecognized. The Nebraska drift, treated as a time-rock unit, comprises the *Nebraskan Stage* (glacial).

When the Nebraskan ice disappeared, the till that it had formed began to be weathered. Most of the topography seems to have been that of a nearly flat, poorly drained ground-moraine plain, upon which chemical weathering was effective and erosion negligible. The weathering continued until an average thickness of more than 8 feet of gumbotil was formed by alteration of the Nebraska till. Beds of peat, containing tree stumps and branches, and water-laid sediments, containing remains of animals that indicate a cool temperate climate, are associated with the gumbotil. All these deposits belong to the *Aftonian Stage* (interglacial).

A second Pleistocene glaciation is shown by the occurrence of till and fluvioglacial sand and gravel above the Nebraska drift and Afton gumbotil. The younger deposits, called Kansas drift, occupy about the same area as the Nebraska, and their average thickness is about 50 feet. The Kansan glacier advanced from the Keewatin center, as shown by its rock constituents. An ancient drift in central Ohio, which contains copper derived from the Lake Superior region, is possibly equivalent to the Kansas. The Kansas drift comprises the *Kansan Stage* (glacial).

After melting of the Kansan ice, the poorly drained ground-moraine deposits were subjected to weathering, and an average thickness of 12 feet of gumbotil was formed on the Kansas till before the next glaciation occurred. Deposits of peat, loess, and gravel were formed at this time. These materials represent the *Yarmouthian Stage* (interglacial).

A third ice sheet, termed Illinoian, came from the Labrador center and extended over a large part of Illinois, Indiana, and Ohio. A lobe of the glacier extended westward into Iowa, displacing the Mississippi River for a time. The average thickness of the Illinois drift is about 30 feet. Large areas of its surface are nearly flat ground moraine, but in some belts, the topography is distinctly hummocky, denoting terminal and recessional moraines. The Illinois drift makes up the *Illinoian Stage* (glacial).

During another interglacial age that followed, the Illinois till was weathered to form 4 to 6 feet of gumbotil in many places. Peat occurs locally. The prolonged weathering that produced the gumbotil was followed by deposition of loess, which consists of wind-blown materials spread widely over the weathered Kansas drift in Iowa, Missouri, Nebraska, and Kansas, and over weathered Illinois drift in Illinois and Indiana. Volcanic ash, interbedded with the loess, has been found in western Iowa. Calcareous materials of the loess were leached to a depth of 3 to 5 feet before glacial ice advanced again over parts of the region. These nonglacial deposits are classed as the *Sangamonian Stage* (interglacial).

The youngest of the drift sheets is the Wisconsin. Its distinctive youthful features are the almost unmodified glacial topography and slight weathering, which contrast greatly with the characters of the older glacial deposits. Although ice of Wisconsinan time did not reach as far south, in general, as preceding glacial invasions, the area covered by Wisconsin drift is much more extensive than that in which any of the older drifts are now found. The obvious reason for this is that, wherever the Wisconsin deposits occur, they overlie and conceal older drift, unless the latter was removed before deposition of the Wisconsin. The margins of the Wisconsinan ice sheets were strongly lobate, as shown by the looped arrangement of the terminal and recessional moraines, and the distribution of the lobes indicates that the ice movement was influenced by major topographic features of the area invaded, being accelerated by broad smooth lowlands and impeded by rough uplands. Thus we find that the hummocky morainal belts of the Wisconsin drift are concentric with the Great Lakes depressions. The Wisconsin glacial deposits comprise the *Wisconsinan Stage* (glacial).

Study of deposits left by the various Wisconsinan ice lobes, shows that the history of this glaciation is complex. It is known that the edge of the ice advanced, retreated, advanced again, receded, halted, receded, and so on, with innumerable local variations. In places, after the advance and partial retreat of one lobe, an adjoining lobe overrode deposits previously left by the other. It appears that in the early part (Iowan) of the late Pleistocene glaciation, the Keewatin center was most important. Later, the greatest center of radiation was in the Labrador region, from which the ice pushed southwestward as far as central Illinois; and still later, the chief center of radiation seems to have shifted westward to a region south of Hudson Bay. The ice then advanced southward over territory in Ohio and farther east, which had not been glaciated previously, and lobes extended far south also in Iowa and the Dakotas.

The glacial deposits classed as Wisconsin include four main divisions, that represent separate advances and retreats of a single great ice sheet during this epoch.

304. Superposed deposits of glacial till and loess exposed in a railway cut near Rhodes, Iowa. Comparatively fresh Wisconsin till at the top of the cut rests on wind-laid Peoria loess, which in turn lies on Kansas till that has a well-marked weathered zone (gumbotil) at the top. Such a sequence of deposits demonstrates some of the complexities of the glacial record. *(W. C. Alden, U. S. Geol. Survey.)*

1. The Iowa drift occurs in Iowa, Minnesota, and probably farther west. Although leaching of this drift has reached a depth of about 6 feet, all of the time since retreat of the Iowan ice sheet has been insufficient to produce gumbotil. The Iowan glaciation is thus relatively recent. Extensive deposition of loess (Peoria) is the next recorded item of Wisconsinan history. The loess is clearly of wind-blown origin, as indicated by occurrence of the thickest accumulations (nearly 100 feet) along the tops of the bluffs and uplands adjacent to the large river valleys, and a progressive thinning away from them. Presumably, it was derived from silt exposed in flats of the valley bottoms, which was swirled aloft by air currents and sifted over adjacent land. The Iowa drift and associated deposits form the *Iowan Substage*.

2. The Tazewell drift forms the surface of a large part of Illinois, Indiana, and southwestern Ohio. It is younger than the Peoria loess,

which it overlies. Not much difference in amount of weathering is shown by early and late parts of the Wisconsin drift, but the topography of Tazewell areas is more modified by erosion and has fewer lakes and swamps than younger divisions of the drift. The Tazewell drift is classed as the *Tazewellian Substage*.

3. The Cary drift, which is identified in northern and eastern Wisconsin, at the southern tip of Lake Michigan near Chicago, and throughout most of Michigan, Ohio, northern Pennsylvania, and New Jersey, represents the greatest advance of Wisconsinan ice sheets in Ohio and farther east. The Cary drift comprises the *Caryan Substage*.

4. The youngest part of the Wisconsin glacial deposits, named Mankato drift, is least modified by weathering and erosion. It is mostly poorly drained, and its area contains thousands of lakes, ponds, and swamps. This drift is widely distributed west of the Mississippi Valley in Minnesota, Iowa, and the Dakotas, but was restricted in the east to the borders of the Superior, Michigan, Huron, and Ontario lake basins, and the borders of the St. Lawrence Valley. The late Wisconsin glacial deposits cover a large part of Canada and collectively constitute the *Mankatoan Substage*.

Formation of the Great Lakes. One of the most interesting and important physiographic results of continental glaciation in North America was the formation of the Great Lakes, several large temporary glacial lakes now vanished, and an unnumbered multitude of smaller lakes. All these lakes are due to the formation of depressions made by erosion or deposition of the ice, or by the ponding of waters between parts of the glacial ice and the adjacent land.

The recorded history of the Great Lakes began when the ice lobes retreated north of the St. Lawrence-Mississippi divide, and water from the normal drainage and the melting ice rose until it found the lowest available outlet. The levels of water bodies thus formed were maintained until some other outlet at lower elevation was uncovered. Shoreline features, such as beaches and wave-cut cliffs, and deposits on the lake bottoms furnish evidence of successive steps in evolution of the lakes—features that are defined in proportion to the duration of the lake levels.

In addition to the effect of changing positions of the ice front, a general slow tilting of the land surface influenced the history of the lakes. Under the enormous weight of the continental ice sheet, which

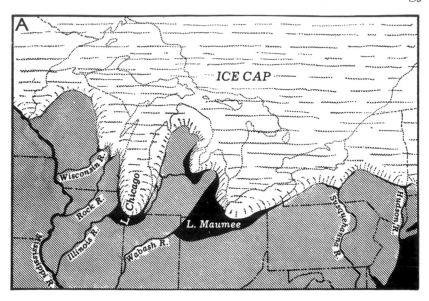

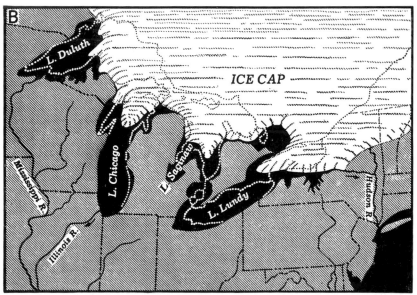

305. Early steps in development of the Great Lakes. Map *A* shows ponding at the tip of the Michigan, Saginaw, and Erie ice lobes, with outlets southwestward to the Mississippi. Map *B* represents a later condition when drainage of the eastern lakes was into the Hudson River.

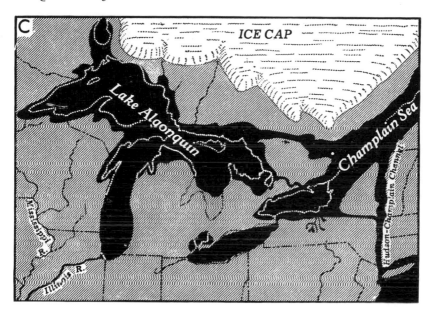

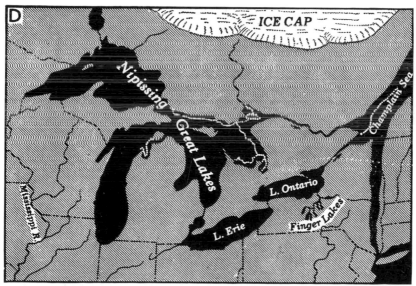

306. Late steps in development of the Great Lakes. Map *C* shows marine invasion caused by depression in the northeast under weight of glacial ice. Map *D* shows how up-warping of the land caused partial withdrawal of the sea. Existence of the Hudson-Champlain channel is doubtful.

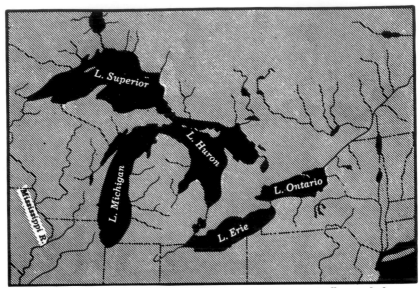

307. The present Great Lakes, which drain by way of Lake Ontario. Differential elevation of country in the northeast, amounting to more than 600 feet near Quebec, has caused withdrawal of the sea to the present Gulf of St. Lawrence.

was thousands of cubic miles in aggregate volume, the northern part of the continent was depressed, but when this weight was removed by melting of the ice, the land rose in resilient manner. The upward movement was slow. It was least in the southwest and greatest in the northeast, where it amounts to some hundreds of feet. The differential nature of the warping is clearly defined by the gently tilted attitude of the lake beaches, which were horizontal originally. The main steps in the development of the Great Lakes are given in the following summary and accompanying maps.

1. Formation of lakes at the tip of the Michigan and Erie ice lobes; outlets by way of Illinois-Des Plaines and Wabash Rivers to the Mississippi.

2. Retreat of ice, forming larger lakes, especially in the Erie basin; abandonment of Wabash River outlet because of the uncovering of a new outlet, which drained waters of the Erie basin northward into a lake formed at the tip of the Saginaw ice lobe, and thence westward across Michigan.

3. Slight retreat of the Huron lobe, causing further lowering of the lake in the Erie basin to the level of a lake in the Huron-Saginaw

basin, with which it was confluent; drainage westward into the Lake Michigan basin and southwest to the Mississippi.

4. Readvance of the Huron ice lobe, separating the Huron-Erie waters from those of Saginaw, raising the lake level of the former but not the latter.

5. Retreat of the ice, forming a lake in the Superior basin and opening outlet for waters of the Huron-Erie basin by way of Mohawk River into the Hudson; outlet of the Lake Michigan basin still southwestward from Chicago.

6. Retreat of the ice, uncovering almost all of the Great Lakes area, with drainage of Lake Erie northward into the Ontario basin. The three upper Great Lakes were combined in a single large water body which drained eastward across Ontario by way of the Trent River Valley, thence eastward by way of the Mohawk. Some water may have been discharged to the outlet at Chicago.

7. Complete withdrawal of the ice from the lakes region, disclosing an outlet for the upper lakes by way of Ottawa River, directly to the St. Lawrence. This region in the northeast was much lower than now, the sea extending into the Champlain Valley and Lake Ontario basin.

8. Differential elevation of country in the north, causing abandonment of the Ottawa River outlet and introducing present conditions.

Retreat of the ice from the Red River basin, northwest of Lake Superior, produced Lake Agassiz, which vastly exceeded in dimensions any of the existing Great Lakes. It is marked by lake deposits and well-formed beaches. The lake drained southeastward by way of valleys now occupied by the Minnesota and Mississippi Rivers. Eventually, when the ice retreated far enough north to permit discharge of waters into Hudson Bay, the lake was drained, except for its present remnants, Lake Winnipeg, Rainy Lake, and other smaller water bodies.

Mountain glaciation. During the Pleistocene Epoch, large quantities of snow and ice accumulated in mountain ranges of the western United States and Canada. Mountain glaciation occurred on a grand scale. At times of maximum growth, the glaciers scoured out and considerably deepened gorges previously cut by the mountain streams. Tongues of ice reached many miles down the valleys and in places spread out as lobes on the adjacent lowlands, building great lateral and terminal moraines. Many topographic features in these mountain areas, where ice is now absent, are due to Pleistocene glaciation. The effects of glaciation are recorded as far south as Arizona and southern California.

Early drift lies on remnants of a piedmont terrace bordering the

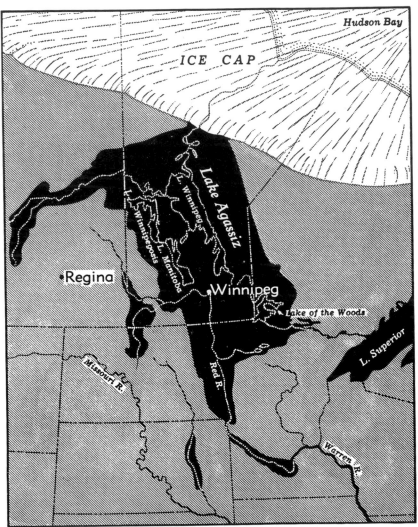

308. Glacial Lake Agassiz. This water body, much larger than any of the modern Great Lakes, occupied most of southern Manitoba; its outlet was southward by way of the present Minnesota and Mississippi River Valleys. When ice that blocked outlet to the north melted, the ponded water was drained from all of the area except depressions that hold modern Lake Winnipeg and near-by lakes. (*Modified from Taylor and Leverett, U. S. Geol. Survey.*)

309. U-shaped valley of the Merced River in Yosemite National Park. This valley, carved in massive igneous rocks that form the core of the Sierra Nevada, shows typical sculpture produced by mountain glaciation. (*F. E. Matthes, U. S. Geol. Survey.*)

Rocky Mountains in Montana. The elevation of the drift-bearing terrace is as much as 1,000 feet above the present drainage. Much younger glacial deposits are found in the lower parts of the valleys, which, subsequent to the early glaciation, were cut far below the high terrace levels. Three, and possibly four, glaciations are recognized in the mountains of western Wyoming. The oldest deposits lie on remnants of high piedmont terraces, which are separated by valleys that have been carved 1,000 feet in bedrock since the early glaciation. The San Juan Mountains of southwestern Colorado, the Sierra Nevada, and many other mountains show evidence of two or more glaciations.

Sculpture and Deposition in Nonglaciated Regions

Features of Quaternary history, which vie in importance with continental glaciation, are the effects of erosion and deposition in areas that were not covered by glaciers. It is in post-Tertiary time that shaping of most details and the outlining of many major topographic forms of the land surface were accomplished. We find proof that in mountain areas impressive canyons, like the Royal Gorge in the Colorado Rockies and Yosemite Valley on the west slope of the Sierra Nevada, are the product of down-cutting in hard rocks, belonging almost wholly to the Quaternary Period. The Colorado River established its southwestward course through Utah and Arizona in Tertiary time, but a preponderant part of the stupendous excavation required to make the Grand Canyon and innumerable other stream-made gashes of the Colorado Plateau region is sculpture effected during Pleistocene and Recent time. Less imposing but equally important, is dissection of vast areas south of the glacial border and east of the Rockies, comprising interior and coastal plains, and uplands like the Ozarks and Appalachians. The configuration of hills and valleys that lie within view of millions of our homes is the product of Quaternary processes of erosion and deposition.

Acceleration of stream work.   The surface of North America at the present time is certainly far more rugged and varied in topography than during many past geologic periods. The continent is larger now than in Tertiary time, and probably it has higher and more numerous mountains. We are sure, at any rate, that upward movements of the earth crust have occurred since the beginning of the Quaternary Period, and that these elevations have accelerated the work of running water. Except along parts of the Pacific border in southern California, however, no evidence of folding of rock strata in connection with uplift is found, and thus we must conclude that the elevation is essentially a differential upwarping. Displacement along fault lines can be proved in some places, as at the eastern base of the Sierra Nevada.

Evidence of the geologically recent uplift is chiefly physiographic. Southward from Oregon along the Pacific shore, marine terraces, bordered by wave-cut cliffs and beaches, now stand at varying elevation above the sea, and they furnish unequivocal proof of differential upward movement of the land with respect to sea level. In mountain areas like the Rockies, Cascades, and Sierra Nevada, evidence of uplift consists of well-defined remnants of peneplain surfaces, which lie at or near summits of the ranges. These surfaces are warped and do not now occur at constant elevation. Study of the relation of the peneplain remnants to adjacent fossil-bearing deposits, which were formed of materials derived from the region of peneplanation, indicates that

310. Summit peneplain in the Front Range of the Rocky Mountains in Colorado. This old erosion surface, shown by smooth topography and accordant summit levels of mountain areas, is being obliterated by erosion of streams and ice. *(W. T. Lee, U. S. Geol. Survey.)*

some peneplains were developed before the close of the Tertiary, but others are seemingly not older than Pliocene or early Pleistocene. The uplift of these surfaces to present elevations, thousands of feet above sea level, and their partial obliteration are Quaternary events, with which accelerated erosion and deposition of many streams are associated.

The Columbia River, which flows through lowland country in eastern Washington, has cut a gorge transecting the Cascade Mountains, which rise as a great barrier blocking the river's path to the sea. Explanation of the cut that the Columbia has made through the barrier is the antecedent position of the river's course; the powerful stream was able to erode its channel at a pace that prevented diversion by reason of upwarping of the Cascades in Quaternary time.

311. Old shore line and wave-built terrace on the east side of Lake Bonneville, near Provo, Utah. The shore line shown in this view is approximately 1,000 feet above the level of present Great Salt Lake. It was made when fresh-water Lake Bonneville, 19,000 square miles in area, occupied the basin. *(W. C. Alden, U. S. Geol. Survey.)*

Lakes in the Great Basin. The Great Basin contains many subordinate depressions in which shallow temporary or permanent lakes are found, most of them saline or alkaline. The largest of these lakes is the Great Salt Lake in Utah. Greatly increased precipitation in this region during Pleistocene time caused such expansion of the lake that the waters of different basins became confluent. The very large lake thus formed is known as Lake Bonneville. At one time, this water body had a maximum depth of about 1,000 feet and covered 19,000 square miles. It was then a fresh-water lake, for an outlet was established northward into Snake River. Subsequently, with increase of evaporation over precipitation, the lake level sank lower and lower, size dwindled, and the water became increasingly salty. Great Salt Lake, the diminutive descendant of Lake Bonneville, has a maximum depth of less than 50 feet and an area of about 1,800 square miles. Large quantities of salt have been deposited in parts of the Bonneville basin, and the existing lake is a brine containing more than 400 million tons of dissolved salt. Former lake levels are clearly marked by beaches and wave-cut cliffs, and by large deltas of sand and gravel that were built out into the lake at the mouths of inflowing streams. These features, and the flat topography of the old lake bottom, are very striking characters of the landscape near Salt Lake City, Provo, and other cities of the Salt Lake Valley. A similar large Quaternary lake in west central Nevada is known as Lake Lahontan. An interesting deposit formed in parts of these lakes is large masses of calcareous tufa.

Development of the Mississippi River system. An outstanding feature of Quaternary history in North America is establishment of the continent's greatest river system—the Mississippi and its tributaries. The carving of broad valleys, the deposition of alluvium over many ten-thousand square miles of flood plains, and the building of one of the world's great deltas form parts of this record. Many important

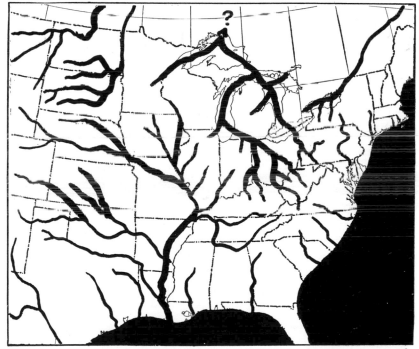

312. Drainage in part of eastern North America at the beginning of Pleistocene time. The location of many preglacial drainage lines is indicated on good evidence, but that of others is by no means well established. Heavily drawn parts of the drainage lines call attention to important divergences from present stream courses.

facts relating to the surface and subsurface geology of the lower Mississippi Valley have been brought to light within the past few years by investigations of the Mississippi River Commission; this work includes very detailed mapping with aid of air photographs, the boring of many thousand test wells, and thorough study of well samples.

At the beginning of Quaternary time, the lowland region of the north central United States was drained principally by streams flowing northward into Canada, the waters of these streams being emptied into Hudson Bay or the St. Lawrence. The diversion of drainage to the Gulf of Mexico and the establishment of the present Mississippi River system are effects of Pleistocene glaciation. First, the northward flowing streams were ponded by the advancing ice. Later the waters of adjacent valleys were united, and eventually outlets southward became located at low points. The Ohio and Missouri Rivers, which

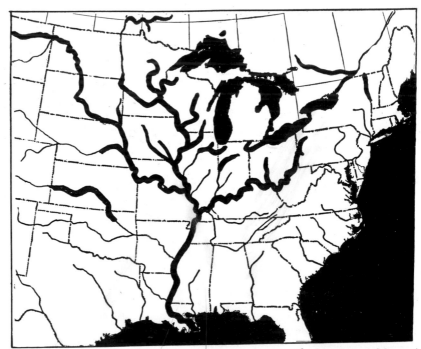

313. Present drainage lines of the area represented in Fig. 312. The Mississippi, Missouri, and Ohio River systems have been developed very largely through effects of glaciation. The heavy lines denote new drainageways developed during the Quaternary Period.

roughly follow the southern border of the glaciated area, were
formed by this diversion of former northward-flowing rivers and
the bringing together of formerly separate drainage lines. As a
result, the Ohio, for example,
flows in a valley that is alternately
wide and very narrow, and its yet
unadjusted gradient changes in
different sections from 0.5 to over
5 feet to the mile.

The Mississippi River established its course in lowland along
the western margin of the Mississippi embayment, which is the
broad northward extension of the
Gulf coastal plain occupied by
Cretaceous and Tertiary sedimentary formations. The Ohio River
drainage established its course in
early Pleistocene time near the
eastern border of the embayment,
and reached the Gulf of Mexico
independently of the Mississippi.
Subsequently, it joined the Mississippi near Natchez, 100 miles from
the Gulf, but the present junction
at Cairo, 550 miles airline distance
north of the delta, was established
only 2,000 years ago, approximately, in Recent time.

The history of erosion and sedimentation in the lower Mississippi

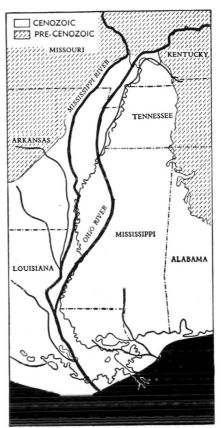

**314. The lower Mississippi Valley at a date
computed to be about 4,500 years ago.** Geological studies for the War Department,
utilizing data from thousands of borings,
have supplied much new information on
deposits of the lower Mississippi Valley
in recent geologic history. At the time
here shown, the Mississippi and Ohio had
separate courses southward to a point below Natchez, Miss. *(After H. N. Fisk,
Mississippi River Commission.)*

Valley during Quaternary time has been shown to be one of alternate
cutting and filling. Epochs of downward erosion are correlated with
times of glaciation, when sea level was lowered by removal of water
to make the many thousand cubic miles of continental ice sheets.

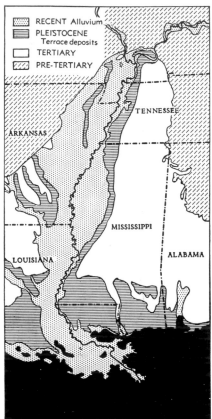

RECENT Alluvium
PLEISTOCENE Terrace deposits
TERTIARY
PRE-TERTIARY

TENNESSEE

ARKANSAS

MISSISSIPPI

LOUISIANA   ALABAMA

315. The lower Mississippi River Valley at the present time. The Mississippi River flood plain, which is geologically of very recent origin, is bordered by Pleistocene terrace deposits arranged in four successively higher steps above the flood plain, the oldest at the top. These indicate alternating times of deposition and valley cutting, which are inferred to correspond to epochs of deglaciation and glaciation. *(After H. N. Fisk, Mississippi River Commission.)*

Steepened gradients then caused the Mississippi and tributary streams to deepen their valleys by headward down-cutting that began at the Gulf. When ice sheets melted, water in large volume was returned to the ocean basins, and the consequent rise in sea level caused the Mississippi and its tributaries to aggrade their valleys. Renewal of glaciation reversed these conditions, because lowering of sea level accelerated stream velocity. This caused erosion of previously deposited alluvium and renewal of downward cutting into Tertiary bedrock. Deglaciation and rise of sea level again inaugurated another cycle of extensive alluviation, but at lower level than the first. In this manner, successive alternating epochs of erosion and deposition have developed the present lower Mississippi Valley, broad flood plain, and great delta. The margins of the valley show the presence of terraces that are upwarped remnants of four main epochs of alluviation, which were recorded during Pleistocene time. The highest of these terraces is about 350 feet above the present flood plain, and each of them has been traced upstream to the vicinity of Cairo.

At Houma, La., 50 miles southwest of New Orleans and about 40 miles from the Gulf, the base of Recent alluvial gravel is nearly 350 feet below sea level. Inasmuch as no evidence of subsidence in Late

Quaternary time is known in this part of Louisiana, the accumulation of this 350 feet of Recent alluvium is inferred to measure part of the rise of sea level since late Pleistocene time, that was produced by melting of the Wisconsinan ice sheet.

Duration of Quaternary Time

Evidence from weathering of drift sheets. An approximate measure of the duration of Pleistocene time is based on depth of leaching and decomposition of the materials of the drift sheets. For example, if calcareous constituents of the late Wisconsin (Mankato) drift have been leached to an average depth of 2½ feet in the time since this glaciation, the observed average depth of leaching of the Iowa drift, of 5 to 6 feet, may be interpreted to mean that the time since the Iowan glaciation is slightly more than twice as long as that since the retreat of the late Wisconsinan glacier. Gumbotil, the ultimate product of chemical decay of till in flat, poorly drained areas, is found at the top of the Illinois, Kansas, and Nebraska tills, but not on the Wisconsin tills, even where the topographic conditions are favorable. Evidently, gumbotils do not begin to be formed until there has been time for leaching of calcium carbonate to a depth of at least 6 feet. Study of these results of weathering of the drift leads to the following determination of the minimum comparative time values represented by the weathering. If the time since maximum spread of the Mankatoan ice is designated as 1, then post-Iowan time is about 2.2, Sangamonian interglacial time about 4.8, Yarmouthian interglacial time 12, and Aftonian interglacial time 8. To convert these values to years, we must know as accurately as possible the time value of 1; and to derive a figure for the duration of the Quaternary Period, the time involved in the glaciations must be added to the figures for interglacial and postglacial times.

Evidence from recession of river falls. Attempts have been made to measure the time since the Wisconsinan ice retreated by study of the rate and total amount of the recession of certain river falls that came into existence immediately after the last glaciation. Chief of these are Niagara Falls and St. Anthony Falls, the latter on the Mississippi River at Minneapolis.

The beginning of Niagara Falls can be dated at the time when the Wisconsinan ice retreated north of the escarpment of Niagaran lime-

316. Niagara Falls looking toward Goat Island and the Canadian Falls. The recession of this falls, as the capping limestone is undercut and carried away, furnishes a measure of the time since waters from Lake Erie established outlet by way of the Niagara River. This river initially tumbled over the Niagara escarpment at a point coinciding with the lower end of the gorge that now extends several miles below the falls.

stone in western New York. Drainage from streams, lakes, and part of the ice front to the west followed the present course of Niagara River and tumbled over the escarpment near the town of Lewiston. From this point, the falls have subsequently receded about 7 miles to their present position, forming Niagara Gorge. Dividing the total length of the gorge by the present average annual amount of recession, which is fairly accurately determined at 3.8 feet, the length of time required for the making of the gorge is figured to be about 10,000 years. This method of computation is inaccurate and gives a value far too low for postglacial time. The observed recession rate of the falls depends on the volume of the discharge of the present Niagara River, which drains all the Great Lakes above Ontario. During much of the past when the waters of Lakes Huron, Michigan, and Superior had a different outlet, the flow of Niagara River was correspondingly reduced, and the rate of recession of the falls greatly retarded. Estimates of the time required for the recession of Niagara Falls from its original position range from 20,000 to 39,000 years.

Saint Anthony Falls originated near the present confluence of the Mississippi and Minnesota Rivers, where the waters of the newly formed Mississippi were precipitated into a broad valley, which had served as the outlet for glacial Lake Agassiz in the North Dakota-Manitoba country. The minimum time required for the recession of these falls, which have receded northward a little over 8 miles, is estimated to be 12,000 to 16,000 years.

Evidence from seasonally banded clay deposits. Another method of time measurement, which is accurate as applied to considerable portions of late Pleistocene and postglacial time, is the study of the seasonally banded layers (varves) of clay or fine silt deposited in temporary glacial lakes. A varve consists of two layers, a thick one and a thin one. The thicker, slightly coarser, and generally lighter colored layers represent the more rapid deposition in the summer period, when the melting of ice was greatest, whereas the thinner, finer, and darker colored deposits represent the winter season. Count of the pairs of bands in any one deposit gives a measure of the years represented in making the deposit, while careful measurements of the successive bands afford basis for correlation of banded deposits in different lakes and areas. The record may be pieced together to give a fairly continuous time record. Study of these banded clays in New England and eastern Canada indicates that the retreat of the ice in this region required 28,000 to 29,000 years.

Estimate of Quaternary time. If we accept 25,000 years as reasonable approximation of time since the beginning of recession of the last Pleistocene ice sheet, the values of preceding interglacial ages indicated by comparative figures previously given are as follows: Aftonian, 200,000 years; Yarmouthian, 300,000 years; and Sangamonian, 120,000 years. A minimum figure for each glacial epoch is 20,000 years. That the times of glaciation, even if 50,000 years long,

317. Banded clay deposits laid down in a glacial lake. Each pair of light and dark bands in this deposit near Kazabazua, Quebec, comprises sedimentation made during one year. It is thus readily possible to compute the time required to make the entire thickness of the deposits. *(Canada Geol. Survey.)*

were short as compared with the duration of interglacial ages. Summation of figures indicates that the Quaternary Period can measure hardly less than 750,000 years, and it is probably 1,000,000 years.

19. Nature and Evolution of Cenozoic Life

Pleistocene flesh-eaters assembled at the Rancho La Brea tar pools in Los Angeles, Calif.

The Age of Mammals and Flowering Plants

The record of changing life on land and in the sea during the Cenozoic Era is better known than in the ancient geologic periods, and this life is particularly interesting to us because here we find the immediate ancestors of living animals and plants. The evolution of many groups of organisms can be traced step by step from primitive generalized forms to specialized modern species. There are also numerous Cenozoic lines that have ended in extinction. Prominence of flowering plants is the main characteristic of Cenozoic time in the plant world.

The outstanding Cenozoic animals are the mammals, which include the highest type of living creatures, and therefore, the era is preeminently the Age of Mammals. This advance seems especially important to us, because we ourselves are mammals. We find in the Tertiary rocks the beginning of most of our modern domestic and wild ani-

C. R. Knight, Chicago Natural History Museum

318. Standing trunk of petrified tree in the Yellowstone Park Fossil Forest. Several successive levels of petrified trees in this area furnish record of Tertiary forests that were killed off by volcanic ash falls. Silica from the volcanic rocks replaced the woody tissue of the plants. *(J. P. Iddings, U. S. Geol. Survey.)*

mals. The fossil record is nearly all that could be asked for. Fossils are abundant and generally very well preserved. A few groups, such as the horses, are well represented by species which show each stage in evolution, from near the beginning to the present, and which show branching of various offshoots.

Plants

CULMINATION OF FLOWERING PLANTS

All collections of fossil plants from Cenozoic deposits show marked similarities to existing floras. The flowering plants or angiosperms, which made their appearance late in the Mesozoic Era, had assumed definite leadership. In an astonishingly short time, geologically speaking, this group has not only come to outnumber all others, but it has spread over practically the entire earth, adapting itself alike to the sweltering heat of the tropics and the bitter cold within 5 to 6 degrees of the Pole; to sea level or hundreds of feet below in some inland basins, and to mountain heights of 14,000 feet or more; to regions having an annual rainfall of 500 inches and burning deserts where rain may fall only at intervals of years. Some find a congenial home in marshes, while others have waded boldly into the water and compete with the algae. In size they range from adults scarcely $\frac{1}{12}$ inch long to the redwood big trees of California, which have a diameter up to 30 feet and attain a maximum known height of 340 feet. In length of life, they range from herbs that die in a summer, to trees like the baobab that may survive for several thousand years. The variety seems illimitable.

Most of the Eocene genera are the same as today, but the species were different from those in later Tertiary epochs and from living forms. The Miocene and Pliocene deposits contain many plants that apparently have persisted without noticeable change.

The Pleistocene glaciers obliterated the vegetation of the north and forced persisting species southward. At times of greatest advance of

319. Fossil leaves from Tertiary formations of the western United States. The leaf at left is a maple *(Acer)*; those at right are two species of walnut *(Juglans)*. One-half natural size.

the ice, such northern trees as the balsam, fir, and tamarack lived in the central United States, but during interglacial ages these invaders moved back northward.

Interglacial plants, in a clay deposit near Toronto, Canada, include remains of the Osage orange, papaw, and others that grow today only in a latitude several hundred miles farther south. The climate around Toronto, therefore, must have been appreciably warmer at that time than now.

Invertebrates

Invertebrate life of the Cenozoic Era is rich and varied. Thousands of fossil species have been collected and described, and each year brings important additions to knowledge. The outstanding characters of Cenozoic invertebrates as a whole are (1) progressively increased resemblance to the living fauna, (2) dominance of pelecypods and gastropods, and (3) common very perfect preservation of the shells, which may be altered hardly at all. Many localities are famous for the abundance and variety of their fossil shells.

PROTOZOANS

In variety of species and uncountable numbers of individuals, the fossil protozoans of the Cenozoic Era exceed all other parts of the geologic record, not excepting the Cretaceous chalk. During the Tertiary, as now, these tiny shells accumulated on the sea bottom in such myriads, that in places they form the major part of deposits hundreds of feet thick. Both sand-shelled and calcareous forms occur abundantly, but the latter are greatly preponderant. Most species are very minute and can be identified only under a microscope. These furnish the chief basis for correlating Tertiary formations in the oil-field regions of the Pacific Coast and Gulf of Mexico.

In warm waters of subtropic and tropic seas, one group of foraminifers built large shells with complex internal structure, the maximum size being about $2\frac{1}{2}$ inches in diameter. These are chiefly disk-shaped (like *Nummulites*).

SPONGES AND CORALS

Since the marine Tertiary deposits that have been studied are almost entirely of shallow-water origin, it is not surprising to find few siliceous sponges, for these live chiefly in deeper water. One of the two orders of calcareous sponges apparently became extinct at the close of the Cretaceous period.

The corals of Cenozoic time are abundant and highly varied. Many new genera and some new families appeared. They belong to the group characterized by sixfold symmetry. Coral reefs are found in the Eocene of Georgia, Florida, Alabama, Mexico, Central America, and the West Indies, and they occur in rocks of this age in parts of the Old World. Miocene, Pliocene, and Pleistocene deposits show that such reefs have become more and more restricted to the tropics.

ECHINODERMS

Living echinoderms include the echinoids, starfishes, crinoids, brittle stars, and holothurians, of which the first two are much the most important.

Among echinoids, practically all the Mesozoic families are represented in the Tertiary and today. Both the regularly symmetrical, rounded shells with coarse spines, and the irregular, flattened or heart-shaped shells with short spines, are common. These echinoderms are essentially at the peak of their career.

Starfishes and brittle stars are well known and varied in modern seas, but their fossil record is not important. A few are found in Tertiary rocks.

Modern crinoids are a vigorous, cosmopolitan stock confined mainly to deeper oceanic waters. About 650 species of living crinoids are known, 90 per cent of which are free-swimming, stemless forms. Tertiary fossil crinoids, however, are extremely rare.

BRYOZOANS AND BRACHIOPODS

Bryozoans are exceedingly abundant in many of the Tertiary strata of North America and Europe, and the number of species is surprisingly large. Nearly 1,000 species have been described from the eastern United States. Some soft marly formations are mainly composed of bryozoan remains which may easily be washed free in any desired quantity for study.

Brachiopods are even less important in the marine faunas of Cenozoic time than in the Mesozoic Era. The number of known species is roughly comparable to that of the present day.

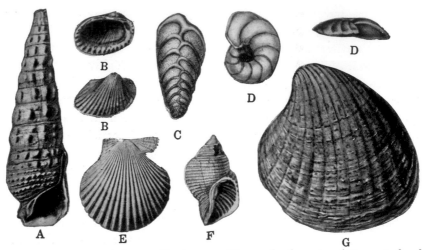

320. A few marine invertebrates of Tertiary age. Thousands of species of Cenozoic fossil invertebrates have been collected and described. Many are closely similar to living species. The forms here shown include foraminifers (*C, Bolivina,* and *D, Cibicides,* Miocene), pelecypods (*B, Scapharca,* Oligocene; *E, Pecten;* and *G, Venericardia,* Eocene), and gastropods (*A, Cerithium,* Pliocene; *F, Cancellaria,* Miocene). Natural size, except *C* and *D,* which are enlarged.

Mollusks

Dominant place among Cenozoic invertebrates was held by the mollusks, even though cephalopods were far less important than in Mesozoic time. Species of pelecypods and gastropods are numbered by thousands. They show no very radical changes in structure, and peculiarly specialized shells, like some of the Cretaceous pelecypods, are absent. There is a progressive trend toward types of the present day, like the common scallops and oysters, or the periwinkles and larger gastropods that one finds along modern seashores. The great majority of Early Tertiary molluscan genera are still living, but the species are almost entirely extinct. Late Tertiary species, however, are closely related to or identical with living forms. The pelecypods and gastropods have always been a fairly conservative, little-changing stock; their abundance and variety in the Cenozoic, which marks the peak of their development, indicate that they have retained a high degree of racial virility and, though ancient in origin, they are expanding rather than declining in importance. The Tertiary and modern gastropods are more highly ornamented on the average than their predecessors.

The great contrast between Mesozoic and Cenozoic marine faunas is seen especially in the cephalopod element. The horde of ammonites that distinguished the older era was completely gone, and only a few nautiloids and two-gilled cephalopods remained. After millions of years in which the cephalopods held a leading place in marine life, they have receded to an inconspicuous part of the background.

Vertebrates

FISHES

The chief characteristic of Cenozoic fishes is the rise of the bony fishes (teleosts) to a position of dominance in which they outnumber all other kinds more than 20 to 1. They include the salmon, herrings, carps, perches, mackerels, and many other familiar and some extinct groups of marine and fresh-water fishes.

A famous Eocene fish fauna occurs in the Green River beds in southwestern Wyoming, where large numbers of beautifully preserved complete skeletons have been collected. Among the marine fishes, there were sharks (*Carcharodon*) that had sharp-edged triangular cutting teeth up to 6 inches long. Based on comparison with similarly shaped teeth of living sharks, it is estimated that some of these fossil species attained a length of 80 feet.

AMPHIBIANS AND REPTILES

Amphibians were relatively no more important in Tertiary and Pleistocene time than now. Fossil salamanders, frogs, and toads occur.

Reptiles of the Tertiary and Quaternary Periods are distinguished chiefly by their modern appearance, dinosaurs and other strange reptilian creatures of Mesozoic times having disappeared. Their Cenozoic descendants included especially large numbers of turtles, crocodiles, lizards, and snakes.

BIRDS

Birds are relatively rare as fossils, but more than 500 genera are known from Cenozoic deposits. These represent most of the modern families, including gulls, ducks, herons, storks, pigeons, grouse, owls, hawks, parrots, and a great many others. Among ostrich-like birds are some of very massive build that attained the gigantic height of about 10 feet; one (*Phororhachis*) had a powerful hooked beak and a skull that measured 2 feet in length.

MAMMALS

The history of mammals dates back at least to Triassic time. Development was almost negligible, however, until the sudden acceleration of evolutional change that occurred in the oldest Tertiary. This led in Eocene time to increase in average size, larger mental capacity, and special adaptations for different modes of life. In the Oligocene Epoch, there was further improvement, with appearance of some new lines and extinction of others. Miocene and Pliocene time was marked by culmination of several groups and continued approach toward modern characters. The peak of the career of mammals in variety and size was attained in the Miocene.

Adaptation of mammals.   The adaptation of mammals to almost all possible modes of life parallels that of the reptiles in Mesozoic time, and except for greater intelligence, the mammals do not seem to have done much better than corresponding reptilian forms. The bat is doubtless a better flying animal than the pterosaur, but the dolphin and whale are hardly more fishlike than the ichthyosaur. Many swift-running mammals of the plains, like the horse and antelope, must excel any of the dinosaurs. The tyrannosaur was a more ponderous and powerful carnivore than any flesh-eating mammal, but the lion or tiger is probably a more efficient and dangerous beast of prey because of a superior brain. The significant point to observe, is that different branches of the mammals gradually fitted themselves for all sorts of life, grazing on the plains and able to run swiftly (horse, deer, bison), living in rivers and swamps (hippopotamus, beaver), dwelling in trees (sloth, monkey), digging underground (mole, rodent), feeding on flesh in the forest (tiger) and plain (wolf), swimming in the sea (dolphin, whale, seal), and flying in the air (bat). Man is able by mechanical means to conquer the physical world and to adapt himself to almost any set of conditions.

This adaptation produces gradual changes of form and structure. It is biologically characteristic and only possible in the youthful, plastic stage of a group. Early in its career, an animal assemblage

321. Restoration of one of the most primitive known hoofed mammals. This creature (*Ectoconus*) is a condylarth from Eocene strata of western United States. (*John Germann, American Museum of Natural History.*)

seems to possess capacity for change, which, as the unit becomes old and fixed, disappears. The generalized types of organisms retain longest the ability to make adjustments when required, and it is from them that new, fecund stocks take origin—certainly not from any specialized end products. So, in the mammals, we witness the birth, plastic spread in many directions, increasing specialization, and in some branches the extinction, which we have learned from observation of the geologic record of life is a characteristic of the evolution of life.

Fossilization of mammals. Remains of mammals are found in stream-laid deposits, lake and swamp beds, wind-blown dust and sand, volcanic ash, asphalt, cave earth, marine sediments (mostly marine mammals), and other materials. The kinds of mammals, numbers, and state of preservation depend largely on the nature of the deposit and its geologic age.

The great majority of Tertiary mammal fossils occur in sediments of ancient valleys and plains; they indicate burial after drowning or suffocation in streams, quicksands, shallow lakes, swamps, or wind deposits. It is easy to imagine how numbers of animals might be caught and buried, for such capture and burial are not infrequent in modern time. Especially in periods of drought, starved and thirst-crazed animals seek watering places in large numbers and, very much weakened, are unable to escape from clinging mud. Or, in exhausted condition, they drink to excess and, especially if the water is strongly mineralized, this is almost immediately fatal.

In arid regions, animals may suffocate in dust storms or die from thirst, and the skeletons become buried in wind-blown sand.

Fossil mammals are not evenly distributed through the beds but are found to occur in "pockets," with numbers of individuals crowded together. Some layers contain numerous fossils, whereas others are entirely barren.

An interesting occurrence of fossil mammals is the Rancho La Brea asphalt deposits near Los Angeles. The asphalt was formed by oxidation and solidification of petroleum that seeped upward through Pleistocene deposits from oil-bearing strata below. In the change from petroleum to asphalt, very viscous, sticky tar pools were formed on the surface of the ground. These pools entrapped a multitude of late Cenozoic mammals and birds, sealing their bones perfectly from decay. Just as in modern time, animals caught in the tar were quickly rendered helpless by the gummy stuff, which bound their feet and eventually engulfed the whole body. The struggles and cries of trapped creatures served to lure carnivorous mammals and birds, which too late discovered themselves in the hopeless predicament of their intended prey. Thus, the skeletons in this deposit include a preponderance of carnivorous mammals and birds, which is unusual, for the carnivores are rarely found in numbers.

Archaic Hoofed Mammals

Early Tertiary formations contain two assemblages of primitive hoofed mammals, which include ancestors of the varied host of later hoofed animals (ungulates), as well as unsuccessful offshoots. One group (condylarths) had five digits on each foot, a generalized type of body, and a long heavy tail, resembling in many ways some of the

322. Uintatheres and a group of tiny four-toed Eocene horses. The uintatheres are the largest and most specialized of the primitive hoofed mammals. *(C. R. Knight, Chicago Natural History Museum.)*

early clawed mammals. The skull was long and low, the brain case small, and the teeth unspecialized and low-crowned. A typical representative of these animals had about the size of a small shepherd dog. They disappeared before middle Eocene time.

The second group (amblypods) were distinguished by stout limbs ending in short blunt feet, like those of an elephant, by the archaic nature of their teeth and skull, and by their small brain capacity. The earliest of these animals, which lived in Paleocene time, was smaller than a sheep, but one of the late forms (uintathere), of Eocene age, had the appearance and bulk of a small elephant, except that it had no trunk. The top of the long skull carried three pairs of horns, the front pair, above the nose, possibly sheathed with horn, as in the rhinoceros, the middle pair above the eyes and the back pair at the base of the skull being rounded at the ends and probably covered with skin, as in the giraffe. The top of the back part of the skull is peculiarly dish-shaped, leaving little space for the brain, which was indeed small. The males carried long curved tusks projecting downward from the upper jaws.

Odd-toed Hoofed Mammals

One of the chief divisions of hoofed mammals is the so-called "odd-toed" group (perissodactyls), in which the central toe is larger than the others because it bears more of the weight. It includes the horse, man's comrade and most valued domestic animal, and mammals such as the rhinoceroses, tapirs, and the very strange extinct animals called "titanotheres" and "chalicotheres."

Horses. The horse is a highly and efficiently specialized mammal, distinguished chiefly by characters of the limbs and teeth. The limbs are wonderfully fitted for running, which is the horse's chief means of self-preservation. The teeth are specially adapted for grazing on the tough grasses of the plains.

The limbs and feet of the horse differ from those of all other hoofed mammals in that there is but a single functional toe on each foot. Comparison with other animals shows that the horse walks on the very tip of fingers and toes, the wrist is the "knee," the ankle is the "hock," and the elbow and real knee are close up to the body. Thus, the long slender limb of the horse has been developed essentially by lengthening the lower bones; the upper ones, which remain relatively short, carry the powerful well-bunched muscles that propel the lower limbs by means of thin strong ligaments. Although the lower limb consists of a single digit, the bones are so increased in size that they form an adequate support. The joints are fitted with a tongue-and-groove arrangement, so that only forward and backward motion is possible. All together, the limb structure is so perfectly designed for running swiftly, that one may well doubt the possibility of further development along this line in an animal of the size of the horse.

The teeth consist of long-crowned cropping teeth (incisors) in front, very long-crowned grinding teeth (molars and premolars) behind, and in the males, but rarely in females, tusks or canines. The incisors are peculiar in having a deep pit in the cutting face of the tooth, which is due to an infolding of the hard enamel, like the pushed-in end of the finger of a glove. As the teeth are worn down, the size of the pit is reduced; this is used in determining a horse's age. The grinding teeth are nearly square in cross section, and the three elements of the tooth structure—enamel, dentine, and cement—are

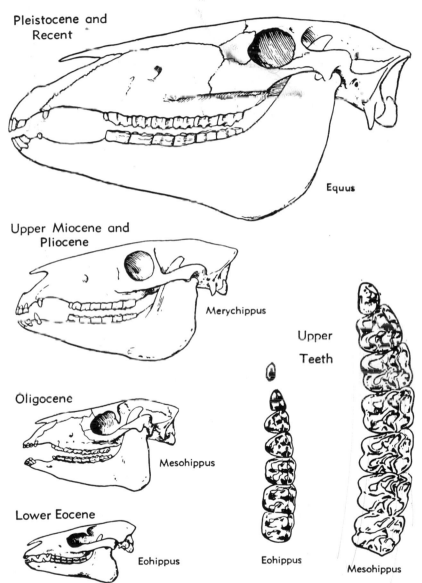

Pleistocene and Recent

Equus

Upper Miocene and Pliocene

Merychippus

Upper Teeth

Oligocene

Mesohippus

Lower Eocene

Eohippus

Eohippus

Mesohippus

323. Skulls and teeth of Cenozoic fossil horses, showing evolution in shape and size. (*After Scott.*)

elaborately infolded, so as to give a characteristic pattern of the resistant enamel upon the wearing surface. The teeth have an excessively long crown, so that years of wear are compensated by gradual outward growth of the grinders. In extreme old age, they are worn down near the roots. The premolars of the horse have assumed the characters of the molars. The long grinding teeth are accommodated in the skull by a deep lower jaw and by elongation of the skull, the eye orbit being pushed well back so as to give room for the teeth in the upper jaw.

Horses have attained a size that is exceeded only by a few kinds of land mammals. Some horses reach a shoulder height of 6 feet 4 inches and a weight of 2,400 pounds. The horse is a very intelligent animal. The brain is not only large but is of a relatively high type, well convoluted. Like man and the elephant, the horse has shown the ability to adapt himself to all climatic environments. In the natural wild state, however, horses are restricted to parts of Asia and Africa, all living horses of other continents, including the wild mustangs of western North America, having been introduced by man.

Evolution of horses. The oldest known horses are diminutive creatures, about 1 foot high, skeletons of which occur in Eocene deposits of North America and southern England. These might really fail of recognition as primitive horses, except for the almost complete series of intergrading fossils in later Cenozoic rocks that definitely connect them with living horses. The small Eocene horses had four complete toes on the forefoot, and three, with remnant of a fourth, on the hind foot. The two bones of the forearm and foreleg are separate and normal, The animal was adapted for running but did not walk on the tips of the digits, as later horses. The teeth are very unlike those of the modern horse in that the crown is short and the grinding surface consists of cusps that begin to show the structure of the teeth only in later types. These teeth were fitted for browsing rather than grazing, and suggest that the earliest horses were creatures of the forests and not of the open plains.

Younger Tertiary beds contain larger and less primitive fossil horses. Climatic changes in Oligocene and Miocene time, with decrease of forests and increase of meadow and plains country, were probably responsible for the chief modifications seen in the several types of fossil horses from deposits belonging to these epochs. There was a distinct

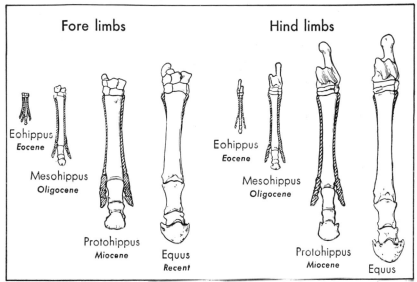

324. The lower part of the limbs of Cenozoic horses. The chief evolutionary change is progressive enlargement of the central digit and gradual disappearance of the side toes. (*Modified from Scott.*)

but gradual increase in size, the toes on each foot were reduced to three, and the teeth, especially in some, became more like those of the modern horse.

Pliocene horses carried these modifications farther, and we find here the first one-toed horse, in which the remnants of side toes are represented merely by bony splints below the wrist and ankle. Some Pliocene horses, however, still retained complete side toes.

Pleistocene deposits of North and South America contain abundant remains of horses which are essentially modern, but, for unexplained reasons, horses became extinct in the Western Hemisphere before the beginning of the Recent geologic epoch. If Old World species, which are probably migrants or descendants of migrants from North America, had not survived, we should know the horse only as we do the amblypod, from fossil bones.

The evolution of the horse, more completely shown by discovered fossils than probably any other mammal group, reveals clearly (1) lengthening of the limbs, (2) change of foot posture from digits with much of the length to only the tip in contact with the ground, (3) reduction in the number of digits on each foot to one, (4) reduction of smaller bones (ulna and fibula) of the limbs, (5) modification and complication of the teeth from a type adapted for browsing to one adapted for grazing, (6) elongation of the skull and neck, and (7) marked increase in size.

Rhinoceroses. The fossil record of rhinoceroses is second only to that of the horses in abundance and completeness. Modern representatives of this family are restricted to Africa, India, Java, and Sumatra, and therefore they seem quite foreign to the North American continent. Yet rhinoceroses were very much at home here during most of Tertiary time, and it is indeed probable that they originated in the western United States. They migrated to all parts of the world except South America and Australia.

The modern rhinoceroses are large beasts, 4 to 6½ feet high at the shoulders, with long body, short elephant-like legs, and a long head that bears one horn on the nose, or one on the nose and another on the forehead. These horns are unlike those of other horned mammals, such as deer or cattle, in that they consist of solid horny substance without a bone core. The horns are not preserved as fossils, but their place of attachment is shown by roughened thickenings of the skull. Living rhinoceroses have three toes on each foot, the central one the largest; this is true of many fossil forms also, but the more primitive had four toes on the front feet. The initial five-toed ancestor is unknown.

Middle Eocene beds contain several species of primitive rhinoceroses about the size of a sheep. From this stock, characterized by the unspecialized nature of the skeleton, came at least four divergent lines of descent: (1) relatively light-bodied, hornless animals with slender limbs adapted for running (hyracodonts); (2) large-bodied, short, and heavy-legged aquatic animals (amynodonts); (3) gigantic long-necked, long-headed hornless forms (baluchitheres); and (4) the true rhinoceroses, which are generally horned.

The Oligocene, Miocene, and lower Paleocene beds of western America contain abundant remains of rhinoceroses, some deposits forming veritable bone beds. One type (*Teleoceras*), which lived in large numbers along streams and marshy areas in western Nebraska and Kansas in late Miocene and early Pliocene time, had a long, large barrel-like body and absurdly short legs.

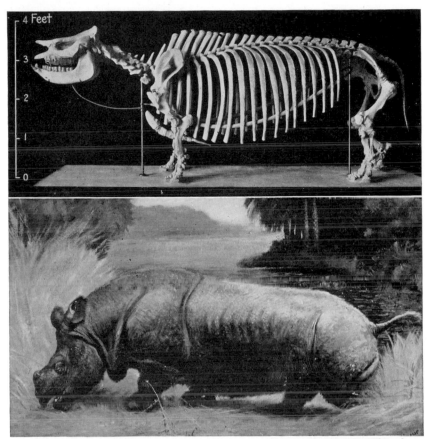

325. Skeleton and restoration of a Pliocene rhinoceros from western Kansas. This short-legged, barrel-bodied rhinoceros *(Teleoceras)* inhabited stream valleys of the plains region in Late Tertiary time. *(American Museum of Natural History.)*

Although not known in North America, we may notice the baluchi-theres (named from Baluchistan, central Asia, where they were dis-covered). These are the largest known land mammals, attaining a height of more than 16 feet at the shoulders and a total length of about 25 feet. The head, armed with two powerful tusks, was about 4½ feet long and the neck was also unusually extended. The legs were long and the whole appearance somewhat giraffe-like, but much heavier. This branch of the rhinoceros group doubtless fed on the foliage of trees. It lived in the late Oligocene or early Miocene.

Titanotheres. This is an interesting branch of the odd-toed hoofed

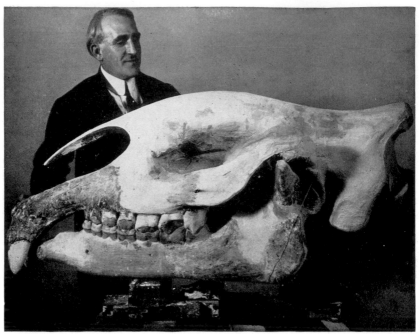

326. Skull of *Baluchitherium*, largest of known land mammals. (*American Museum of Natural History.*)

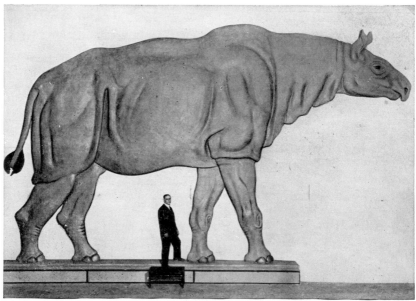

327. Restoration of *Baluchitherium*. This hornless rhinoceros, which roamed central Asia in mid-Tertiary time, stood more than 16 feet high at the shoulders. (*American Museum of Natural History.*)

328. Restoration of large rhinoceros-like titanotheres. Skeletons of these animals, with remains of large turtles and many other forms, come from Oligocene deposits of the Black Hills region. (*C. R. Knight, Chicago Natural History Museum.*)

mammals that inhabited the western United States in Early Tertiary time. The group is most abundantly represented by fossils from North America, but is now known also from Asia and Europe. The earliest known titanothere was a trifle smaller than a sheep, the skull long and narrow, bearing tusks but no horns. The forelimbs had four toes and the hind limbs three. Later titanotheres increased in size to elephantine proportions. The limbs were stout and pillar-like, and, as in the elephant, the short feet were supported by thick pads. The most striking modifications are seen in the skull, which developed bony knobs and eventually great bony paired horns over the nose. The skull became long, very broad, and strengthened to withstand the impact when the horns were put to use. Despite the large bulk of the later titanotheres, the brain was very small, not larger than a man's fist, indicating a low order of intelligence.

Chalicotheres. The strangest perissodactyls are animals called "chalicotheres," from North America and Europe, which are found in middle Eocene to lower Pliocene beds. The skull and remainder of the skeleton, except limbs and feet, are not greatly unlike those of a horse, although there are many differences. The feet are armed with great claws, and when the first specimens were discovered, in disconnected form, they were referred to an order entirely different from that in which the skull had been placed. Complete skeletons now known show that the horselike body and clawed feet actually belong together. That this grotesque animal fed on plants is plainly shown by the teeth. The claws probably served in grubbing roots and tubers. Some of the chalicotheres considerably exceed a good-sized horse in height and bulk.

Even-toed Hoofed Mammals

The great group of even-toed hoofed mammals (artiodactyls) is distinguished by characters of the limbs and teeth, which separate them readily from the odd-toed mammals and yet serve clearly to show relationship between such apparently unlike animals as the pig, camel, deer, giraffe, and hippopotamus. The axis of the foot lies between the third and fourth digits, which are equal in size and symmetrical. The number of toes is four or two, although in some primitive forms a vestige of the fifth toe remains. A peculiar and very characteristic structure of the ankle bones is found in all. There are two types of chewing teeth, the more primitive having conelike cusps, and the more specialized showing crescent-shaped grinding ridges of enamel. Even-toed hoofed animals are very abundant as fossils, the remains of different kinds being found in each of the Cenozoic stages from lower Eocene to Recent.

Oreodonts. The most common kind of mammals in some of the Oligocene deposits of the western United States are extinct creatures having the size of a small sheep and combining certain characters of pig, deer, and camel. They are called "oreodonts." These animals are restricted to North America and are known from Eocene to early Pliocene times. During part of their career, they must have roamed the plains and river valleys in enormous numbers. Skeletons are frequently found in little-disturbed condition. An interesting specimen, mounted by students at the South Dakota School of Mines, shows the well-formed skeleton of an unborn young oreodont within the body of the mother.

Giant pigs and peccaries. The swine may claim rank as one of the "first families" of the Tertiary. They trace their ancestry to Eocene time, and were represented in North America as late as the Pleisto-

329. Part of western Nebraska in Miocene time. The wild hogs (entelodonts) shown in foreground were about 6 feet high at the shoulders; at right is a chalicothere. *(C. R. Knight, Chicago Natural History Museum.)*

cene by large, highly developed peccaries. The strangest, or at least the most uncouth, are giant pigs (entelodonts) that lived in the Oligocene and early Miocene Epochs. These attained a height of 6 feet at the shoulders and were exceeded in bulk among members of the swine family only by the hippopotamus. The skull of the giant pig was very elongate, and it bore peculiar bony excrescences below the eyes and on the underside of the jaw. There were stout but not long tusks. The brain was almost reptile-like in its diminutive size; the animal must have been profoundly stupid.

Camels. The desert regions of central Asia and northern Africa are the home of one living genus of camels, and the cold parts of South America of the other (llama). The ancestral dwelling place of this family, however, was North America. They developed gradually along various lines, increasing greatly in size and in specialization of teeth and limbs. Late in the Tertiary Period, they migrated to the Old World and into South America, while after mid-Pleistocene time, they became extinct in the continent of their birth. The earliest known camels, from upper Eocene beds, were smaller than a tiny lamb. The forefoot had four toes, but the hind foot was already so modified that there were only two functional toes, although vestiges of two

330. A herd of Miocene camels. Skeletal remains show that these llama-like camels roamed North American western plains in large numbers. (*E. M. Fulda, American Museum of Natural History.*)

others are present. The development of the camels shows many interesting parallels with that of the horses, but the irreducible number of toes on each foot is two, instead of one. Some of the mid-Tertiary American camels were slender, graceful creatures resembling antelopes, and one kind is distinguished by its extremely elongated neck and long legs, an adaptation like that of the giraffe for browsing on leaves of trees.

Deer and cattle. Interesting representatives of the deer family are found as fossils in the American Tertiary as far back as the Oligocene. Some were hornless, others had short pronglike horns, and still others had antlers with branches. One very peculiar group, which is really distinct from the true deer, had a pair of prominent bony plates above the eyes and another pair on the nose. The moose and caribou are immigrants from the Old World that are first known on this continent in Pleistocene time.

The cattle family is represented in America by the bison, muskox, and wild sheep. Domestic cattle and sheep are derived from Asiatic species and have been introduced in the Western Hemisphere by man.

The bison, which roamed the plains in such enormous herds before the advance of civilization destroyed them, were present in the Pleistocene Epoch but are not known earlier. One kind of fossil bison was distinctly larger than the Recent species and was characterized by a huge hump; another had a hornspread of more than 6 feet. There is proof that man was contemporaneous with some of these extinct species of bison.

ELEPHANTS

Elephants rank with the horse in point of interest and instructiveness of the fossil record. The lineage of this largest living land mammal may be traced far back in Tertiary time, and the gradual acquirement of proboscidian peculiarities may be observed step by step. Like the horse and man, the elephant is one of the few kinds of mammals that became adapted to almost all sorts of environments and spread over practically the whole world. Teeth and bones of elephants are found in stream and other deposits of Pleistocene age

331. A shovel-toothed elephant *(Platybelodon)* **from Late Tertiary deposits of the western United States.** In Miocene and Pliocene time, this specialized branch of the elephant stock was distributed from the Dakotas to Texas. Probably their spadelike teeth and lower jaw were used for grubbing succulent roots in swampy ground. *(American Museum of Natural History.)*

in almost every part of the United States, testifying to the abundance and wide distribution of these animals in North America until comparatively recent time.

The chief distinguishing characters of the elephants are in the head, which is unusually massive and abnormally shortened, and bears the long powerful trunk. The shape of the skull, the enormously thick but light cranial bones, and the short neck are all modifications that aid in carrying the weight of the head. The trunk is a very muscular development of the upper lip and nose, the nostrils running the entire length to the tip. Elephants are not the only animals with an elongated proboscis or trunk, but no others have this organ so highly developed. Since elongation of the snout is always correlated with a recession of the nasal bones and with a thickening of adjacent bones for muscular attachment, it is possible to determine, from study of a fossil skull, whether an animal had a trunk, and approximately how large it was.

The teeth of the elephant are distinctive. The tusks are remarkably enlarged long incisors, which in the African elephant may exceed 10 feet in length, 2 feet in circumference at the base, and weigh 230 pounds or more apiece. Some of the fossil elephants had tusks 13 feet, or exceptionally even 16 feet, in length. The grinding teeth are very large, and there is normally only one tooth on each side of the upper and lower jaws. However, as a tooth is worn down to the roots, it is gradually displaced by a new one that pushes in from behind. Thus the grinding teeth grow in successively, the last or backmost molars appearing at about age forty-five and serving for the rest of the animal's life. The character of these teeth differs notably in different species, that of the modern Indian elephant having numerous parallel grinding ridges, that of the African elephant having a simpler pattern, and those of several extinct forms showing a series of large conelike cusps.

Evolution of the elephants.   The earliest definitely distinguishable representative (*Palaeomastodon*) of the elephant family occurs in lower Oligocene deposits of northern Africa and southern Asia. This animal had about the size and build of a small baby elephant, but the trunk was undoubtedly very short, the head and neck relatively more elongate, and all the grinding teeth were present at the same

332. Grinding surface of an elephant tooth from Pleistocene deposits in Kansas. This tooth, very similar to the molars of living elephants, shows the projecting transverse ridges of hard enamel that adapt the tooth for grinding. *(University of Kansas, Natural History Museum.)*

time. There were short downward-curving tusks in the upper jaw and very short tusks also in the long lower jaw.

In Miocene time, different kinds of elephants are known to have spread to Europe and North America. One type (*Dinotherium*), which occurs in Europe and Asia, had no tusks on the upper jaw, but on the lower there were large tusks curving downward and backward. Other kinds had four large straight tusks, two on the upper jaw and two on the lower. Some of these are found in North America. They continued into the Pliocene Epoch, a specimen of this age from Nebraska having a lower jaw and flat shovel-like tusks at least 6 feet long.

The most abundant and best-known fossil elephants in North America are those of the great Ice Age. One type, called the American mastodon, is distinguished partly by the large-cusped grinding teeth, which differ markedly from those of the true elephants. The mastodon had about the height of the modern Indian elephant but was much stockier. It was apparently a forest-dwelling animal. Its remains have

333. Largest of the American fossil elephants, of Pleistocene age. This animal (*Archidisko-don*) is known as the "imperial elephant." (*American Museum of Natural History.*)

been found chiefly in drainage excavations in boggy lands of the Northern States, one specimen found in New York having a quantity of long shaggy dark brown hair with the bones. True elephants are represented in North America: by the imperial elephant, which had remarkably long curving tusks and attained a height of 13 feet; the columbian elephant, which was somewhat smaller than the imperial; and the hairy or woolly mammoth. This last was circumpolar in range, being known in Europe and northern Asia, as well as on this continent. It had a thick coat of coarse long black hair, with a dense brown wool covering beneath. Specimens of this animal have been discovered frozen in the Siberian tundras.

The main evolutionary changes in the development of the elephants are increase of size; modification in shape and structure of bones of the skull; loss of incisors and canines, except two incisors of each jaw (or of one jaw) that are modified as tusks; increase in size and complexity of the grinding teeth; their reduction in number; development of the peculiar method of tooth succession; and the growth of the trunk.

Carnivores

The carnivorous mammals, including chiefly the cat and dog families, are distinguished by clawed feet and by teeth adapted for grasping and cutting flesh, the long sharp canines and shearlike molars. In the early part of Tertiary time, there were primitive flesh-eaters (creodonts), which in some respects resembled the early hoofed mammals but in others show ancestral relationship to the later carnivores.

The best-known cats of Tertiary time are the sabertooths, characterized by unusual enlargement of the canines of the upper jaw. These animals were evidently ferocious beasts of prey that ranged over the whole Northern Hemisphere, and late in the Tertiary extended to South America. The culmination of this race is found in a Pleistocene cat (*Smilodon*) of the western United States, which had great curved scimitar-like upper canines 8 inches or more in length. It is hard to

334. The Pleistocene saber-tooth cat of the western United States. This beast of prey (*Smilodon*), as large and powerful as the African lion, was much specialized in its dentition. (*C. R. Knight, American Museum of Natural History.*)

understand how these great tusks, blocking entrance to the mouth, could have been used effectively, unless the creature could open its mouth much more widely than any living cat. There were only one or two large cutting teeth at the back of each jaw—indeed, the entire dentition includes but 12 to 14 teeth. The form and structure of the skeleton indicate an unusually powerful animal.

Fossil dogs are well known from late Cenozoic deposits, but the doglike animals of earlier time are increasingly generalized. Dogs are a central line of carnivore evolution among the mammals, several lines of which became extinct during the Tertiary.

20. The Geologic Record of Man

Neanderthal cave man.

F. L. Jaques, American Museum of Natural History

The bare-skinned, warm-blooded animal called man, which has been the dominant creature of the earth during at least the last several thousand years, differs from all other living things in his ability to reason, and to devise and make tools for use in accomplishing all sorts of purposes. Many past and present inhabitants of the earth have achieved high specialization of structure that adapt them to different modes of life, but no other has learned to make and use implements or has achieved the mental and spiritual consciousness leading to ethical, aesthetic, and religious concepts such as those belonging to man. Accordingly, we say that man stands apart from the lower animals.

Because man seems to belong in a sphere of his own, it is appropriate to inquire whether his origin is different from that of the rest of the organic world. Is he a wholly distinct type of being that suddenly appeared in a fully developed state very recently—say, about 4,000 B. C.—by special creation? Or, opposed to this, do we find evidence that antiquity of man on the earth is measured in many ten-thousand or even several hundred-thousand years? Do we observe that early human types are less sharply differentiated from lower animals than men composing the modern Caucasian, Mongolian, and Negro races are distinguished from one another?

Study of man's origin, his expanding distribution over the earth, and his physical and cultural development prior to earliest written history, belongs in the field of geology, though the later parts of the prehistoric human record are commonly embraced in archaeology.

Evidence of Man's Origin

Several independent lines of evidence throw light on the question of how man originated. All testimony points toward his derivation by processes of evolution such as have produced the many other kinds of animals inhabiting the earth. It indicates, furthermore, that he developed during Late Tertiary or very Early Quaternary geologic history from the branch of mammals that includes the lemurs, apes, and monkeys. This branch comprises animals that collectively are known as the "primates" (Latin *primus,* first), a name given by Linnaeus to signify their development to first rank in the animal kingdom. The chief lines of evidence relating to man's origin are found in studies of comparative anatomy, embryology, vestigial organs, blood tests, and paleontology.

Structural relationship. Man's body very plainly is patterned on the mammalian plan. Part for part, his skeleton, musculature, nervous system, and internal organs correspond to those of other mammals, identity of features being especially close between man and other primates. Most closely similar to man in physical structure are the gorilla and chimpanzee, and not much less like man are the orangutan and gibbon. At least one-fourth of man's structural peculiarities also characterize the gorilla or chimpanzee, or both, but are not found in other animals. A few features are common to man and the orangutan or gibbon, but not to others. An example of these peculiarities is one of the wristbones (centrale) that is lacking in adult man, gorilla, and chimpanzee, but is present in all three before birth, and is found generally in all other adult primates. Another example is the air chambers that branch off the nasal cavity, which are identical in number and arrangement in man, gorilla, and chimpanzee, but different in other primates. Such facts have rational

335. Gorilla, largest of the living manlike apes. Although the gorilla corresponds closely to man in many features of structure and embryological development, his hands and feet are considerably modified from human form. *(Peabody Museum, Yale University.)*

meaning if these animals are related in evolutionary development. They are surely not duplication of characters produced by pure chance.

The developing human embryo undergoes a series of peculiar changes in the mother's womb, and it is a significant fact that in only

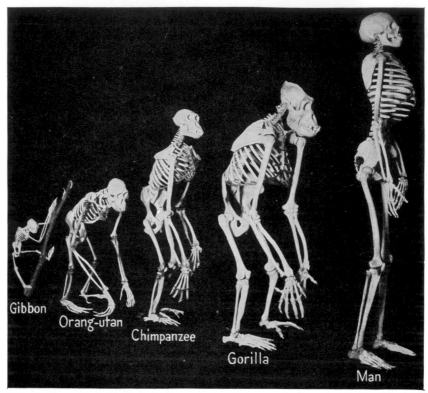

336. Skeletons of man and of the four primates that most closely resemble him. *(Peabody Museum, Yale University.)*

four other living mammals—gorilla, chimpanzee, orangutan, and gibbon—are identical changes found to occur. One of these similar features of development is the appearance of an external jointed tail that is seen in the fifth week of development but shrivels and disappears by the eighth week.

Sensitive tests based on biochemical properties of blood have been found to be a reliable measure of biologic relationship. This sort of study proves that man is close kin to the manlike apes and more distantly related to other primates. Confirming such evidence is observation that diseases of man much more readily affect the gorilla and chimpanzee, for example, than any of the monkeys, and when some of these are successfully inoculated, they are likely to have the disease in mildest form.

Fossil remains. Whereas structural relationships just considered provide strong inferential basis of man's antiquity and common ancestry with the higher apes, the discovery of fossilized human remains, buried in association with extinct Pleistocene animals of various sorts, furnishes indisputable proof that races of men existed on the earth during the Ice Age. Almost certain, but not established beyond doubt, is appearance of the earliest creatures classifiable as human during the Pliocene Epoch of Tertiary time. No skeletal remains of Pliocene man have been found, but stone implements (*eoliths*), classifiable as marking the beginning of human culture, are found buried in Pliocene deposits. Thus, fossil remains give convincing confirmation of conclusions concerning man's origin based on other lines of study. We shall now review main features in the fossil record.

Ape Men of Eastern Asia

Relatively numerous kinds of human fossils, representing primitive types of men that possess many apelike characters, have been reported from eastern Asia. These fossils have been obtained from the island of Java in the East Indies and from China. They occur in river terrace and cave deposits containing undisturbed remains of extinct mammals, which are interpreted to denote mid-Pleistocene age.

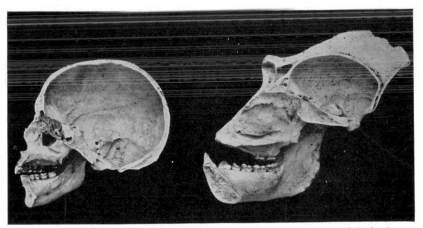

337. Skulls of man and gorilla cut longitudinally to show comparative size of the brain case. The prominent eyebrow ridge above the orbit and the sagittal crest on the top of the skull of the gorilla are features which, with the low facial angle and absence of chin, distinguish the apes from men. (*Peabody Museum, Yale University.*)

338. An early member of the order of primates. This animal *(Notharctus)*, which is represented by nearly complete skeletal remains in Eocene deposits of North America, may be a very distant ancestor of man. *(F. L. Jaques, American Museum of Natural History.)*

Ape man of Java. The first discovery of very ancient primitive man in Asia was in 1892 when excavation in ash beds on the banks of the Solo River in eastern Java yielded human teeth and bones associated with remains of various extinct animals, then thought to represent latest Pliocene or earliest Pleistocene time. The fossils are now considered to belong to the middle part of the Pleistocene Epoch and are estimated to be approximately 400,000 to 500,000 years old. The first found evidence of human existence in such remote past time consisted of three teeth, the top part of a skull, and an upper leg bone (femur). The skullcap is apelike in having very prominent bony ridges over the eye orbits, but it differs greatly from that of any ape in lacking a median crest and in having a very much larger brain cavity. The

339. Restoration of the Java ape man (*Pithecanthropus*). (*J. H. McGregor, American Museum of Natural History.*)

size of the brain of this early Java man was approximately two-thirds that of a modern adult European and roughly twice as large as that of the biggest ape brain, which is found in a full-grown gorilla. A cast of the interior of the Java ape man's skullcap shows the position and shape of brain convolutions, and this definitely confirms classification of the owner of the skull as a primitive human being who probably possessed at least the rudiments of speech. The structure of the leg bone shows that it belonged to an erect-walking primate. Inasmuch as the skull and leg bone were found some 20 feet apart, although in the same deposit, it is by no means certain that they belong to the same individual. They are confidently judged, however, to represent a race of erect-walking primitive men and accordingly have been named *Pithecanthropus erectus* (erect ape man).

Excavation of the Solo River deposits, especially in the years from 1936 to 1939, has yielded important additional remains of *Pithecanthropus*. These include three more skullcaps, upper and lower jaws, four leg bones, and the skull of a child. They agree in character with the original find and furnish information, previously wanting, concerning the face. Despite lack of most of the skeleton, the essential nature of the Java ape man is fairly well known.

China ape man. In 1927, or shortly before, paleontological collecting from limestone caves some 40 miles southwest of Peking, China, resulted in finding three teeth that belong either to a primitive man or a large manlike ape. In 1929, a well-preserved skullcap, almost identical in size and shape to that of the Java ape man, was discovered. The human affinities of these fossils could no longer remain doubtful, and the name *Sinanthropus pekingensis* (China man of Peking) was applied. Subsequent excavations of the cave deposits have yielded a full series of skeletal remains belonging to about three dozen young and adult individuals of both sexes. Although no complete skull has been found, comparison of different specimens now provide full knowledge of the skull, including the lower jaw. It is judged that the Peking man belongs to the same race as the Java ape man, and therefore may be called *Pithecanthropus* instead of *Sinanthropus*.

Stone implements and remains of hearths prove that the Peking ape man was a user of tools and knew how to make fire. The fact that every brain case has been broken open from below indicates that the brains were sought for food, and we must judge that the *Pithecanthropus* individuals of China were cannibals. This is confirmed by the condition of the limb bones, all of which have been split so as to get at the marrow.

Associated extinct fossils near Peking indicate that the Chinese ape men belong to mid-Pleistocene time like those of eastern Java.

Giant primates. In recent years, fragmentary jaws and teeth of gigantic ape men or manlike apes (*Meganthropus*, *Gigantopithecus*) have been found in Java and southern China. These indicate creatures considerably larger than the biggest full-sized gorilla. They are not well enough known to permit more than a guess as to whether they are in the direct line of human ancestry or an offshoot branch of primates.

Primitive Human and Near-Human Remains from Africa

Cave deposits in the Transvaal and Rhodesia, South Africa, have yielded varyingly complete skulls and other bones that prove existence of primitive human and near-human beings. As judged by fossil animals found with them, they probably belong to late Pleistocene time. Some of these primate fossils are more like apes than men, even though the brain capacity is slightly larger than that of a gorilla and dentition closely follows the human pattern.

One almost perfect skull from Rhodesia undoubtedly represents a human type, but it is unusual in that it combines several very primitive characters with others that are specialized. There are very heavy brow ridges and the face rather suggests that of an ape, but the brain case has only slightly smaller capacity than that of an adult modern European. Rhodesian man is not very unlike early human cave dwellers of western Europe who lived during late Pleistocene time.

Prehistoric Men in Europe

River terraces and cave deposits in various parts of western Euope have yielded fairly numerous cultural remains of prehistoric man. These show definitely progressive advancement of his skill in making weapons and many sorts of implements. Except skeletons of late Pleistocene and early Recent age, fossil human bones are uncommon.

Heidelberg man. Perhaps the oldest human bone yet discovered anywhere in the world is a man's jaw found in a deposit of river sand about 80 feet below the surface near the German town of Heidelberg. Associated bones of elephants, rhinoceroses, lions, and other mammals indicate the age of the deposit as early Pleistocene. The jaw is very large and heavily built. It lacks a chin prominence, but the teeth and other structural features have definite human characters. Nothing is known of the cultural stage of Heidelberg human beings, because no man-made implements have been found in the river deposit associated with the bone.

English "dawn man." The incomplete skull and lower jaw of a primitive man have been found in early Pleistocene deposits known as the Piltdown gravels in southeastern England. These human remains have been named *Eoanthropus*, the "dawn man." The skull denotes a type much more modern than that of the eastern Asia ape men, but the lower jaw is so much like that of a large ape that question has been raised as to whether the jaw and skull actually belong together. Inasmuch as no bones of large apes have been found in Pleistocene deposits of northwestern Europe, it is reasonable to judge that the skull and jaw, discovered a few feet apart in the Piltdown beds, belong to the oldest known human inhabitant of England.

Neanderthal man. A race of prehistoric men that during the last interglacial age of Pleistocene time and the early part of the final (Würmian) glaciation lived throughout Europe, western Asia, and the north coast of Africa, is Neanderthal man. This name is derived from the locality in western Germany where the first recognized specimen was found in a cave deposit in 1856. Many complete skeletons now are known, and the bones are associated in many places with an abundance of stone implements that show a high degree of skill in

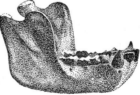

Heidelberg man   Chimpanzee   Modern man

340. The jaw of Heidelberg man compared to that of an ape and modern man. *(K. F. Mather, "Sons of the Earth," W. W. Norton & Company, Inc.)*

341. Restoration of Neanderthal man. (*J. H. McGregor, American Museum of Natural History.*)

manufacture. The Neanderthalers were primarily cave dwellers and hunters. The average height of adult men was not over 5½ feet, and of women about 5 feet. The brain capacity was as large as that of the highest type of living races, but the shape of the skull, especially the receding forehead and heavy eyebrow ridges, is quite unlike the rounded contours of the modern European head. The jaw was chinless, and there are many other structural differences between the Neanderthal race and modern man.

Modern man. In late Pleistocene time, during the retreating phase of the last ice sheets, a new race of men, decidedly unlike the Neanderthalers who suddenly disappeared, took possession of Europe. The newcomers, sometimes known as Cro-Magnon man, from a locality in France where many skeletal remains have been found, are entirely indistinguishable structurally from well-built modern men. Their bones are especially abundant in cave deposits of central France, and altogether about 100 nearly complete skeletons are known. Many of the males exceed 6 feet in height. The skulls have a high forehead and well-rounded contours, and the lower jaws bear a well-developed chin. These prehistoric "modern" men were skilled workers in flint and bone, and they have left records of artistic talent in paintings and sculpture found in many caves.

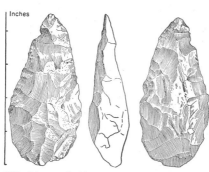

342. Edge and side views of an early Stone Age flint used for striking blows or for cutting and scraping. (*K. F. Mather, "Sons of the Earth," W. W. Norton & Co., Inc.*)

Early Man in the Americas

Extensive and varied remains of prehistoric human cultures have been found in both North and South America, but there is no proof that the oldest of these belongs as far back as 25,000 B. C. Man's antiquity in the Western Hemisphere does not seem to approach that of the early and middle Pleistocene remains found in various parts of the Old World. Moreover, information concerning man in the Americas is derived mostly from his works, rather than from skeletal remains. It is true that human bones have been found associated with fossil skeletal parts of extinct mammals, such as camels, elephants, and ground sloths, but either it is not established that the human remains are as old as the associated mammals (occurrence together being due

343. Carving on a cave wall at Les Combarelles, in central France. (*After l'Abbé H. Breuil.*)

344. Ponderous rock tables constructed by prehistoric man near Morbihan, France. *(Frank Carney.)*

to secondary deposition) or there is no reason to suppose that the extinct mammals themselves are very ancient.

Folsom remains. The oldest American flint implements are those of so-called Folsom man, named from a locality in New Mexico where specimens of this sort of prehistoric human handicraft were first discovered. Most common are spearheads, which are readily differentiated from flints shaped by the later American Indians, all of which lack the sort of groove that is cut on each side of the Folsom points. Some of the latter implements have been found embedded in matrix between bones of extinct species of bison and one in northeastern Colorado was found beneath the pelvis of a fossil mammoth. These finds satisfactorily prove a considerable antiquity, even though age in years can only be estimated.

Patagonian early man. Seemingly, the oldest authentic human remains yet found in the New World are several human skeletons found in two caves in Patagonia, South America. These bones were found near the bottom of undisturbed earth and ashes that largely fill the caves, and associated with them were bones of an extinct sloth and American wild horse. Excavation showed four distinct layers of successive human cultures in deposits that had accumulated above the skeletons. The skulls are of mongoloid type, not very unlike those of

345. Inscriptions on sandstone of the Colorado River canyon, about 85 miles below the mouth of Green River, Utah. These carvings, well preserved in the dry air of the Southwest, are not demonstrably of great antiquity, but they were made by men unknown to modern Indians.

some American Indians. They are by no means primitive in structural characters.

Probable migration from eastern Asia. Comparatively modern, though prehistoric, are remarkable stone structures and carvings that are records of early Inca, Maya, and other cultures of South and Central America, but in places there are relics of a very different pre-Inca people. These may represent some of the earliest invaders of America who, in all probability, migrated from eastern Asia by way of the Bering Strait, which now narrowly divides Alaska from the eastern tip of Siberia.

During late Pleistocene time, it is very probable that man need not have traveled by water in order to reach Alaska, and it is not necessary to postulate existence of an ice bridge in order to permit passage of land animals from one continent to the other. Water that was removed from ocean areas to make the enormous volume of glacial ice during Pleistocene time is computed to have lowered the mean sea level by an amount greater than 300 feet. Submarine surveys in the Bering region show that, if the present sea level dropped only a little more than 100 feet, a dry roadway could be built so as to join North America with Asia. Not only is this northwestern route a most plausible pathway for migration but no other reasonably possible alternative route is offered. The Asiatic origin of the Indian inhabitants of both North and South America is shown by their physical character, for extremely close resemblance between Indian and Mongolian types persists to the present day. We conclude that the earliest human inhabitants of the Americas were all immigrants who traveled eastward from Asia, and that Indian tribes of North and South America are descendants of Asiatic immigrants. The first arrivals probably came in the late part of Pleistocene time, perhaps 25,000 years ago, and in course of time spread throughout vast areas of game-filled wilderness and plains country in the Americas. Eventually they peopled both continents and built civilizations that were old when Columbus crossed the Atlantic.

nated by the first name, generally derived from the Greek, and the individual kind (species) by the second name, generally derived from the Latin. For example, *Felis domesticus*, the common cat; *Felis leo*, the lion; *Felis concolor*, the puma; and a number of others are all species of the genus of cats. Obviously they are all closely related to one another. *Smilodon* and *Hoplophoneus* are extinct genera of cats characterized by unusually elongated saber-like canine teeth, and distinguished in other respects from modern *Felis*, but we group together all the cats in the family Felidae.

Thus, in ascending scale of comprehensiveness, there are species, genus, family, order, class, phylum, and kingdom. All animals and plants may be classified according to this plan, but, because of differences in knowledge or judgment as to the relationship and points of distinction between organisms, there is by no means complete accord among biologists on the subject of classification.

The main plan of organization of the plant and animal kingdoms, omitting certain divisions that are unimportant as fossils, is given in the following tabular outline. Divisions comprised of extinct organisms are marked by an asterisk (*).

Main Divisions of the Plant and Animal Kingdoms

PLANTS

Thallophyta, cellular tissue plants lacking distinction of root, stem, or leaf.
  Schizophyta, one-celled plants; bacteria.
  Algae, seaweeds and diatoms.
  Fungi, mushrooms and molds; unimportant as fossils.
Bryophyta, plants having leafy stems; mosses and liverworts; unimportant as fossils.
Pteridophyta, plants having roots, leaves, and woody-fiber stems; ferns.
Arthrophyta, plants provided with jointed stem, allied to ferns; horsetails and calamites.
Lepidophyta, plants characterized by scalelike leaves, allied to ferns; club mosses, lepidodendrons, and sigillarias.
Pteridospermophyta, extinct seed ferns.
Cycadophyta, palmlike plants; cycads.
Coniferophyta, conifers like the pine and spruce, and the fossil cordaites.
Angiospermophyta, all flowering plants.

ANIMALS

Protozoa, one-celled animals.
  Foraminifera, mostly calcareous, in part arenaceous-shelled protozoans.

Radiolaria, mostly siliceous-shelled.

Porifera, the sponges; body wall porous, many with calcareous or siliceous skeleton.

Coelenterata, body cavity serving to carry on all vital functions.

    Hydrozoa, small, body cavity lacking radial partitions.

    Stromatoporoidea, colonial, secreting massive laminated base.

    Graptolitoidea, delicate stemlike growths along which the individuals are arranged in series (possibly may belong with bryozoans).

    Anthozoa, the corals; body cavity divided by radial partitions.

Echinoderma, spiny-skinned animals.

    Pelmatozoa, stemmed echinoderms.

      Cystoidea, bladder-like form, plates irregularly arranged.

      Blastoidea, small symmetrical, budlike.

      Crinoidea, calyx composed of regularly arranged plates, arms free.

    Asterozoa, starfishes, brittle stars.

    Echinozoa, sea urchins, holothurians.

Vermes, worms, generally unimportant as fossils.

Bryozoa, minute colonial animals that secrete a variety of beautiful and delicate calcareous skeletons.

Brachiopoda, bivalves in which one shell is larger than the other and, typically, each bilaterally symmetrical.

Mollusca, soft-bodied invertebrates, highly developed.

    Pelecypoda, bivalves in which the two shells are the same in size, and generally symmetrical one to the other.

    Gastropoda, a single cap-shaped or spirally coiled shell, undivided.

    Cephalopoda, straight or spirally coiled shell divided into numerous chambers, or shell solid, internal.

Arthropoda, segmented animals, typically with a pair of jointed appendages to each segment.

    Branchiata, gills developed in connection with the appendages.

      Crustacea, mostly aquatic, provided with antennae.

        Trilobita, primitive marine crustacea having a longitudinally three-lobed shell.

      Ostracoda, small, bivalved crustacea.

      Malacostraca, crabs, lobsters.

    Arachnida, mostly air-breathers, lacking antennae.

      Merostomata, horseshoe crabs, eurypterids.

      Euarachnida, scorpions, spiders.

    Insecta, insects.

Vertebrata, animals with a notochord or backbone.

    Pisces, the fishes.

      Agnatha, primitive jawless fishes, mostly having prominent external bony covering of the anterior region; ostracoderms and cyclostomes.

      Placodermi, primitive jaw-bearing, plate-armored fishes, including the joint-neck arthrodires and sharklike fishes.

Chondrichthyes, cartilaginous jawed fishes; sharks, skates, rays.

Osteichthyes, bony fishes having well-developed jaws.

    Choanichthyes, fishes having internal nostrils; include crossopterygian (lobe-finned) fishes, which are ancestral to amphibians.

    Actinopterygii, ray-finned fishes; include most modern bony fishes.

Amphibia, cold-blooded animals provided with limbs and undergoing metamorphosis from water- to air-breathing; salamanders, frogs.

Reptilia, cold-blooded, air-breathing animals.

    Cotylosauria, primitive land reptiles.

    Chelonia, turtles.

    Ichthyosauria, short-necked, aquatic reptiles.

    Sauropterygia, long-necked, aquatic reptiles.

    Squamata, lizards, snakes, and extinct aquatic reptiles; mosasaurs.

    Thecodontia, ancestral stock of dinosaurs, pterosaurs, and crocodiles; includes phytosaurs.

    Crocodilia, crocodiles, alligators.

    Pterosauria, flying reptiles.

    Saurischia, a great group of dinosaurs, having lizard-like pelvic structure.

    Ornithischia, another group of dinosaurs, having birdlike pelvic structure.

  Pelycosauria, primitive mammal-like reptiles, some provided with tall fin along the back.

    Therapsida, progressive mammal-like reptiles that probably include ancestors of the mammals.

Aves, the birds.

Mammalia, the mammals, warm-blooded, suckle the young.

  Prototheria, egg-laying mammals.

  Metatheria, young born immature and carried in a pouch.

  Eutheria, young well-developed before birth.

    Insectivora, insect eaters.

    Chiroptera, bats.

    Primates, mammals provided with nails; apes, monkeys, man.

    Carnivora, flesh-eaters.

    Amblypoda, clumsy, archaic, hoofed mammals.

    Dinocerata, primitive hoofed mammals; includes uintatheres.

    Proboscidea, elephants.

    Sirenia, sea cows, manatees.

    Condylarthra, ancestral stock of hoofed mammals.

    Notoungulata, a distinctive South American assemblage of hoofed mammals.

    Litopterna, another South American hoofed mammal group.

    Perissodactyla, odd-toed mammals; horses, rhinoceroses, tapirs, titanotheres.

    Artiodactyla, even-toed mammals; sheep, cattle, swine.

    Edentata, sloths, armadillos.

    Cetacea, whales, dolphins.

    Rodentia, gnawing mammals; hares, beavers, rats, gophers.

Protozoans

The most primitive and simple animals, the protozoans, consist of a single cell in which are performed all the various functions of life, such as assimilation of food, excretion, respiration, reaction to external stimuli, and reproduction. The protozoans are exceedingly varied, but only two classes, (1) Foraminifera and (2) Radiolaria, secrete hard parts that are capable of preservation as fossils. The vast majority of protozoans are aquatic, and almost all the shelled forms live in the sea.

Foraminifera. These are the most important shell-bearing protozoans. Their shell or test, composed of calcium carbonate or sand grains cemented by calcium carbonate, iron oxide, or a complex organic compound known as chitin, is perforated by one or more minute openings (*foramina*). The simplest types consist of a single globular or cylindrical chamber with a rounded aperture. A more advanced type has an initial chamber surrounded spirally by a long undivided tube. In still more complex shells, there are several chambers arranged spirally, in a straight line, or coil, or in two or more rows.

Radiolaria. These secrete a very delicate and beautiful skeleton generally composed of silica.

Sponges

The sponges (Porifera), together with all higher types of animals, are distinguished from protozoans by the fact that the body is composed of many cells, which differ in function and are mutually interdependent. Accordingly, animals above the rank of the protozoans are sometimes grouped under the name Metazoa.

In simplest form, the sponge is a hollow, globular, or cylindrical structure with a large opening at the top. The body walls are pierced by numerous small openings. These passageways are lined by cells provided with mobile, hairlike appendages, which by a rhythmic motion produce gentle water currents toward the interior cavity of the animal, and thence outward by the large vent at the top. There is wide variation in the shape and size of different species of sponges, and through development of buds and branches, there may be much difference in the form of individuals of the same species. The sponges are aquatic creatures, mostly marine. Some of them have no hard parts

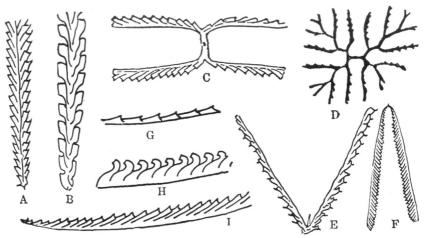

348. Representative forms of graptolites showing types of branching of colonies and cups of individual animals. *A, Diplograptus* (×3.5); *B, Climacograptus* (×6.5); *C, Tetragraptus* (×2.5); *D, Goniograptus* (×2); *E, Dicellograptus* (×3); *F, Didymograptus* (×1.5); *G, Cyrtograptus* (×5.5); *H, I, Monograptus* (×2.5). *A-F*, Ordovician; *G-I*, Silurian. *(After Ruedemann.)*

of them secrete a calcareous or horny skeleton. Corals are chiefly inhabitants of the very shallow parts of the sea.

Structurally, the body of the coral polyp differs from that of the hydrozoan in the presence of numerous radial walls of membrane (*mesenteries*), some of which project inward only a short distance from the circumference of the body, others reaching and joining a slit-like gullet that extends part way downward from the mouth. The calcium carbonate skeleton is normally secreted by the outer portion of the body wall, which thus encases the lower part of the coral in a cylindrical or conical tube, or forms a flattish basal expansion. Radial calcareous walls (*septa*) are built by infolded parts of the body covering. The upper edges of these walls generally slope inward from the outer calcareous wall (*theca*), so as to form a central depression (*calyx*). In Mesozoic and younger corals, there are typically six dominant radiating walls; in most Paleozoic forms, there are only four such primary walls. Among the latter, one or more of these four may be repressed so as to form a furrow (*fossula*) or furrows in the calyx. At successive stages in the life of the coral polyp, it may draw upward slightly and deposit a new basal platform (*tabula*) across the tube, and vacated spaces between the radial walls may be partitioned off by small oblique plates (*dissepiments*). Some corals secrete a central rodlike axis (*column*), which may project into the calyx. These and other structures give complexity and wide variation to the hard parts of different species of corals, which make them the more useful as markers of strata that contain them.

Echinoderms

The echinoderms (spiny skin) comprise a host of exclusively marine animals that are highly varied in appearance and size, but nearly all are characterized by radial symmetry and by the presence of a skeleton consisting of crystalline calcarcous plates embedded in the skin. Most familiar to visitors at the seashore are the starfish and sea urchin, which crawl about on the shallow sea bottom. Less generally

349. Model of a sea anemone. This coelenterate is closely related to the corals but lacks hard parts. (*American Museum of Natural History.*)

known, but important geologically, is a group of sedentary echinoderms, the crinoids, which are represented by living species, and the cystoids and blastoids, both of which are confined to rocks of Paleozoic age. The mouth is located on the ventral side. In free-moving echinoderms, the ventral side is normally downward, but in attached forms it is upward, and the animal is fastened by a stalk growing from the dorsal side. The echinoderms are much more highly organized than the coelenterates, for they have a true digestive canal, a distinct body cavity, a vascular and water circulatory system, a more highly developed nervous system, complex skeletal and structural elements, and an exclusively sexual mode of reproduction.

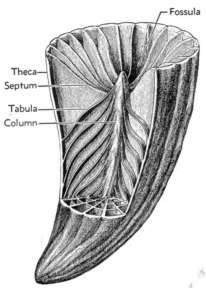

350. Diagram showing structure of a simple horn coral *(Lophophyllidium)*. About one third of the upper part of the corallite is cut away so as to show the internal structure.

CYSTOIDS

The most primitive and oldest known echinoderms are the cystoids, which have a skeleton of irregularly arranged plates joined rigidly together to form a saclike calyx, 1 or 2 inches in average diameter. The calyx was attached to the sea bottom or some foreign object by a short stem. Like other sedentary echinoderms, the cystoids fed on microscopic organic matter in the sea water, which was carried to the mouth along canals (*ambulacral grooves*) on the upper surface of the calyx or on the arms. Some species had two or more rather simple arms; a majority show peculiar perforations of the plates.

BLASTOIDS

A second group of the stemmed echinoderms is known as the blastoids. These have a symmetrical, budlike calyx, about ½ inch in average diameter, composed of 13 plates. Five food-groove ambulacral areas extend downward from the summit along the sides. Exceptionally well-preserved specimens show a multitude of threadlike armlets attached to the borders of the food grooves. Bundles of flattened tubes (*hydro-spires*), which probably functioned as respiratory organs, occur inside the calyx.

CRINOIDS

The most important group of sedentary echinoderms is that of the crinoids. Most of them are long-stemmed animals having a calyx composed of regularly arranged plates and provided with well-developed movable arms.

The stem consists of numerous superimposed button-like disks, each with a rounded or five-angled

351. Side view of the calyx of an Ordovician cystoid (*Canadacystis*). The plates are irregularly arranged; this genus lacks arms.

opening through the center. Lateral appendages (*cirri*) may occur at intervals, and near the base they may be modified into rootlike branches that serve for attachment. The length of the stem is ordinarily not greater than 2 feet, but some Mesozoic crinoids have stems 50 feet long.

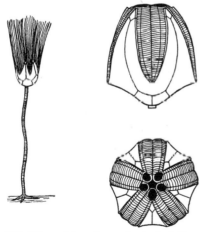

352. Side and top views of a typical blastoid (*Pentremites*). The symmetrical budlike shape and prominent ambulacral grooves are shown. Blastoids have a stem and armlets, called brachioles, that are attached along edges of the ambulacra, as shown at left.

The calyx is cup-shaped or globular and encloses the more important organs of the animal. The lower (dorsal) portion, below the arms, is characterized by regularly disposed plates, the shape and arrangement of which are constant in each species. The primary symmetry is always fivefold (pentameral) but in very many crinoids the introduction of an additional plate or series of plates (*anals*) on one side of the calyx introduces a bilateral symmetry. The crinoids are classified mainly on the basis of the plate arrangements of the calyx. If the plates become separated after death of the animal, or if stem or arm pieces only are found, it is not pos-

353. A modern crinoid *(Metacrinus)* **from the southwestern Pacific, showing crown and branchlets on stem.** Natural size.

sible ordinarily to identify the species to which these parts belonged. The upper (ventral) part of the calyx is generally formed of numerous irregularly arranged plates. The mouth is centrally located and externally visible in some forms, but concealed beneath the ventral covering in others. The anal vent is also located on the upper surface of the calyx, sometimes at the end of an elevated tube.

The arms of the crinoid are movable columns of small channeled plates arranged in single or double alternating series. The furrow along the arms, covered by small plates, carries water, with its contained microscopic food matter, to the mouth. Among all the more highly organized crinoids, each plate segment of the arms carries a small branchlet (*pinnule*), similar to the arm in structure and function. Various numbers of arms and types of branching are observed, but the arrangement of arms in all species shows a basic fivefold symmetry.

Living crinoids are highly gregarious and inhabit mainly the shallow, clear, moderately warm portions of the sea.

ECHINOIDS

The echinoids are distinguished from other echinoderms by the general form and plan of their shell, but especially by the covering of the shell by innumerable movable spines. In one large group of echinoids the shell is a slightly flattened globe with a moderately large opening for the mouth, centrally located on the underside, and a small anal aperture near the center of the dorsal side. The shell is composed of 20 columns of plates arranged in double rows, five of the pairs of rows containing specialized perforated plates (*ambulacra*) through which the delicate "tube feet" or tentacles that are used in locomotion or for respiration are protruded. The spines vary greatly in size, and there may be two or three orders of sizes on the same shell. They have a socket-like hollow at the base, which articulates with a rounded tubercle on the plates of the shell and is movable by muscle fibers that are attached slightly above the base. The function of the spines is to support the test, to aid in locomotion, and to serve as a means of defense. Within the mouth of most echinoids is a complicated jaw or masticatory apparatus, known as the Aristotle's lantern.

A second group of echinoids is distinguished by the more or less irregular outline of the shell which in a large number of species is heart-shaped, by the excentric position of the mouth and anus, and in part by modification of the ambulacral areas into petal-shaped spaces on the dorsal side of the shell.

Bryozoans

With exception of a single genus, bryozoans are exclusively colonial animals that secrete a calcareous, horny, or membranous covering that in different species exhibits a multitudinous variety of form and structure. Of course, only the calcareous forms are adapted for preservation as fossils. The most primitive bryozoans build a simple, chainlike series of tubes, one budding from another. By branching and lateral confluence of tubes, the more complex types of colonial structures are produced. Some grow in slender tufts; some spread over shells or other foreign objects in a delicate network of interwoven threads; or they form thin, leaflike expansions, rounded branches, lacy fronds, or massive subglobular bodies. There are several thousand described fossil species ranging in age from Ordovician to Recent, and during parts of geologic time the bryozoans were important rock builders.

Superficially, the bryozoans resemble certain hydrozoans, but they differ from them radically in the possession of a distinct body cavity, an alimentary canal, a highly developed nervous system, and delicate

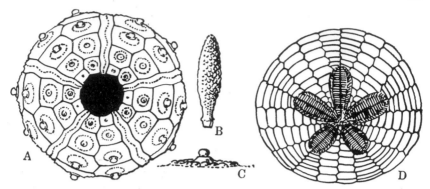

354. Fossil echinoids. *A, Dorocidaris,* Lower Cretaceous, Texas; bottom view of test showing narrow ambulacral areas and large interambulacral plates, each bearing a rounded spine base. *B, Cidaris,* Jurassic, California; side view of a large spine. *C, Dorocidaris,* side view of interambulacral plate. *D, Dendraster,* Pleistocene, California; top view of test showing petal-like ambulacral areas.

respiratory tentacles surrounding the mouth. The colonial skeleton (*zoarium*) has various structural peculiarities, which, with the almost microscopic size of the individual habitations (*zooecia*), make it easy to distinguish the bryozoans from other organisms. Many bryozoans were widely distributed geographically but short-ranging vertically; they are therefore good index fossils of the formations in which they occur.

Features that are most important in the evolution and classification of the bryozoans are (1) characters of the zooecial apertures, (2) internal structures, and (3) the mode of colonial growth, which determines the form of the zoarium.

Brachiopods

Brachiopods are marine shelled animals that are related to the bryozoans. Their external form, average size, and complete absence of colonial development, however, do not remotely suggest the bryozoans.

Brachiopods have two unequal shells or valves, each of which is bilaterally symmetrical. They consist of calcium carbonate in the great majority of species, but some have chitinous shells, impregnated with calcium phosphate and carbonate. The form of the shell is variable. Generally both valves are convex, but they may be nearly flat; one or other of the valves may be convex while the opposite is concave: or one valve may be cone-shaped, the other fitting like a lid upon it. The posterior portion of the shell, where the valves are hinged or held closely together, is pointed in a beak. One of the valves is designated as pedicle (or ventral) and the other as brachial (or dorsal). During all or part of the existence of the brachiopod after the free-swimming larva settles down, the shell is attached to the sea bottom by a fleshy stalk (*pedicle*) that projects posteriorly between the valves or through

an opening in the pedicle valve, which generally is dorsal in position. With increasing age, the pedicle opening may become closed and the pedicle itself atrophied. Some brachiopods are anchored by projecting spines or are cemented to foreign objects by the whole or part of the surface of the ventral valve.

Some brachiopods are smooth, except for concentric markings that indicate interrupted growth. The greater number develop radiating striae, ribs, or plications that ornament and strengthen the shell materially. The median portion and front margin of one valve are frequently depressed (*sinus*), while the corresponding part of the opposite valve is elevated (*fold*). Spines may be developed in various parts or over

355. A colony of modern bryozoans (Bugula). Each small tube of the colony houses an individual animal. Much enlarged. *(American Museum of Natural History.)*

the entire surface. Between the beak and the hinge line in many species, a flattened or curved triangular space (*cardinal area*) is observed. It is more highly developed in the pedicle valve and is bisected by a small triangular opening (*delthyrium*) for the pedicle. The opening may be partly closed by a plate (*deltidium*) secreted by the pedicle, or by a pair of plates (*deltidial plates*) secreted by an extension of the mantle that builds the pedicle valve. The shells of most living species are light-colored and unornamented, but some bear vivid color markings. It is interesting to find at least some fossil brachiopods in which traces of

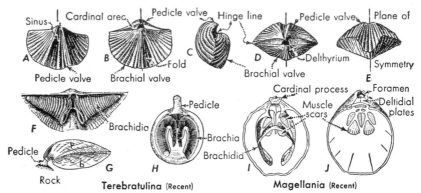

356. Form and structural features of brachiopods. *A-F, Spirifer,* from Devonian rocks; *G-J,* living species. *(F-J, after Winifred Goldring, New York State Museum.)*

color patterns are preserved. The large, externally sculptured brachiopods of Paleozoic time must have been objects of much beauty.

The more primitive brachiopods have no definite hinge structure, the valves being held together merely by muscles. More advanced shells have hinge teeth on the pedicle valve that fit into sockets on the brachial valve, and the hinge line may be considerably extended laterally. The valves are pulled together by muscles attached to the interior and are opened by other muscles extending from the floor of the pedicle valve to the end of a lever-like projection (*cardinal process*), near the beak of the brachial valve, which passes between and beyond the hinge teeth. These structures may be supplemented and supported by plates of various shape and position inside the shell. Finally, in all advanced types of brachiopods, the delicate fleshy arms (*brachia*) that serve to propel food particles toward the mouth are supported by calcified projections attached near the beak of the brachial valve. These may consist of moderately short, curved processes (*crura*), of a loop, or of two thin, spirally coiled ribbons.

Mollusks

PELECYPODS

Pelecypods are bivalved aquatic animals with a bilaterally symmetrical body, fairly well-developed digestive, circulatory, and nervous systems, and a muscular foot that may be used in locomotion.

They have no head, and in this respect they are more primitive than the gastropods (snails) and cephalopods, which are grouped with pelecypods in the phylum Mollusca. In most pelecypods the membranous mantle that encloses the body and secretes the shell is extended backward out of the shell and forms two tubes (*siphons*). These carry currents of water, of which the inflowing one carries oxygen for respiration and microscopic organic matter for food, and the outflowing one serves to remove waste products. The tubes can be drawn inside the shell, except where they are unusually elongated. Most clams live on the bottom of the shallow parts of the sea, but some, like the mussels, have become adapted to fresh waters. They may crawl about slowly or burrow into mud, sand, or even into wood and stone. The scallop (*Pecten*) can swim a little by clapping its valves together and by forcing water alternately from one side and the other.

The two valves of the pelecypod are typically equal in size and symmetrical one with the other; they are carried on the right and

357. A typical modern marine clam *(Arca grandis)* distributed along the Atlantic Coast from Cape Cod to the West Indies. *(American Museum of Natural History.)*

left sides of the animal, the line of hingement being dorsal. This is
very different from the two valves of the brachiopod, which are dorsal
and ventral, one larger than the other, and each valve divisible into
equal symmetrical halves. The foot of the pelecypod projects forward
on the ventral side between the valves, and the siphons backward.
The beak of each valve generally, but not invariably, points forward
and is located in front of the mid-length of the shell. By this and
other means the fossil shell may be oriented readily. The valves are
held together in most pelecypods by two large muscles (*adductors*),
but in some, like the oyster, there is only one such muscle. The valves
are fastened together at the hinge by an elastic ligament, which, if
external, is placed under tension and, if internal, under compression,
when the muscles close the shell. When the muscles relax, the shell
springs open automatically. Articulation of the two valves is aided in
very many species by different types of teeth and sockets along the
hinge line; the interlocking of these serves to hinder slipping or twisting of one valve on the other. The external ornamentation comprises

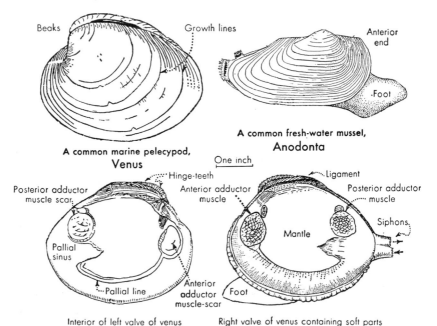

358. A fresh-water and marine clam showing structural features. (*Modified from Winifred
Goldring, New York State Museum.*)

concentric growth lines, projecting lamellae, ridges, ribs, folds, nodes, and spines. Certain fossil species have a subtriangular space (*cardinal area*) set off by a slight groove between the beak and the hinge line; in others and in many living forms there is a heart-shaped area (*lunule*) bounded by a ridge or groove in front of the beaks, and a more elongated one (*escutcheon*) extending backward from the beaks.

On the inside of the shell are attachment scars of the muscles. A slight furrow (*pallial line*), which marks the place of attachment of the mantle, parallels the ventral border of many pelecypods, and a strong deflection of this furrow (*pallial sinus*) in some shows where the siphons are drawn into the shell. These internal features are clearly defined on some fossil molds. The fact that the inner pearly layer of pelecypod shells consists of aragonite explains the frequent removal of the shell substance by solution, for aragonite, though identical with calcite in composition, is more soluble. In collecting fossils, one often finds that brachiopods and other shells made up of calcite are well preserved, whereas pelecypods and gastropods, whose original shell was largely composed of aragonite, are represented only by molds.

The structures of the hinge region, musculature, and general form of the shell are chief features used in classsifying the pelecypods. In spite of a wide variety of forms, the group has been rather conservative throughout its long period of existence.

GASTROPODS

The gastropods, or snails, have a distinct head, which carries mouth, eyes, ears, and tentacles. They are also distinguished by having a broad foot, on which they may crawl slowly, and by the possession of a single spirally coiled or cap-shaped shell, on account of which they are frequently termed "univalves." Some gastropods, however, have no shell at all. The mouth is armed with horny plates and a rasplike process (*radula*). The esophagus leads into a long coiled intestine, surrounded by a large liver, kidneys, and various glands. A heart and many-branching blood vessels make up the circulatory system, and two cerebral and numerous other paired ganglia, with their connections, compose the nervous system. Most gastropods have tufted or leaflike gills, originally paired, but generally becoming single by the atrophy of one. Reproductive organs are specialized. Gastropods are most abundant in the shallow seas, but they live also in fresh waters

359. A large marine gastropod showing color pattern (Triton tritonis), photographed with mirror image. *(American Museum of Natural History.)*

and many are air-breathers. They feed mostly on plants but some, including the drills, which can bore a neat round hole through other shells, are carnivorous. A few are scavengers.

The shell of the gastropods, secreted by the mantle on the dorsal side of the body, consists essentially of calcium carbonate in the form of aragonite and hence, like the pearly shell substance in pelecypods, is subject to solution or alteration rather readily in fossilization. Generally, the spire is strongly elevated and screwlike, being carried on the back of the animal with the apex pointed upward and backward, and the aperture downward and forward. Most shells are right-handed; that is, the aperture when held downward and facing the observer is on the right side. A few are left-handed. Some shells are coiled in a plane. Each complete coil is termed a *whorl*. The whorls may wind around a solid axis (*columella*) or leave an open space (*umbilicus*).

The aperture is generally rounded but may be notched by canals carrying the siphon, which conducts water to the gills, and the anal tube. The position and character of these notches are indicated on the earlier formed whorls by the configuration of the shell and by deflection of the growth lines. External ornamentation is highly varied; it consists of revolving and transverse lines, grooves, ribs, frills, and spines. In addition, many gastropod shells are beautifully decorated with a diversity of brilliant or delicate hues and patterns.

The body of the gastropod is united to the shell by muscular attachment, and generally the animal may draw itself entirely inside for protection. In many species an accessory plate (*operculum*) secreted by the foot then closes the aperture. This plate is commonly composed

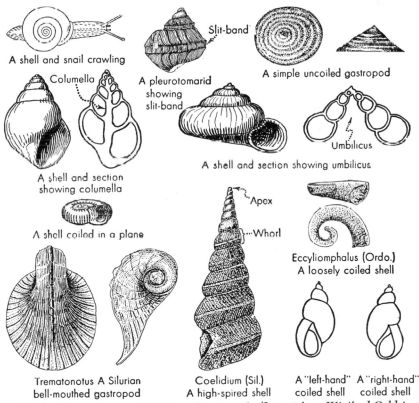

A shell and snail crawling

A pleurotomarid showing slit-band

Slit-band

A simple uncoiled gastropod

Columella

A shell and section showing columella

A shell and section showing umbilicus

Umbilicus

A shell coiled in a plane

Apex

Whorl

Eccyliomphalus (Ordo.) A loosely coiled shell

Trematonotus A Silurian bell-mouthed gastropod

Coelidium (Sil.) A high-spired shell

A "left-hand" coiled shell

A "right-hand" coiled shell

360. Typical form and structural features of gastropods. *(In part from Winifred Goldring, New York State Museum.)*

of horny material and is not fossilized, but rarely it is calcareous and may be preserved.

A subordinate division among the gastropods, which, however, was very important in parts of Paleozoic time, is that of the *pteropods*. These are rather small, free-swimming forms in which the foot is modified into two winglike fins. The shell is generally a narrow and straight pointed tube, which is circular or triangular in cross section. Somewhat similar are the *conularids,* which have a shell that is rounded or quadrangular in section. It is possible that these last may be a type of worm.

CEPHALOPODS

The cephalopods are the most highly organized class of mollusks. They include the largest and most powerful of all invertebrate animals, and they are one of the most important groups of fossils. The best-known living cephalopods are the pearly nautilus, which has a coiled, many-chambered shell, and the cuttlefishes, some of which have internal shelly structures. The head is well defined in most types and is provided with large eyes. The mouth contains jaws armed with a powerful horny beak and is surrounded by fleshy tentacles, which are used in grasping objects. Among cuttlefishes, the tentacles bear strong sucker disks and hooks. The foot is transformed into a muscular funnel-shaped swimming organ through which water may be ejected so as to propel the cephaloped rapidly backward or sideward. Cephalopods breathe by gills and are exclusively marine. The nervous, circulatory, digestive, and reproductive systems and the sense organs are all specialized and well developed.

Two main classes of cephalopods are distinguished: (1) the *tetrabranchiates,* which have four gills and a chambered external shell, and (2) the *dibranchiates,* which have two gills and an internal shell, or none at all. The first group is represented by thousands of fossil species, but only one, the nautilus, is still living; the second had a great development in Mesozoic time and includes a variety of living species.

Nautiloid cephalopods. The shell of the nautilus is coiled in a plane and is bilaterally symmetrical. In life the aperture is directed forward, the shell twisting spirally backward and upward above the animal. Accordingly, the outer, convex part of the coiled tube is ventral, and the inner, concave part, is dorsal. In side view, only the last-formed coil (*whorl*) of the shell may be seen, for in the nautilus each coil extends laterally so as to envelope and conceal the inner ones. The cross section of each embracing whorl is therefore strongly crescentic. This type of shell is said to be deeply *involute*, and it is evidently an advanced or specialized form of coiling. Among fossil nautiloids there are many examples in which the outer whorl only partly embraces the inner, and many in which the coils are barely in contact at their outer and inner margins. Then there are coiled shells in which the whorls do not touch. There are also curved but uncoiled

361. Exterior of the chambered nautilus *(Nautilus pompilius)* The unabraded shell (as shown at left), which has growth lines and color markings, does not reveal sutures (union of internal chambers with outer shell). (*American Museum of Natural History.*)

362. Section view of the chambered nautilus *(Nautilus pompilius).*

shells, and finally the most primitive type of all, which is straight.

   The body of the nautilus occupies only the end portion of the outer whorl, this part of the shell being known as the body chamber. At the inner end of the body chamber is a cross plate (*septum*), which is concave toward the aperture, and at regular short spaces throughout the unoccupied parts of the shell, are similar partitions, which were formed at successive stages in the growth of the animal. These septa and the chambers into which they divide the nautilus shell are characteristic features which serve to distinguish it very readily from that of planospirally coiled gastropods. Observation shows that each septum is pierced by a round opening, which provides passage for a tube (*siphon*) that extends back to the embryonic chamber in the center of the shell. In many of the ancient nautiloids the siphon was encased in a calcareous tube (*siphuncle*), which, of course, may be preserved in the fossils. The junctions of the septa with the outer wall of the shell are termed *sutures;* they cannot be seen from the exterior unless the outer shell is broken or worn away. The sutures of early Paleozoic cephalopods are straight or gently curved, but those of later time became angulated and extremely complex in pattern. External ornamentation consists merely of color bands and faint curving growth lines in the modern nautilus. The majority of fossil nautiloids have smooth shells, but some had strong ribs or spines, and a few preserve indications of a color pattern.

Arthropods

TRILOBITES

The most interesting of all invertebrate fossils to the average person are trilobites. This is due partly to the easily recognized character of the head, eyes, segmented body, and tail, and partly to the obvious biologic advancement and approach to such familiar creatures as lobsters, crabs, and insects. Indeed, trilobites are probably the direct or indirect ancestors of all other joint-legged invertebrates (Arthropoda), which surpass in number of species all other classes of animals combined. For this reason, and because the trilobites are very numerous and valuable index fossils in many Paleozoic formations, they occupy a position of importance.

Trilobites were protected on the dorsal side by a hard shelly carapace consisting of chitin impregnated by calcium carbonate. The shell is longitudinally three-lobed, with an axial and two side (*pleural*) regions that are commonly well defined on head (*cephalon*), thorax, and tail (*pygidium*). Since the trilobite skeleton is rather easily separated into segments, one finds these fragments much more frequently than a complete test. As shown by a few remarkable well-preserved fossils, these animals had delicate antennae, numerous legs that were used for crawling or swimming, and breathing organs.

Straight   Curved   Loose-coiled   Evolute coiled   Moderately involute   Highly involute

363. The form of cephalopod shells shown by side and sectional views.

The central lobe of the head (*glabella*) is generally well defined. Typically, it is divided transversely into five lobes, which represent the original segments that consolidated to form the head and correspond to the five pairs of appendages on the ventral side of the head. The lateral portions of the head are each divided by a line of parting (*facial suture*) into an inner portion (*fixed cheek*) attached to the glabella and an outer (*free cheek*) that carries the eyes. In primitive

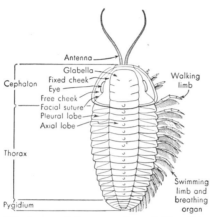

types of trilobites, the fixed cheeks make up nearly the whole of the lateral lobes of the head shield, the facial suture being marginal. In more advanced orders, the free cheek shows clearly on the dorsal side, the suture intersecting the posterior or lateral margin of the head shield. Most trilobites had a pair of raised, outward-facing compound eyes provided with numerous facets, and in some there was a simple eye located centrally at the rear of the glabella. As many as 15,000 facets may occur on one

364. Structural features of a trilobite (*Triarthrus*, Ordovician).

of the compound eyes. Some trilobites were blind. The segments of the thorax were jointed and permitted slight movement, but flexibility sufficient to bring the tail under the head, and thus protect the vulnerable ventral parts, was not developed in the earliest, most primitive genera. The pygidium, like the head shield, was formed by fusion of several segments, for its superficial markings and the paired appendages beneath it indicate ancestral separated segments.

Stages in the development of the trilobite individual are determinable by means of the successively castoff, or molted, shells. During the larval stage, when only head and tail shields were present, there were commonly several molts; during the adolescent stage, there were molts at the time of adding each thoracic segment; during adult life, there were further molts, which permitted increase in size but did not increase the number of segments. The characters exhibited during these changes are significant in establishing the direction of evolutionary modification in the different groups of trilobites, for the life history of the individual recapitulates more or less completely the history of the race.

OSTRACODES

Ostracodes are minute, commonly microscopic, bivalve crustaceans, which (excepting two families) are restricted to the sea. They occur in vast numbers, and a study of the microscopic fossils that may be washed out of most marine shale or shaly limestone deposits shows that ostracodes are common and highly varied in rocks of all ages back to the Early Ordovician. The majority of genera and species are not long-ranging vertically, which fact, together with wide geographic distribution and large numbers, makes them valuable index fossils. In recent years they have served especially in helping to identify and correlate the rocks penetrated in oil wells, for, in spite of the action of drilling tools, many perfect specimens can often be found in the well cuttings.

The valves of the ostracode shell are generally somewhat elliptical in outline; commonly they have a straight hinge line and exhibit a diversity of surface markings, which consist chiefly of raised lobes and depressed grooves or pits. Some have a beautiful network surface ornamentation, broad flangelike frills, or projecting spines.

Fishes

Fishes have the form and general structure that are best adapted to a mobile life in water. The body is typically compressed, spindle-shaped, and streamlined to offer minimum resistance to motion. The head, which is fastened to the body without a neck, bears the eyes, mouth, and gills. The sharks and lampreys have a series of separate openings for the gills, which are exposed on each side; in other fishes, these are all concealed by an operculum. The body is generally protected by a shingle-like covering of scales, but it may be armored by bony plates, by a flexible mail of quadrangular enamel-like plates, by small toothlike structures embedded in the skin, or it may have only a leathery skin.

Fins, which enable the fishes to swim easily, belong in two groups: (1) the unpaired fins, which are median projections from the back (dorsal fin), tail (caudal fin), and venter (anal fin); and (2) the paired fins, which consist of pectoral fins, located one on each side near the head, and the pelvic fins, located typically farther back but in front of the anal fin. Three types of tail fins are observed: (1) *diphycercal,* which extends symmetrically and evenly around the end of the vertebral column; (2) *heterocercal,* in which the end of the vertebral column is bent upward (or rarely downward) and the arrangement of the fin is unsymmetrical; and (3) *homocercal,* a more or less fan-shaped symmetrical tail fin that is developed at the abrupt termination of the vertebral column. The fins are supported near the base by cartilaginous or bony structures and farther out by horny rays, or in the paired fins of certain species, by a skeletal structure that suggests the limb bones of higher vertebrates.

The lungfishes possess an internal organ of respiration, which is absent in most other fishes. The higher types (bony fishes) have instead an *air bladder,* which functions as a hydrostatic organ.

Several different classifications of the fishes have been proposed, the difference in grouping being due to uncertainty as to the significance and relationships of various structures. Present knowledge favors recognition of four main classes: (1) primitive jawless fishes (Agnatha), which include the ostracoderms; (2) plate-armored fishes (Placodermi), having primitive jaws and a bony skeleton; (3) sharks and related fishes (Chondrichthyes), having an advanced type of jaw structure but no bony skeleton; and (4) other fishes (Osteichthyes), which have advanced jaw structure and retain a bony skeleton.

Amphibians

Amphibians resemble the fishes in living for a part or all of their lives in water, and breathing by means of gills, in being cold-blooded, in the possession by some forms of a diphycercal tail fin, in the presence of a body covering of scales in many of the fossil species, and in the nature of their eggs and the way these are laid in water without further attention from the parents. They differ from fishes in having legs with fingers and toes (although in some amphibians one or both pairs of limbs have been lost); in the possession by the majority of species of functional lungs, which make them independent of water as a surrounding medium in adult life; and in the structure of the heart, the mobile muscular tongue, and other features. The amphibians were derived from crossopterygian fishes.

Index

P